MW00535038

TOOLS OF THE TRADE

Introduction

to

Advanced

Mathematics

TOOLS OF THE TRADE

Introduction

to

Advanced

Mathematics

Paul J. Sally, Jr.

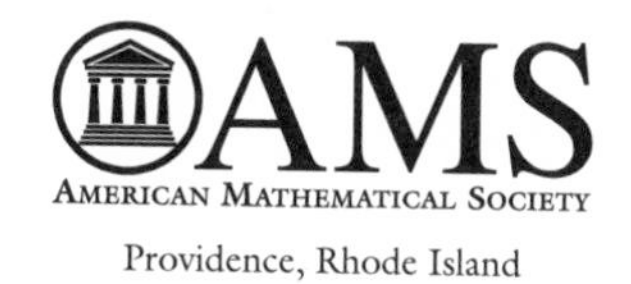

Providence, Rhode Island

2000 *Mathematics Subject Classification.* Primary 26–01;
Secondary 26A03, 26A06, 12J25.

For additional information and updates on this book, visit
www.ams.org/bookpages/mbk-55

Library of Congress Cataloging-in-Publication Data

Sally, Paul.
Tools of the trade : an introduction to advanced mathematics / Paul J. Sally, Jr.
p. cm.
Includes index.
ISBN 978-0-8218-4634-6 (alk. paper)
1. Mathematics—Textbooks. I. Title.

QA37.3.S25 2008
510—dc22 2008024594

♾ The paper used in this book is acid-free and falls within the guidelines
established to ensure permanence and durability.
Visit the AMS home page at http://www.ams.org/

10 9 8 7 6 5 4 3 2 1 13 12 11 10 09 08

This book is dedicated to the memory of my father, Paul Joseph Sally. He was born in 1897 into an Irish family then living in Scotland. His family immigrated to the United States in 1907 and lived in Philadelphia.

He left school after the eighth grade and worked at Friends Hospital to help support his family. He joined the Army in 1917 and thereby obtained his citizenship. He fought in World War I and was among the first U.S. troops that landed in Europe. He was a highly intelligent man with unmatched skills as a bricklayer, plasterer, and roofer. He knew the tools of his trade.

Paul J. Sally, Jr.
May 2008

Table of Contents

Introduction

When structuring an undergraduate mathematics program, ordinarily the faculty designs the initial set of courses to provide techniques that permit a student to solve problems of a more or less computational nature. So, for example, students might begin with a one variable calculus course and proceed through multi-variable calculus, ordinary differential equations, and linear algebra without ever encountering the fundamental ideas that underlie this mathematics. If the students are to learn to do mathematics well, they must at some stage come to grips with the idea of proof in a serious way.

In this book, we attempt to provide enough background so that students can gain familiarity and facility with the mathematics required to pursue demanding upper-level courses. The material is designed to provide the depth and rigor necessary for a serious study of advanced topics in mathematics, especially analysis.

There are several unusual features in this book. First, the exercises, of which there are many, are spread throughout the body of the text. They do not occur at the ends of the chapters. Instead Chapters 1–4 close with special projects that allow the teachers and students to extend the material covered in the text to a much wider range of topics. These projects are an integral part of the book, and the results in them are often cited in later chapters. They can be used as a regular part of the class, a source of independent study for the students, or as an Inquiry Based Learning (IBL) experience in which the students study the material and present it to the class. At the end of Chapter 5, there is a collection of Challenge Problems that are intended to test the students' understanding of the material in all five chapters as well as their mathematical creativity. Some of these problems are rather simple while others should challenge even the most able students.

We now give an outline of the content of the individual chapters. Chapter 1 begins with set theory, counting principles, and equivalence relations. This is followed by an axiomatic approach to the integers and the presentation of several basic facts about divisibility and number theory. The notions of a commutative ring with 1 and a field are introduced. Modular systems are given as examples of these structures. The ordered field of rational numbers is constructed as the field of quotients of the integers. Finally, cardinality, especially countability, is discussed. Several equivalent forms of the axiom of choice are stated and the equivalences proved.

Chapter 2 is about linear algebra. The first part of the chapter is devoted to abstract linear algebra up through linear transformations and determinants. In particular, the properties of determinants are attacked with bare knuckles. The final section of the chapter is devoted to geometric linear algebra. This is a study of the algebra and geometry of Euclidean n-space with respect to the usual distance. It is a preparation for the study of metric spaces in Chapter 4 as well as for the geometric ideas that occur in advanced calculus.

Chapter 3 begins with an axiomatic approach to the real numbers as an ordered field in which the least upper bound property holds. Several fundamental topics are addressed including some specific ideas about rational approximation of real numbers. Next, beginning with the rational numbers as an ordered field, the real numbers are constructed via the method of equivalence classes of Cauchy sequences. After this construction, the standard convergence theorems in the real numbers are proved. This includes the one-dimensional versions of the Bolzano-Weierstrass theorem and the Heine-Borel theorem. The last sections involve the construction of the complex numbers and their arithmetic properties. We also study the topic of convergence in the complex numbers.

In Chapter 4, the stakes are raised a bit. There is a complete and thorough treatment of metric spaces and their topology. Such spaces as bounded real valued functions on a set with the sup norm, the infinite-dimensional ℓ^p spaces, and others are given careful treatment. The equivalence between compactness and sequential compactness is proved, and the standard method of completing a metric space is presented. Here it is noted that this process cannot be used to complete the rational numbers to the real numbers since the completeness of the real numbers is fundamental to the proof. At the end of the chapter, several topics such as convexity and connectedness are analyzed.

Chapter 5 is a compendium of results that follow naturally from the theory of complete metric spaces developed in Chapter 4. These results are essential in further developments in advanced mathematics. The Contraction Mapping Theorem has a number of very useful applications, for example, in the proof of the Inverse Function Theorem. We give an application to the solution of ordinary differential equations. The Baire Category theorem is most often used in functional analysis. We give an application to uniformly bounded families of continuous functions on a complete metric space. The Stone–Weierstrass theorem concerns dense families of functions in the algebra of continuous functions on a compact metric space. In particular, this theorem implies the density of the polynomials in the algebra of continuous functions on closed bounded intervals in $\mathbb{R}$. The final section contains the most basic example of completing a metric space, that is, the p-adic completion of the rational numbers relative to a prime p. Along with being an example of the completion process, the p-adic completion yields a family of locally compact fields that currently is prominent in research in number theory, automorphic forms, mathematical physics, and other areas.

As pointed out above, each chapter ends with a set of special projects that are intended to broaden and deepen students' understanding of advanced mathematics. The first project in Chapter 1 is a series of exercises in elementary number theory that serves as an introduction to the subject and provides necessary material for the construction of the p-adic numbers in Chapter 5. Next, we introduce the idea of completely independent axiom systems, so that students working through this project might have some idea of the role of axioms in mathematics. Finally, we discuss ordered integral domains. We ask the students to show that the integers, as an ordered integral domain in which the Well Ordering Principle holds, are contained in every ordered integral domain. This leads naturally to the conclusion that every ordered field contains the rational numbers.

The projects at the end of Chapter 2 provide a set of exercises for the student that form a primer on basic group theory, with special emphasis on the general linear group and its subgroups.

The projects at the end of Chapter 3 present the students with an opportunity to investigate the following topics: an alternate construction of the real numbers using Dedekind cuts; an introduction to the convergence of infinite series; and a careful analysis of the decimal expansions of real numbers. The material about the convergence of infinite series is used extensively throughout the remaining chapters.

The projects in Chapter 4 provide an insight into advanced mathematics. They begin with an exploration for students of general point set topology, building on the theory of metric spaces covered in Chapter 4. Next, the students are asked to study a proof of the Fundamental Theorem of Algebra which establishes one of the basic facts in advanced mathematics.

The first three chapters of this book are used in a one quarter transition course at the University of Chicago. A substantial portion, but not all, of the material in the first three chapters can be covered in ten weeks. The remaining material in the book is used in the first quarter of "Analysis in $\mathbb{R}^n$." This course is intended as an advanced multivariable calculus course for sophomores. It covers geometric linear algebra from Chapter 2, some convergence theorems in $\mathbb{R}$ and $\mathbb{C}$ in Chapter 3, and the theory of metric spaces in Chapter 4, with an introduction to Chapter 5 if time allows. The remaining two quarters of Analysis in $\mathbb{R}^n$ cover differentiation theory and integration theory in $\mathbb{R}^n$ along with the usual theorems in vector calculus. The entire book is more than sufficient for a two quarter or one semester course, and if the projects are covered completely there is more than enough for a three quarter or two semester course.

Acknowledgements

We acknowledge with gratitude the contributions to our book made by our colleagues, students, and friends over the span of twenty years or more. It is not possible to mention by name all those with whom we have had conversations about this material, but we express appreciation to them here.

We thank Harvey Friedman, Bill Fulton, Dennis Hirschfeldt, David Leep, Raghavan Narasimhan, and Madhav Nori for their advice and assistance.

We thank John Conlon, Dan Gardner, Matt Gelvin, Grant Larsen, Alex Munk, Kevin Tucker and Shaffiq Welji for their careful, critical reading of portions of the manuscript.

We are grateful to Sam Altschul, David Coley, Moon Duchin, Sam Isaacson, Sean Johnson, Tom Koberda, Calvin Lin, Chris Malon, Emily Peters, Sam Raskin, and Ryan Reich for their incisive ideas on the material in this book, as well as their perceptive reading of portions of it.

We are in great debt to Mitya Boyarchenko who contributed significant ideas to the book and to John Boller and Loren Spice, both of whom also contributed ideas to the book and carefully read the final manuscript.

My ultimate debt is owed to those who worked with me to produce this manuscript. The word colleague describes them appropriately. The word amanuensis could be used as a formal title, but they are much more. We argued, discussed, rewrote, reaffirmed and readjusted parts of the manuscript on many occasions. These friends are Chris Jeris, Nick Ramsey, Kaj Gartz, Nick Ramsey (again), and Nick Longo. Without them, etc.

Paul J. Sally, Jr.
Chicago, Illinois
May 2008

Chapter 1

Sets, Functions, and Other Basic Ideas

Dans la présente Note, on va essayer de préciser une terminologie propre à l'étude des ensembles abstraits. Cette étude a pour but principal d'étendre les propriétés des ensembles linéaires à des ensembles de plus en plus généraux, et par voie de conséquence, de disséquer ces propriétés et d'en rechercher pour chacune la véritable origine. Il en résulte que le fond des démonstrations est pour ainsi dire donné d'avance et que la difficulté consiste en grande partie a préciser dans quel cadre elles viendront se placer. Adopter une terminologie, c'est donc tracer d'avance toute la théorie. Au fur et à mesure du développement de cette théorie, la terminolgie a varié et variera encore. Mais il n'est peut-être pas inutile d'en proposer une, adaptée à la situation présente.

- M. M. Fréchet,
Extrait des Comptes rendus du Congrès des Sociétés savantes en 1924.

In this chapter, we introduce various types of notation to label definitions, theorems, and formulas. We even use examples of sets whose elements are natural numbers before we formally define the natural numbers. We expect the reader will have no problem with this.

1. Sets and Elements

You are probably familiar with the notion of a set as a "collection", or a "bunch", or maybe even a "set" of objects. Formally, we begin our discussion of sets with two undefined terms, that is, "set" and "membership in a set." So we might say that a set is a thing that is a collection of other things called the elements of the set. In practice, this sort of "definition by synonym" suffices for most mathematicians. If A is a set, we write $x \in A$ to denote membership in A, and we say that *x is an element of the set A*.

2. Equality, Inclusion, and Notation

If A and B are sets, we say that $A = B$ (*A is equal to B*) if they have the same elements. That is, if $x \in A$, then $x \in B$, and conversely if $x \in B$, then $x \in A$. This is used to prove that two sets, which at first glance might not appear to be equal, are indeed equal. Examples of this are given below, and many more are in the exercises. There is one very special set that plays an important role – the *empty set*, which contains no elements. The empty set is denoted $\varnothing$.

$A = B$ $\varnothing$

The next idea is that of a subset. We say that A is a *subset* of B if for any $x \in A$, we have $x \in B$. If A is a subset of B, we write $A \subseteq B$. We also say that *B contains A* (some people even say that B is a *superset* of A, but that is the only time you will see that word in this book). When $A \subseteq B$, it may be the case that B is actually "bigger" than A, that is, there is an element $b \in B$ such that b is not in A, or symbolically, $b \notin A$. In this case, we say that A is a *proper subset* of B, and, if we wish to emphasize this, we write $A \subsetneq B$. However, keep in mind that when we write $A \subseteq B$, A can certainly be a proper subset of B.

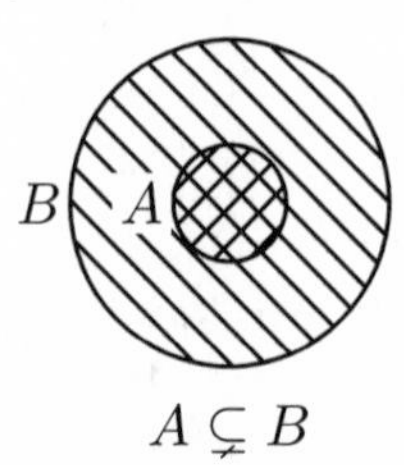

$A \subsetneq B$

Exercise 1.2.1. *If A is a set, show that $A \subseteq A$.*

Exercise 1.2.2. *If A and B are sets, show that $A = B$ if and only if $A \subseteq B$ and $B \subseteq A$.*

Exercise 1.2.3. *Suppose that A, B, and C are sets. If $A \subseteq B$ and $B \subseteq C$, show that $A \subseteq C$.*

Exercise 1.2.4. *Show that if A is a set, then $\varnothing \subseteq A$.*

To be fair, we should observe that all of this is a bit fuzzy logically and may even seem to be tautological. Nonetheless, if you assume the appropriate properties for the symbol $\in$, and you practice enough, you will feel comfortable with this whole business.

There are two *quantifiers* which we use regularly throughout this book. The first is $\forall$ which reads "for all," and the second is $\exists$ which reads "there exists." Also, the phrase "such that" will often be replaced by the symbol $\ni$, and we abbreviate the phrase "if and only if" by iff.

We usually just assume that all of the sets we consider are contained in some "big" set that is large enough to include all the objects we need. This big set or *universal set* is often denoted by the symbol X. Nevertheless, it is possible for a set to be "too big" (see Section 8). When a quantifier appears without a domain, as in the definition of equality, we mean to consider all objects in the current universe as our domain. Don't get the mistaken idea that the elements of the universal set X must all look the "same". For example, X can contain equilateral polygons, purple Buicks, real numbers, fried green tomatoes, etc.

There is an abbreviated notation for the set of all objects $x \in X$ that satisfy some condition $P(x)$. This notation means that P is a proposition, which is either true or false depending on the value of x. For the set of all $x \in X$ such that $P(x)$ is true, we write $\{x \in X \mid P(x)\}$. We may write simply $\{x \mid P(x)\}$ which again is meant to imply that we take only those x in some designated universe. For example, "the set of x such that x is even" is not sufficiently precise about the universe. It would be better to say, for example, "the set of real numbers x such that x is an even integer."

There will be cases when we list the elements of a set. If the set is small enough, for instance, the set of the first five letters of the alphabet, we write $A = \{a, b, c, d, e\}$. If the set is very large (maybe even infinite), but there is no ambiguity, we may simply list the first few elements of the set and describe the set to the reader. For example, we write the natural numbers as $\mathbb{N} = \{1, 2, 3, 4, \ldots, n, \ldots\}$. This familiar "dot, dot, dot" signifies that you should use your brain and continue as indicated.

3. The Algebra of Sets

This section is about taking subsets of a universal set X and putting them together in different ways to create new subsets of X. In fact, that's what most of mathematics is all about, building new things from old things. As was the case in Sections 1 and 2, most students will have seen this material, so let's cut right to the chase.

Definition 1.3.1. *Let A and B be sets. The* union *of A and B, denoted $A \cup B$, is defined by*

$$A \cup B = \{x \in X \mid x \in A \text{ or } x \in B\}.$$

Note that the "or" in this definition is inclusive (as opposed to "either–or"). That is, even if x is an element of both A and B, then x is still an element of $A \cup B$.

Definition 1.3.2. *Let A and B be sets. The* intersection *of A and B, denoted $A \cap B$, is defined by*

$$A \cap B = \{x \in X \mid x \in A \text{ and } x \in B\}.$$

Here, there is no doubt about what "and" means. "And" is "and."

$A \cup B$ $\qquad$ $A \cap B$

Definition 1.3.3. *Let A and B be sets. We say that A and B are* disjoint *if $A \cap B = \varnothing$. If $\mathcal{C}$ is a collection of sets, any two of which are disjoint, then the elements of $\mathcal{C}$ are said to be* pairwise disjoint.

Definition 1.3.4. *Let A and B be sets. The* difference *of A and B, denoted $A \setminus B$, and read "A minus B", is defined by*

$$A \setminus B = \{x \in A \mid x \notin B\}.$$

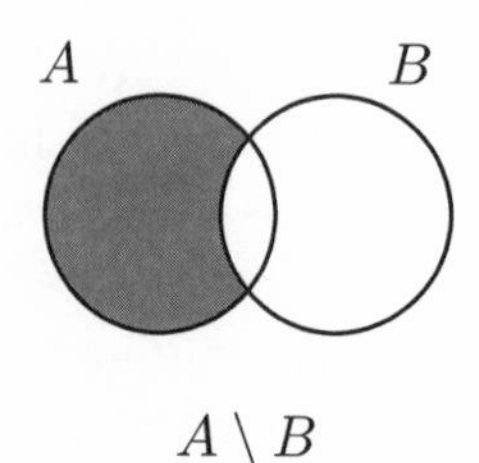

$A \setminus B$

At this point, it is useful to remark that union and intersection are obviously commutative, that is $A \cup B = B \cup A$ and $A \cap B = B \cap A$. However, difference is not commutative. For example, let $A = \{a\}$ and $B = \varnothing$. The reader may find it amusing to experiment with the difference of various pairs of sets.

The cure for the non-commutativity of the difference is provided by the symmetric difference.

Definition 1.3.5. *Let A and B be sets. The* symmetric difference *of A and B, denoted $A \triangle B$, is defined by*

$$A \triangle B = (A \setminus B) \cup (B \setminus A).$$

A B

$A \triangle B$

Obviously, the symmetric difference is a commutative operation. Finally, we define the complement of a subset A of a universal set X.

Definition 1.3.6. *Let $A \subseteq X$. The* complement *of A (in X), denoted ${}^{c}A$, is defined by*

$${}^{c}A = X \setminus A.$$

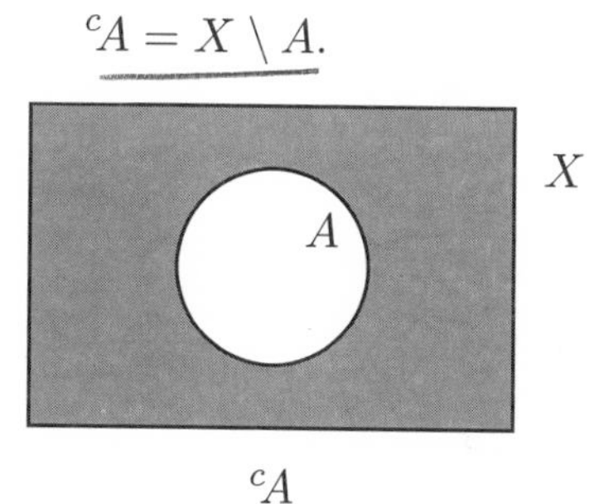

${}^{c}A$

There are many identities among sets that result from using the above operations. We illustrate a few and then assign a multitude of problems for practice.

Example 1.3.7. *This example shows that intersection is distributive over union. That is $A \cap (B \cup C) = (A \cap B) \cup (A \cap C)$.*

Take $x \in X$. Then $x \in A \cap (B \cup C)$ iff $x \in A$ and $x \in B \cup C$ iff ($x \in A$ and $x \in B$) or ($x \in A$ and $x \in C$). Now this means that $x \in A \cap B$ or $x \in A \cap C$, that is $x \in (A \cap B) \cup (A \cap C)$. Notice that in this proof, we simply replace symbols by words and use the common understandings of these words.

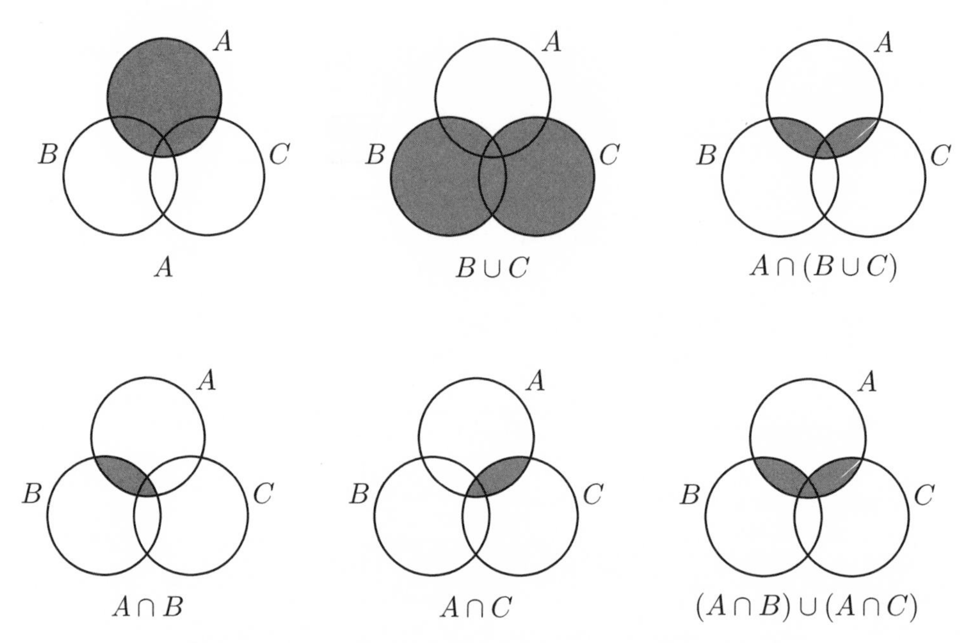

Illustration of the proof of the example

Example 1.3.8 (DeMorgan's Law I). $^c(A \cup B) = {}^cA \cap {}^cB$.

Take $x \in X$. *Then* $x \in {}^c(A \cup B)$ *iff* $x \in X \setminus (A \cup B)$ *iff* $x \in X$ *and* $x \notin A \cup B$ *iff* $(x \in X$ *and* $x \notin A)$ *and* $(x \in X$ *and* $x \notin B)$ *iff* $x \in {}^cA$ *and* $x \in {}^cB$ *iff* $x \in {}^cA \cap {}^cB$.

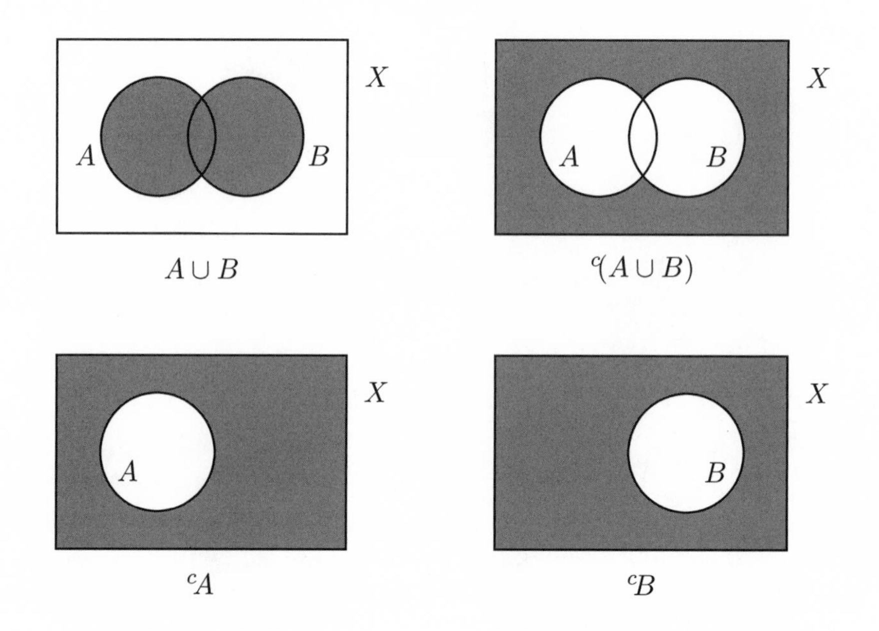

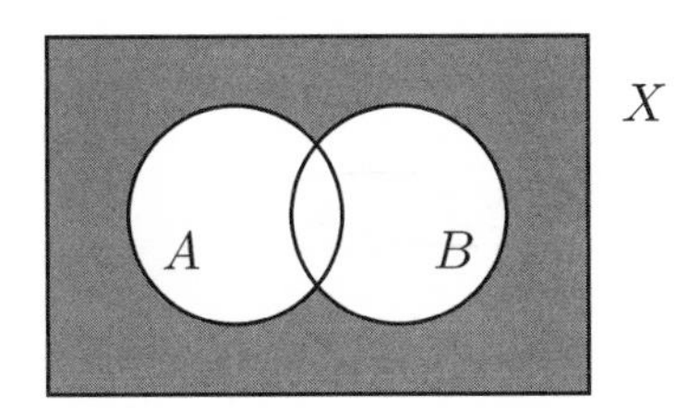

${}^cA \cap {}^cB$

Illustration of the proof of the example

As the book progresses, occasionally we will need to show, for certain pairs of sets A and B, that $A \subseteq B$ or perhaps that $A = B$. Such inclusions and equalities can be difficult to prove. The following list of exercises will help the reader to develop skills in this direction.

Exercise 1.3.9. *Prove the following equalities. As in* 1.3.7 *and* 1.3.8*, diagrams will illuminate the situation, but they will not suffice for proof. The sets A, B, C are subsets of some universe X.*

(*i*) $A \cup (B \cup C) = (A \cup B) \cup C$ *(Associative law for union).*

(*ii*) $A \cap (B \cap C) = (A \cap B) \cap C$ *(Associative law for intersection).*

(*iii*) $A \triangle (B \triangle C) = (A \triangle B) \triangle C$ *(Associative law for symmetric difference).*

(*iv*) $A \cup \varnothing = A$ *(The empty set is an identity for union).*

(*v*) $A \triangle \varnothing = A$ *(The empty set is an identity for symmetric difference).*

(*vi*) $A \cap X = A$ *(The universe is an identity for intersection).*

(*vii*) $A \cup B = \varnothing$ *iff* $A = \varnothing$ *and* $B = \varnothing$.

(*viii*) $A \cap B = X$ *iff* $A = X$ *and* $B = X$.

(*ix*) $A \triangle B = \varnothing$ *iff* $A = B$.

(*x*) $A \cap (B \triangle C) = (A \cap B) \triangle (A \cap C)$ *(Distributive law of intersection over symmetric difference).*

(*xi*) $A \cup (B \cap C) = (A \cup B) \cap (A \cup C)$ *(Distributive law of union over intersection).*

(*xii*) ${}^c(A \cap B) = {}^cA \cup {}^cB$ *(DeMorgan's Law II).*

It is obvious that the concepts of union and intersection can be extended to any finite number of sets $A_1, A_2, \ldots, A_n$. These are written $\bigcup_{i=1}^n A_i$ and $\bigcap_{i=1}^n A_i$. More generally, we can extend union and intersection to any collection of sets. We select an *index set I*, and write $\bigcup_{i \in I} A_i$ and $\bigcap_{i \in I} A_i$. Here, I could be finite or infinite. This is discussed later in the chapter.

4. Cartesian Products, Counting, and Power Sets

The Cartesian product of two sets may be familiar from the example of the coordinate or Euclidean plane. This is the set of all pairs (x, y) of real numbers where x denotes the "first coordinate" and y denotes the "second coordinate." The symbol (x, y) is called an *ordered pair*. This is not equal to the ordered pair (y, x), unless $y = x$. That is, the position of the coordinates makes a difference. For example, in the coordinate plane, the point $(1, 2)$ is not the same as the point $(2, 1)$, whereas the sets $\{1, 2\}$ and $\{2, 1\}$ are the same since they have the same elements and order is irrelevant. There is a formal definition of ordered pair, namely $(a, b) = \{\{a\}, \{a, b\}\}$. We are more concerned with a working principle. We say that two ordered pairs (x, y) and (x', y') are equal iff $x = x'$ and $y = y'$.

Definition 1.4.1. *Let A and B be sets. The* Cartesian product *of A and B, denoted $A \times B$, is defined by*

$$A \times B = \{(a, b) \mid a \in A \text{ and } b \in B\}.$$

Thus, the Cartesian product of A and B is the set of all ordered pairs in which the first coordinate comes from the set A, and the second coordinate comes from the set B. Notice that we have created a new universal set of ordered pairs of elements of the old universal set X. This will cause no difficulty for the moment.

For future use, we make the following definition of a relation on a set X.

Definition 1.4.2. *A* relation *on a set X is a subset of $X \times X$.*

Example 1.4.3. *If $A = \{a, b, c\}$ and $B = \{1, 2, 3\}$, then $A \times B = \{(a, 1), (a, 2), (a, 3), (b, 1), (b, 2), (b, 3), (c, 1), (c, 2), (c, 3)\}$.*

Exercise 1.4.4. *Write out $B \times A$ where A and B are as in the example above. Observe that the elements of $B \times A$ are different from those of $A \times B$.*

Exercise 1.4.5. *Prove that $A \times \varnothing = \varnothing \times A = \varnothing$.*

Exercise 1.4.6. *Suppose $A \neq \varnothing$ and $B \neq \varnothing$. Show $A \times B = B \times A$ iff $A = B$.*

There is a fundamental counting principle that accompanies the Cartesian product.

Theorem 1.4.7. *(Fundamental Counting Principle) If A has m elements and B has n elements, then $A \times B$ has mn elements.*

This is simple to prove by drawing little trees or using some other artifice. A formal proof by induction is very straightforward and will be given as an exercise later in the chapter. This counting principle is the basis for most of the combinatorial formulas in finite probability theory. We will have occasion to use this formula in only a few instances since most of the sets with which we deal in analysis have an infinite number of elements.

We discuss the terms "finite set" and "infinite set" in Section 8. We denote the number of elements in a set A by ${}^{\#}A$. So our fundamental counting principle says

$$ {}^{\#}(A \times B) = ({}^{\#}A)({}^{\#}B) \text{ if } A \text{ and } B \text{ are finite.} $$

To generalize this fundamental counting principle to a finite number of finite sets, we must first define the Cartesian product of these sets. Suppose that $A_1, A_2, \ldots, A_n$ are subsets of X.

Definition 1.4.8. *The n-fold Cartesian product of sets $A_1, \ldots, A_n$ is $A_1 \times A_2 \times \cdots \times A_n = \{(a_1, a_2, \ldots, a_n) \mid a_j \in A_j \text{ for } 1 \leq j \leq n\}$. This is the set of ordered n-tuples, with each coordinate coming from the appropriate subset.*

Exercise 1.4.9. *If A_1 has k_1 elements, A_2 has k_2 elements, $\ldots$, A_n has k_n elements, show that ${}^{\#}(A_1 \times A_2 \times \cdots \times A_n) = ({}^{\#}A_1)\,({}^{\#}A_2)\,\cdots\,({}^{\#}A_n) = k_1 k_2 \cdots k_n$. Hint: this can be proved drawing pictures but a formal proof is better.*

Another counting principle has to do with the union of two sets. When counting the number of elements in $A \cup B$, we cannot simply add ${}^{\#}A$ and ${}^{\#}B$ since the intersection might be non-empty (that is, not the empty set), so we would be counting the number of elements in the intersection twice.

Exercise 1.4.10. *Inclusion-Exclusion Principle*

(i) *If A and B are finite sets and $A \cap B = \varnothing$, show that*

$$ {}^{\#}(A \cup B) = {}^{\#}A + {}^{\#}B. $$

(ii) *If A and B are finite sets, show that*

$$ {}^{\#}(A \cup B) = {}^{\#}A + {}^{\#}B - {}^{\#}(A \cap B). $$

(iii) *Do it for three sets; that is if A,B, and C are finite sets, show that*

$$ {}^{\#}(A \cup B \cup C) = {}^{\#}A + {}^{\#}B + {}^{\#}C - {}^{\#}(A \cap B) - {}^{\#}(A \cap C) - {}^{\#}(B \cap C) + {}^{\#}(A \cap B \cap C). $$

(iv) *Generalize the previous exercise to any finite number of finite sets.*

The next thing to look at is the collection of all subsets of a given set. The idea here is to start with a universe X and study all the subsets of X.

Exercise 1.4.11.

(i) *Let $X = \{1\}$. Write a list of the subsets of X.*

(ii) *Let $X = \{1, 2\}$. Write a list of the subsets of X.*

(*iii*) *On the basis of this information, make a conjecture about the number of subsets of a set with n elements.*

Definition 1.4.12. *Let X be a set. The* power set *of X, denoted $\wp(X)$, is the collection of all subsets of X.*

Here is the counting principle that goes with $\wp(X)$.

Theorem 1.4.13. *If X is a set with n elements, then $\wp(X)$ has 2^n elements.*

Proof. Enumerate the elements of X: $x_1, x_2, \ldots, x_n$. Given a subset A of X, we construct a sequence $c_1, c_2, \ldots, c_n$ of 0's and 1's as follows. Let $c_i = 1$ if $x_i \in A$ and $c_i = 0$ if $x_i \notin A$. Thus, the subset A corresponds to a unique sequence of length n consisting of 0's and 1's. Similarly, given a sequence of 0's and 1's of length n, one can construct a unique subset of X. But how many sequences of length n are there consisting of 0's and 1's? By the fundamental counting principle, there are 2^n such sequences.

5. Some Sets of Numbers

The set of natural numbers is the collection $\mathbb{N} = \{1, 2, 3, \ldots, n, \ldots\}$. We have already used these numbers to index theorems and examples, and in examples themselves. Now, we wish to take a more formal approach towards a familiar set of numbers, namely the integers. The integers form the collection $\{0, 1, -1, 2, -2, \ldots\}$ which we study in elementary arithmetic. We denote the integers by the symbol $\mathbb{Z}$ (from the German word *Zahlen*). The operations in the integers are addition $(+)$ and multiplication $(\cdot)$, and here are the rules. We expect that the reader is well versed in the arithmetic of the integers, but we are stating these properties explicitly for two reasons. First, these properties are used in arithmetic from the earliest grades, but are seldom justified. Second, these properties will be used to describe other algebraic structures that we will meet later.

Rules of Arithmetic in $\mathbb{Z}$

(A1)	If $a, b \in \mathbb{Z}$, then $a + b \in \mathbb{Z}$.	Closure
(M1)	If $a, b \in \mathbb{Z}$, then $a \cdot b \in \mathbb{Z}$.	
(A2)	If $a, b, c \in \mathbb{Z}$, then $a + (b + c) = (a + b) + c$.	Associativity
(M2)	If $a, b, c \in \mathbb{Z}$, then $a \cdot (b \cdot c) = (a \cdot b) \cdot c$.	
(A3)	If $a, b \in \mathbb{Z}$, then $a + b = b + a$.	Commutativity
(M3)	If $a, b \in \mathbb{Z}$, then $a \cdot b = b \cdot a$.	
(A4)	$\exists 0 \in \mathbb{Z} \ni \forall a \in \mathbb{Z},\ a + 0 = 0 + a = a$.	Identity
(M4)	$\exists 1 \in \mathbb{Z} \ni 1 \neq 0$ and $\forall a \in \mathbb{Z},\ a \cdot 1 = 1 \cdot a = a$.	
(A5)	$\forall a \in \mathbb{Z},\ \exists -a \in \mathbb{Z} \ni a + (-a) = (-a) + a = 0$.	Additive inverses

In general, elements in $\mathbb{Z}$ do not have multiplicative inverses in $\mathbb{Z}$. That is, given an element $a \in \mathbb{Z}$, we cannot necessarily find another element $b \in \mathbb{Z}$ so that $ab = 1$. However, some integers do have multiplicative inverses, namely 1 and -1.

The operations of addition and multiplication are tied together by the distributive law.

(D) If $a, b, c \in \mathbb{Z}$, then $a \cdot (b + c) = (a \cdot b) + (a \cdot c)$.

Without the distributive law, there would be no connection between addition and multiplication. The richness of the structure is embodied in the interaction between the two operations.

Let's stop and investigate some of the implications of these 10 axioms.

Facts 1.5.1.

(1) *The additive identity is unique.*

Proof. *Suppose that* 0 *and* $0'$ *are additive identities. Then* $0 = 0 + 0' = 0'$.

(2) *The multiplicative identity is unique.*

Proof. *Do it.*

(3) *Additive inverses are unique.*

Proof. *Suppose that* $a \in \mathbb{Z}$ *and* $a + a' = 0$. *Then* $-a + (a + a') = -a + 0$. *So, by associativity and other things,* $((-a) + a) + a' = -a$, *and finally* $0 + a' = -a$, *or* $a' = -a$.

(4) *(Cancellation for addition) If* $a, b, c \in \mathbb{Z}$ *and* $a + b = a + c$, *then* $b = c$.

Proof. *If* $a + b = a + c$, *then* $-a + (a + b) = -a + (a + c)$, *etc.*

Question: Why don't we have cancellation for multiplication based on (M1)– (M4)?

Answer: Because we don't have multiplicative inverses (especially for 0).

(5) *If* $a \in \mathbb{Z}$, *then* $a \cdot 0 = 0$.

Proof. *We can write*

$$\begin{aligned} a \cdot 0 &= a \cdot (0 + 0) \\ (a \cdot 0) + 0 &= a \cdot 0 + a \cdot 0 \end{aligned}$$

by properties of the additive identity and the distributive law. Now cancel to get $a \cdot 0 = 0$.

This is really quite something, and it emphasizes the role of the distributive law. What we have here is multiplication by the additive identity reproducing the additive identity. We have more interaction between multiplication and addition in the following statements.

(6) *If* $a \in \mathbb{Z}$, *then* $(-1) \cdot a = -a$.

Proof. *We can write* $a+(-1)\cdot a = 1\cdot a+(-1)\cdot a = (1+(-1))\cdot a = 0 \cdot a = 0$. *But additive inverses are unique, so* $-a = (-1) \cdot a$.

Notice that, when convenient, we drop the dot which signifies multiplication.

Exercise 1.5.2. *If* $a, b \in \mathbb{Z}$, *then* $(-a)b = a(-b) = -(ab)$.

Exercise 1.5.3. *If* $a, b \in \mathbb{Z}$, *then* $(-a)(-b) = ab$.

Now, what other properties do the integers have? Cancellation for multiplication should be familiar, but in the integers, cancellation for multiplication doesn't follow from the first 10 axioms. We now state it as an additional axiom for the integers.

(C) If $a, b, c \in \mathbb{Z}$ with $a \neq 0$ and $ab = ac$, then $b = c$.

Why is $a = 0$ excluded?

Exercise 1.5.4. *Cancellation can be phrased in another way. Show that the statement "if* $a, b \in \mathbb{Z}$ *and* $ab = 0$, *then either* $a = 0$ *or* $b = 0$*" is equivalent to cancellation.*

What else do we have for the integers? We have inequalities. The $<$ sign should be familiar to you. It is a relation on $\mathbb{Z}$ that is subject to the following *rules of order.*

(O1) If $a, b \in \mathbb{Z}$, then one and only one of the following holds: $a < b$, $a = b$, or $b < a$. (Trichotomy)

(O2) If $a, b, c \in \mathbb{Z}$ with $a < b$ and $b < c$, then $a < c$. (Transitivity)

(O3) If $a, b, c \in \mathbb{Z}$ and $a < b$, then $a + c < b + c$. (Addition)

(O4) If $a, b, c \in \mathbb{Z}$, $a < b$, and $0 < c$, then $ac < bc$. (Multiplication by positive elements)

We adopt the usual notation. That is, if $a < b$, we say that "a is less than b." If $a < b$ or $a = b$, we say that "a is less than or equal to b" and write $a \leq b$. If $a < b$ we may also write $b > a$ and say that "b is greater than a." The statement $b \geq a$ is now self-explanatory.

Here are some examples of fundamental exercises and facts which go with the order axioms. For these statements and the following exercises, let $a, b, c \in \mathbb{Z}$.

Facts 1.5.5.

(1) $a > 0$ *iff* $-a < 0$.

Proof. *Suppose* $a > 0$. *Add* $-a$ *to both sides.*

(2) *If* $a > 0$ *and* $b > 0$, *then* $ab > 0$.

Proof. *Suppose* $a > 0$. *Then, since* $b > 0$, $ab > 0 \cdot b = 0$.

(3) *If* $a > 0$ *and* $b < 0$, *then* $ab < 0$.

Proof. *Suppose* $a > 0$ *and* $b < 0$. *Then* $-b > 0$ *and* $a(-b) = -(ab) > 0$. *So* $ab < 0$.

(4) *If* $a < 0$ *and* $b < 0$, *then* $ab > 0$.

Proof. *If* $a < 0$ *and* $b < 0$, *then* $-a > 0$ *and* $-b > 0$. *Hence* $(-a)(-b) = ab > 0$.

(5) *If* $a \neq 0$, *then* $a^2 > 0$.

Proof. *If* $a > 0$, *use Fact 2. If* $a < 0$, *use Fact 4.*

(6) $1 > 0$.

Proof. $1 = 1^2$.

(7) *If* $a > b$ *and* $c < 0$, *then* $ac < bc$.

Proof. *If* $a > b$, *then* $a - b > 0$. *Since* $-c > 0$, $(-c)(a - b) = -ac + bc > 0$. *Hence,* $bc > ac$.

(8) *If* $a > b$, *then* $-a < -b$.

Proof. *Let* $c = -1$ *and use Fact 7.*

Are you having fun yet? Good, try these exercises.

Exercise 1.5.6. *Suppose that* $0 < a$ *and* $0 < b$. *Show that* $a < b$ *iff* $a^2 < b^2$.

Exercise 1.5.7. *Suppose that* $a < 0$ *and* $b < 0$. *Show that* $a < b$ *iff* $b^2 < a^2$.

Exercise 1.5.8. *Show that* $2ab \leq (a^2 + b^2)$.

The set $\mathbb{N}$ of positive elements in $\mathbb{Z}$ is the set of elements that are greater than 0. It is clear that $\mathbb{N}$ is closed under addition and multiplication. If we add trichotomy, these properties lead to an alternate characterization of order.

Exercise 1.5.9. *Suppose now that we have only the first 11 axioms for* $\mathbb{Z}$ *(that is, through cancellation). Let* P *be a set of integers with the following properties.*

(1) *If* $a \in \mathbb{Z}$, *then one and only one of the following holds:* $a \in P$, $a = 0$, *or* $-a \in P$.

(2) *If* $a, b \in P$, *then* $a + b \in P$ *and* $ab \in P$.

For $a, b \in \mathbb{Z}$, define $a < b$ if $b - a \in P$. Show that this relation satisfies (O1)–(O4). Moreover, if we have a relation that satisfies (O1)–(O4), and we define $P = \{a \in \mathbb{Z} \mid a > 0\}$, then show that P satisfies properties 1 and 2 above.

Exercise 1.5.10. *Show that the cancellation axiom (C) can be proved using the properties for addition and multiplication and the order axioms.*

So far, the integers have five axioms for addition, four for multiplication, one for the distributive law, one for cancellation (which is superfluous), and four for order. There is one more axiom, which plays a crucial role. It is called the *Well-Ordering Principle.* This Principle assures us that 1 is the smallest positive integer. This should not come as a surprise but we do need something to confirm this. In the rational numbers, which we construct later, the first fifteen axioms are satisfied, but there is actually no smallest positive element.

Well-Ordering Principle for $\mathbb{Z}$. If A is a non-empty subset of the positive integers, then A has a least element. That is, there exists an element $a_0 \in A$, such that for all $a \in A$, $a_0 \leq a$.

That does it! We now have 15 properties, which completely characterize the integers. Most of the work with the Well-Ordering Principle will be done later. However, here are a couple of facts which follow immediately from the Well-Ordering Principle.

Facts 1.5.11.

(1) *There are no integers between 0 and 1.*

Proof. *Let $A = \{a \in \mathbb{Z} \mid 0 < a < 1\}$. If $A \neq \varnothing$, then it has a least element a_0 which is in A. So, $0 < a_0 < 1$, and, by property (O4), $0 < a_0^2 < a_0$. But then $a_0^2 \in A$ and a_0 is not the least element.*

(2) *(Mathematical Induction) Let A be a set of positive integers such that $1 \in A$, and if $k \in A$, then $k + 1 \in A$. Then A is the set of all positive integers.*

Proof. *Suppose there exists a positive integer which is not in A, and let A' be the set of all such positive integers. Then A' is a non-empty subset of the positive integers, and hence has a least element c. Now $c > 1$ since $1 \in A$, and there is no integer between 0 and 1. So $c - 1$ is an integer greater than 0. Since $c - 1 < c$, it follows that $c - 1 \in A$. And, so, $(c - 1) + 1 = c$ is also in A, which is a contradiction.*

Exercise 1.5.12. *If n, k are non-negative integers, we define the* binomial coefficient $\binom{n}{k}$ *by*

$$\binom{n}{k} = \frac{n!}{k!(n-k)!}$$

where $n! = n(n-1)\cdots 2\cdot 1$, and we set $0! = 1$. Prove the Binomial Theorem*: If $a, b \in \mathbb{Z}$ and n is a positive integer, then*

$$(a+b)^n = \sum_{k=0}^{n} \binom{n}{k} a^k b^{n-k}.$$

(Use Mathematical Induction.)

Remark 1.5.13. *Observe that the binomial coefficient $\binom{n}{k}$ represents the number of ways of choosing k objects from n objects where order does not matter. The binomial coefficient $\binom{n}{k}$ is the number of subsets of k elements in a set with n elements. Of course the binomial theorem implies that $\sum_{k=0}^{n} \binom{n}{k} = 2^n$, the total number of subsets of a set with n elements.*

Exercise 1.5.14.

(i) *Prove by induction that if A and B are finite sets, A with n elements and B with m elements, then $A \times B$ has nm elements.*

(ii) *Prove by induction the corresponding results for k sets.*

6. Equivalence Relations and the Construction of $\mathbb{Q}$

Recall that a relation on a set X is simply a subset of $X \times X$. For example, we can define a relation on $\mathbb{Z}$ by setting $\mathcal{R}$ equal to $\{(a, b) \mid a, b \in \mathbb{Z} \text{ and } a < b\}$.

Equivalence relations are everywhere in mathematics, and we really mean that. What an equivalence relation does is take a set and partition it into subsets. Some equivalence relations appear to be very natural, some appear to be supernatural, and others appear to make no sense at all.

Definition 1.6.1. *Let X be a set. An* equivalence relation *on X is a relation $\mathcal{R}$ on X such that*

(ER1) *For all $a \in X$, $(a, a) \in \mathcal{R}$. (Reflexive)*

(ER2) *For $a, b \in X$, if $(a, b) \in \mathcal{R}$, then $(b, a) \in \mathcal{R}$. (Symmetric)*

(ER3) *For $a, b, c \in X$, if (a, b) and $(b, c) \in \mathcal{R}$, then $(a, c) \in \mathcal{R}$. (Transitive)*

The "twiddle" (or "tilde") notation $(\sim)$ is often used in mathematics. That is, if $(a, b) \in \mathcal{R}$, we write $a \sim b$. Then the definition of equivalence relation becomes

(ER1) For all $a \in X$, $a \sim a$. (Reflexive)

(ER2) For $a, b \in X$, if $a \sim b$ then $b \sim a$. (Symmetric)

(ER3) For $a, b, c \in X$, if $a \sim b$ and $b \sim c$, then $a \sim c$. (Transitive)

Again, speaking loosely, we can refer to $\sim$ as an equivalence relation on X.

Exercise 1.6.2. *Let $\mathcal{R}$ be a relation on X that satisfies*

(a) *For all $a \in X$, $(a, a) \in \mathcal{R}$, and*

(b) *for $a, b, c \in X$, if $(a, b), (b, c) \in \mathcal{R}$, then $(c, a) \in \mathcal{R}$.*

Show that $\mathcal{R}$ is an equivalence relation.

Example 1.6.3. *The most basic example of an equivalence relation is equality. That is, $a \sim b$ iff $a = b$. Prove this, but please don't write anything.*

Example 1.6.4. *If A and B are triangles in the plane, write $A \sim B$ if and only if A is similar to B.*

Example 1.6.5. *Let n be an integer greater than or equal to 2. If $a, b \in \mathbb{Z}$, we say that $a \sim b$ iff $a - b$ is a multiple of n, that is, n divides $a - b$.*

This last example requires a little more elucidation. So, we present a brief discussion about divisibility in $\mathbb{Z}$.

Definition 1.6.6. *Suppose that a and b are integers. We say that a* divides *b, written $a|b$, if there is an element $c \in \mathbb{Z}$ such that $b = ac$. The number a is called a* divisor *of b.*

We need the following facts about divisibility.

Facts 1.6.7.

(1) *If $a \in \mathbb{Z}$, then $a|a$.*

(2) *If $a|b$, then $a| - b$.*

(3) *If $a|b$ and $b|c$, then $a|c$.*

These facts are easy to prove. For example, if $a|b$ and $b|c$, there are integers h and k such that $b = ha$ and $c = kb$. But then $c = (hk)a$, and that does it.

Exercise 1.6.8. *Show that, if $a \in \mathbb{Z}$, then $a|0$.*

Exercise 1.6.9. *Show that, if a and b are integers such that $a|b$ and $b|a$, then $a = \pm b$.*

Exercise 1.6.10. *Show that, if $c|a$ and $c|b$, and $s, t \in \mathbb{Z}$, then $c|(sa + tb)$.*

There is one other type of integer which should be familiar to the reader.

Definition 1.6.11. *Let p be a positive integer greater than or equal to 2. We say that p is* prime *if the only positive divisors of p are 1 and p.*

If n is a positive integer greater than 2 that is not prime, then n is called *composite*. So, if n is composite, there exist integers a and b both greater than or equal to 2, such that $n = ab$.

Exercise 1.6.12. *Let n be a positive integer greater than or equal to 2. Then there exists a prime p such that p divides n.*

The partitioning into subsets relative to an equivalence relation comes about as follows. If $a \in X$, we write $C(a) = \{b \in X \mid b \sim a\}$. The set $C(a)$ is called *the class of a* or *the equivalence class containing a*. Here are the properties of equivalence classes.

Theorem 1.6.13. *(Properties of equivalence classes)*

(1) $a \in C(a)$.
   Proof. *Reflexivity.*

(2) *If $a \sim b$, then $C(a) = C(b)$.*
   Proof. *Transitivity.*

(3) *If a is not equivalent to b ($a \nsim b$), then $C(a) \cap C(b) = \varnothing$.*
   Proof. *If $c \in C(a) \cap C(b)$, then $c \sim a$ and $c \sim b$, so $a \sim b$.*
   So we conclude that $C(a) \cap C(b) \neq \varnothing$ iff $C(a) = C(b)$.

(4) $\bigcup_{a \in X} C(a) = X$.
   Proof. *Use 1 above.*

This all means that an equivalence relation on a set X partitions X into a collection of pairwise disjoint subsets. Although this looks quite special, it's really not that impressive. For example, take a set X and break it up into pairwise disjoint non-empty subsets whose union is all of X. Then, for $a, b \in X$, define $a \sim b$ if a and b are in the same subset.

Exercise 1.6.14. *Prove that this is an equivalence relation on X.*

One more important example of an equivalence relation gives a method for constructing the rational numbers $\mathbb{Q}$ from the integers $\mathbb{Z}$ using the properties discussed in the last section. We consider the set $F = \{(a, b) \mid a, b \in \mathbb{Z} \text{ and } b \neq 0\}$. We are thinking (for example) of the pair $(2, 3)$ as the fraction $2/3$. For $(a, b), (c, d) \in F$, we define $(a, b) \sim (c, d)$ if $ad = bc$. Thus, for instance, $(2, 3) \sim (8, 12) \sim (-6, -9)$.

Exercise 1.6.15. *Show that $\sim$ is an equivalence relation on F.*

The set of equivalence classes determined by this equivalence relation is called the *rational numbers* and is denoted by $\mathbb{Q}$. You should be extremely happy about this since it explains all that business about equivalent fractions that you encountered in elementary school. What a relief!

We have several things to do with this example. First, we have to add and multiply rational numbers, that is, add and multiply equivalence classes. The fundamental principle to be established here is that, when we add or multiply equivalence classes, we do it by selecting an element from each equivalence class and adding or multiplying these. We must be certain that the result is independent of the representatives that we choose in the equivalence classes. For simplicity, we denote the class of (a, b) by $\{(a, b)\}$ rather than $C((a, b))$.

For $\{(a, b)\}, \{(c, d)\} \in \mathbb{Q}$, we define $\{(a, b)\} + \{(c, d)\} = \{(ad + bc, bd)\}$ and $\{(a, b)\} \cdot \{(c, d)\} = \{(ac, bd)\}$. What we must establish is the fact that if $(a, b) \sim (a', b')$ and $(c, d) \sim (c', d')$, then $(ad + bc, bd) \sim (a'd' + b'c', b'd')$ and $(ac, bd) \sim (a'c', b'd')$. All this requires is a little elementary algebra, but, for your sake, we'll actually do one and you can do the other. Of course, we do the easier of the two and leave the more complicated one for you. So, here goes: $(a, b) \sim (a', b')$ means that $ab' = a'b$, and $(c, d) \sim (c', d')$ means that $cd' = c'd$. Multiplying the first equality by cd', and then substituting $cd' = c'd$ on the right hand side of the resulting equation, we get the desired equality $acb'd' = a'c'bd$.

Exercise 1.6.16. *You do addition. It's messy.*

When we are defining some operation which combines equivalence classes, we often do this by choosing representatives from each class and then showing that it doesn't make any difference which representatives are chosen. We have a formal name for this. We say that the operation under consideration is *well-defined* if the result is independent of the representatives chosen in the equivalence classes.

Throughout this book, we will encounter equivalence relations on a regular basis. You will be fortunate enough to have the opportunity to prove that these are actually equivalence relations.

What properties are satisfied by addition and multiplication as defined above? For example, what about the associativity of addition? We must prove that $(\{(a, b)\} + \{(c, d)\}) + \{(e, f)\} = \{(a, b)\} + (\{(c, d)\} + \{(e, f)\})$. Well,

$$\begin{aligned}(\{(a, b)\} + \{(c, d)\}) + \{(e, f)\} &= \{(ad + bc, bd)\} + \{(e, f)\} \\ &= \{((ad + bc)f + (bd)e, (bd)f)\}.\end{aligned}$$

Now we use associativity and distributivity in $\mathbb{Z}$ to rearrange things in an appropriate fashion. This gives $\{(((ad)f + (bc)f) + (bd)e, (bd)f)\}$, and using the acrobatics of parentheses, we get $\{(a(df) + b(cf + de), b(df))\} = \{(a, b)\} + (\{(c, d)\} + \{(e, f)\})$. This is all rather simple. To prove various properties of addition and multiplication in $\mathbb{Q}$, we reduce them to known properties from $\mathbb{Z}$.

Exercise 1.6.17.

(*i*) *Prove the associative law for multiplication in* $\mathbb{Q}$.

(*ii*) *Prove the commutative laws for addition and multiplication in* $\mathbb{Q}$.

(*iii*) *Show that* $\{(0,1)\}$ *is an additive identity in* $\mathbb{Q}$.

(*iv*) *Show that* $\{(1,1)\}$ *is a multiplicative identity in* $\mathbb{Q}$.

(*v*) *Show that* $\{(-a,b)\}$ *is an additive inverse for* $\{(a,b)\}$.

(*vi*) *Prove the distributive law for* $\mathbb{Q}$.

Notice here that if $\{(a,b)\} \neq \{(0,1)\}$, that is, $a \neq 0$, then $\{(a,b)\} \cdot \{(b,a)\} = \{(1,1)\}$. Thus, in $\mathbb{Q}$, we have multiplicative inverses for nonzero elements.

Let's tidy this up a bit. First of all, we have no intention of going around writing rational numbers as equivalence classes of ordered pairs of integers. So let's decide once and for all to write the rational number $\{(a,b)\}$ as a/b. Most of the time this fraction will be reduced to lowest terms, but, if it is not reduced to lowest terms, it will certainly be in the same equivalence class as a fraction which is reduced to lowest terms. With this, addition and multiplication of rational numbers have their usual definition:

$$\begin{aligned} \frac{a}{b} + \frac{c}{d} &= \frac{ad+bc}{bd}, \\ \frac{a}{b} \cdot \frac{c}{d} &= \frac{ac}{bd}. \end{aligned}$$

Now consider the axioms for the integers (A1)–(A5), (M1)–(M4), and (D). All of these hold for the rational numbers, and there is another multiplicative property, multiplicative inverses.

(M5) If $a \neq 0$, then there is an element a^{-1} such that $aa^{-1} = a^{-1}a = 1$.

The operations of addition and multiplication are sometimes called *binary operations* or *internal laws of composition.*

Definition 1.6.18. *Let R be a non-empty set. An* internal law of composition (ILC) *on R is a map $\circ : R \times R \to R$. If $a, b \in R$, then we usually write* $\circ((a,b)) = a \circ b$.

Of course, the more properties that are satisfied by internal laws of composition, the better life gets.

Definition 1.6.19. *A set with two internal laws of composition, $+$ and $\cdot$, that satisfy (A1)–(A5), (M1)–(M4), and (D) is called a* commutative ring with 1. *If, in addition, cancellation (C) holds for multiplication, the commutative ring with* 1 *is called an* integral domain. *If (M5) also holds, the structure is called a* field.

Note that the word "commutative" in this definition refers not to the commutativity of addition but to the commutativity of multiplication. Thus, in our latest terminology, $\mathbb{Z}$ is an integral domain and $\mathbb{Q}$ is a field. What about cancellation for multiplication? This followed from order in $\mathbb{Z}$, but for $\mathbb{Q}$ (or any field for that matter) cancellation for multiplication holds automatically.

Exercise 1.6.20. *Prove this.*

Exercise 1.6.21. *Let X be a non-empty set and $R = \wp(X)$. Show that R with symmetric difference as addition and intersection as multiplication is a commutative ring with 1. When is R a field?*

There is another definition which will prove useful in our discussions about these various algebraic structures.

Definition 1.6.22. *Suppose that R is a commutative ring with 1. A subset R_0 of R is a* subring *if R_0 is a ring itself with the same operations of addition and multiplication as in R. We don't necessarily require that R_0 have a multiplicative identity. In the case when it does not, we call R_0 simply a* commutative ring.

The same idea can be used to define *subintegral domain*. Finally, if F is a field and F_0 is a subset of F, we say that F_0 is a *subfield* if it is a field with the same operations of addition and multiplication as in F.

Exercise 1.6.23.

(*i*) *Let R be a ring and R_0 a non-empty subset of R. Show that R_0 is a subring iff, for any $a, b \in R_0$, we have $a - b$ and ab in R_0.*

(*ii*) *If F is a field and F_0 is non-empty subset of F, are the properties in i enough to ensure that F_0 is a subfield?*

What about order in $\mathbb{Q}$? It is simple to extend the order from $\mathbb{Z}$ to $\mathbb{Q}$. We do this using the notion of a set of positive elements. We say that $a/b \in \mathbb{Q}$ is positive if $ab > 0$ in $\mathbb{Z}$.

Exercise 1.6.24. *Show that the above notion of positivity in $\mathbb{Q}$ satisfies the properties in Exercise* 1.5.9, *or equivalently, the properties of order given in (O1)–(O4).*

Definition 1.6.25. *An integral domain or field in which there is an order relation satisfying (O1)–(O4) is called an* ordered integral domain *or* ordered field *respectively. See Project 1.3 for more about this.*

Remark 1.6.26. *Note that the natural numbers $\mathbb{N}$ may be regarded as a subset of $\mathbb{Z}$, and in turn the integers $\mathbb{Z}$ may be regarded as a subset of $\mathbb{Q}$ by identifying the integer n with the equivalence class $n/1$.*

So what is this all about? We have rules for the integers, and the same rules, along with (M5), are satisfied by the rational numbers. Actually, there are lots of structures other than the integers and the rational numbers that have operations of addition and multiplication, and some of them also carry an order relation.

We want to give two more examples before we leave this section. First, let n be a positive integer greater than or equal to 2 and consider the equivalence relation given in Example 1.6.5. What are the equivalence classes? For example, take $n = 5$. Then we have 5 classes. They are

$$\begin{aligned} C(0) = \overline{0} &= \{0, 5, -5, 10, -10, \dots\} \\ C(1) = \overline{1} &= \{1, 6, -4, 11, -9, \dots\} \\ C(2) = \overline{2} &= \{2, 7, -3, 12, -8, \dots\} \\ C(3) = \overline{3} &= \{3, 8, -2, 13, -7, \dots\} \\ C(4) = \overline{4} &= \{4, 9, -1, 14, -6, \dots\}. \end{aligned}$$

Note that, in this example, we have simplified the notation of equivalence class by denoting the equivalence class $C(a)$ by $\bar{a}$. Observe that $\overline{5} = \overline{0}$, $\overline{6} = \overline{1}$, etc. In general, for an arbitrary n, we will have n classes $\overline{0}, \overline{1}, \dots, \overline{n-1}$. These are called *the equivalence classes modulo n*, or, for short, *mod n*. Moreover, for any integer a, we denote the equivalence class in which a lies by $\bar{a}$. Of course, it is always true that $\bar{a}$ is equal to one of the classes $\overline{0}, \overline{1}, \dots, \overline{n-1}$. Let's define addition and multiplication mod n.

Definition 1.6.27. *Denote the set of equivalence classes $\overline{0}, \overline{1}, \dots, \overline{n-1}$ by $\mathbb{Z}_n$. For $\bar{a}, \bar{b} \in \mathbb{Z}_n$, define $\bar{a} + \bar{b} = \overline{a+b}$ and $\bar{a}\bar{b} = \overline{ab}$.*

Exercise 1.6.28.

(*i*) *Show that addition and multiplication in $\mathbb{Z}_n$ are well-defined.*

(*ii*) *Show that, with these operations, $\mathbb{Z}_n$ is a commutative ring with 1.*

(*iii*) *Show that $\mathbb{Z}_n$ cannot satisfy the order axioms no matter how $>$ is defined.*

(*iv*) *Show that $\mathbb{Z}_2$ is a field but $\mathbb{Z}_4$ is not.*

(*v*) *For p prime, show that $\mathbb{Z}_p$ is a field.*

The second example is the real numbers denoted by $\mathbb{R}$. A construction and complete discussion of the real numbers is given in Chapter 3. For the moment, however, it will suffice to say that the real numbers are an ordered field that contains $\mathbb{Q}$ and has one additional property called the least upper bound property. In Chapter 2, we use the real numbers as an example without being concerned with this additional property.

7. Functions

If you think equivalence relations are everywhere, wait until you see functions. We would all be better off if functions were introduced in kindergarten and studied regularly thereafter. The concept of a function is one of the most important ideas in mathematics. We give the informal definition first because it is much closer to the way people think about functions in practice.

Informally, a function from a set A to a set B is a correspondence between elements of A and elements of B such that each element of A is associated to exactly one element of B. This includes the familiar numerical functions of calculus, where, most often, the sets A and B are the real numbers or subsets thereof. But it also includes many examples which have nothing to do with the concept of numbers.

Example 1.7.1. *Given any set A, there is a unique function from A to A that assigns each element of A to itself. This is called the* identity function *on A.*

What functions do is take elements of a given set and push them into another set (or maybe even the same set). The requirement is that to each element of the first set there must correspond exactly one element of the second. This does not preclude having two distinct elements of the first set correspond to the same element of the second set.

Example 1.7.2. *Let A and B be non-empty sets and choose a fixed element $b \in B$. Define a function from A to B by letting every element of A correspond to b. This is called a* constant function.

Before we go too far with the informal idea, let's give a more formal definition for the notion of function.

Definition 1.7.3. *Let A and B be non-empty sets. A* function *from A to B is a subset of $A \times B$ such that each element of A occurs exactly once as a first coordinate.*

This, of course, is an entirely useless definition, but it does carry with it the idea expressed informally above. That is, to each element of A there corresponds exactly one element of B. When you think of functions you will hardly ever think of ordered pairs. The informal notion of a correspondence satisfying certain properties should be your guide. Here's the notation we use. If A and B are sets and f is a function from A to B, we write $f : A \to B$. If $a \in A$, we write $f(a)$ for the corresponding element of B. So, if we were to write this as an ordered pair, we would write $(a, f(a))$. We also use the notation $a \mapsto f(a)$, read as "a goes to $f(a)$", to indicate that $f(a)$ corresponds to a.

Exercise 1.7.4. *How would you formulate the definition of function if either A or B were the empty set?*

Example 1.7.5. *Take $A = \{a, b, c, d, e\}$ and $B = \{1, 2, 3, 4\}$. Now consider functions from A to B, that is, assign a number to each letter. For example one such function is $\{(a, 1), (b, 2), (c, 3), (d, 4), (e, 2)\}$.*

Exercise 1.7.6. *Determine all the functions from A to B in the previous example.*

Exercise 1.7.7.

(*i*) *If A has n elements and B has m elements, how many functions are there from A to B?*

(*ii*) *Let $B = \{0, 1\}$. Use the conclusion of part i to give an alternate proof of Theorem* 1.4.13.

This is a convenient place to state the *Pigeon Hole Principle.*

Theorem 1.7.8. *(Pigeon Hole Principle) Suppose that m and n are positive integers with $n > m$. If n objects are distributed in m boxes, then some box must contain at least two objects. In terms of functions, the pigeon hole principle can be stated as follows. Suppose that A is a set with n elements, B is a set with m elements, and $n > m$. If $f : A \to B$ is a function, there are at least two distinct elements of A that correspond to the same element of B.*

Exercise 1.7.9. *Prove this any way you choose.*

We turn next to the language of functions. Here is a list of important terms. Let f be a function from A to B. That is, $f : A \to B$.

Definitions 1.7.10.

(a) *The set A is called the* domain *of f.*

(b) *If $A' \subseteq A$, we define $f(A') = \{b \in B \mid \exists a \in A'$ with $f(a) = b\}$. The set $f(A')$ is called the* image of A' in B under f. *In particular, $f(A)$ is the* image of A in B under f. *This is commonly called the* image *of f.*

(c) *Note that there is no reason in the world for thinking that* $f(A) = B$. *If* $f(A) = B$, *we say that* f *is* onto *or* surjective *(*f *is a* surjection*). In general,* B *is called the* range *of* f. *Note that, if we change the range to* $f(A)$, *then* f *is surjective. That is, a function is always surjective onto its image.*

(d) *Along with the property of being a function,* f *may also have the property that each element in the image of* f *corresponds to exactly one element in* A. *This can be written as follows. For any* $a, a' \in A$ *if* $f(a) = f(a')$, *then* $a = a'$. *A function with this property is called* one-to-one *or* injective *(*f *is an* injection*).*

(e) *A function that is one-to-one and onto (that is, injective and surjective) is called* bijective *(*f *is a* bijection*). A bijection between two sets is often called a* one-to-one correspondence *between the sets.*

(f) *Two functions* f *and* g *are the same, or equal, when they have the same domain and same range, and the sets of pairs* $\{(a, f(a))\}$ *and* $\{(a, g(a))\}$ *are identical.*

Exercise 1.7.11. *Determine which of your functions in Exercise* 1.7.6 *are surjective. How many are there? Notice that there are no injections or bijections. Why is this?*

There is a way to combine functions which is very useful for many purposes.

Definition 1.7.12. *Suppose* A, B, *and* C *are sets and* $f : A \to B$ *and* $g : B \to C$ *are functions. The* composition *of* f *and* g *is the function* $g \circ f : A \to C$ *defined by* $(g \circ f)(a) = g(f(a))$.

Of course, you met composition of functions in elementary calculus, and you enjoyed learning the chain rule. There is one very useful property concerning composition of functions, that is, composition of functions is *associative*.

Theorem 1.7.13. *If* A, B, C, *and* D *are sets and* $f : A \to B$, $g : B \to C$, *and* $h : C \to D$ *are functions, then* $h \circ (g \circ f) = (h \circ g) \circ f$.

Proof. Suppose $a \in A$. Then $(h \circ (g \circ f))(a) = h((g \circ f)(a)) = h(g(f(a))) = (h \circ g)(f(a)) = ((h \circ g) \circ f)(a)$. ☠

Let's stop for a minute with the definitions and consider some numerical examples. The sets we work with will be the natural numbers $\mathbb{N}$, the integers

$\mathbb{Z}$, the rational numbers $\mathbb{Q}$, the real numbers $\mathbb{R}$, and the complex numbers $\mathbb{C}$. (You may know what the real and complex numbers are, but we will construct them in Chapter 3.) Often, when writing a function, we will specify a rule that tells us how to associate an element of the range to an element of the domain.

Examples 1.7.14.

(*i*) $f : \mathbb{N} \to \mathbb{N}$, $f(n) = 2n$.

(*ii*) $f : \mathbb{Z} \to \mathbb{Z}$, $f(n) = n + 6$.

(*iii*) $f : \mathbb{N} \to \mathbb{Q}$, $f(n) = n$.

(*iv*) *This is an unusual example. Let* $\mathbb{Q}_+$ *be the set of positive rational numbers written as fractions in base* 10, *and let* $\mathbb{N}$ *be the natural numbers but written in base* 11 *with the numerals being* 0, 1, 2, 3, 4, 5, 6, 7, 8, 9, *d. So, for example, the integer which is written* 21 *in base* 10 *is* 1*d in base* 11, *and* $1222_{(10)} = d11_{(11)}$. *(Incidentally, we are writing the bases in base 10.) Now define a function* $f : \mathbb{Q}_+ \to \mathbb{N}$ *by writing* $\frac{a}{b} = \frac{a_n \dots a_2 a_1}{b_m \dots b_2 b_1}$, *where* a_i *and* b_i *are the* i^{th} *digits of the numerator and denominator (and, of course, integers between* 0 *and* 9*). Then, set* $f(\frac{a}{b}) = a_n \dots a_2 a_1 d b_m \dots b_2 b_1$. *The fraction* $\frac{a}{b}$ *will always be written in lowest terms. For instance, if we take the fraction* 2/3 *in base* 10, *then* $f(2/3) = 2d3$ *in base* 11, *which is the same as the integer* 355 *written in base* 10.

(*v*) *Write the real numbers in terms of their decimal expansions. As usual, we do not allow a real number to end in all* 9*'s repeating. Let* $f : \mathbb{R} \to \mathbb{N}$ *be defined by:* $f(x)$ *equals the third digit of* x *after the decimal point (this is called the* Michelle *function).*

Exercise 1.7.15. *Determine which of the above functions are surjective, injective, or bijective.*

We mentioned above the so-called identity function, and we assign a symbol to it.

Definition 1.7.16. *Let* A *be a set. We give a symbol for the identity function defined in Example* 1.7.1. *The identity function* $I_A : A \to A$ *is defined by* $I_A(a) = a$ *for* $a \in A$.

Now suppose A and B are sets, and $f : A \to B$ is a bijection. Since each element of B comes from only one element of A under the function f, we can define a function $f^{-1} : B \to A$ that sends every element of B back to where it came from.

Definition 1.7.17. *Let $f : A \to B$ be a bijection. Then the* inverse *of f is the function $f^{-1} : B \to A$ defined as follows. If $b \in B$, then we set $f^{-1}(b) = a$ where a is the unique element of A such that $f(a) = b$.*

Exercise 1.7.18. *Show that $f^{-1} \circ f = I_A$ and $f \circ f^{-1} = I_B$.*

Exercise 1.7.19. *Suppose A, B, and C are sets and $f : A \to B$ and $g : B \to C$ are bijections. Show that $g \circ f$ is a bijection. Compute $(g \circ f)^{-1} : C \to A$.*

Exercise 1.7.20. *Given $f : A \to B$, suppose there exist $g, h : B \to A$ so that $f \circ g = I_B$ and $h \circ f = I_A$. Show that f is a bijection and that $g = h = f^{-1}$.*

Exercise 1.7.21. *Let $\mathbb{R}_+$ be the positive real numbers and define $f : \mathbb{R}_+ \to \mathbb{R}_+$ by $f(x) = x^2$. Show that f is a bijection from $\mathbb{R}_+$ to $\mathbb{R}_+$ and find f^{-1}. If we expand the domain and include all real numbers, what happens?*

Exercise 1.7.22. *Define $f : \mathbb{N} \to \mathbb{Z}$ by*

$$f(n) = \begin{cases} \dfrac{n}{2}, & \text{if } n \text{ is even} \\[2ex] \dfrac{1-n}{2}, & \text{if } n \text{ is odd.} \end{cases}$$

Show that f is a bijection.

Whether or nor a function $f : A \to B$ is a bijection, we can take a subset $A' \subseteq A$ and consider its image $f(A') \subseteq B$. Moreover, we can take a subset B' of B and consider the *preimage* of B' in A.

Definition 1.7.23. *Suppose A and B are sets and $f : A \to B$ is a function. If $B' \subseteq B$, then the* preimage *of B' in A is defined as*

$$f^{-1}(B') = \{a \in A \mid f(a) \in B'\}.$$

So, $f^{-1}(B')$ is everything in A that is pushed into B' by the function f. Let's make a few quick observations about the empty set.

(1) $f(\varnothing) = \varnothing$.
(2) $f^{-1}(\varnothing) = \varnothing$.
(3) More generally, if $B' \subseteq B$ and $B' \cap f(A) = \varnothing$, then $f^{-1}(B') = \varnothing$.

Take heed: given any subset $B' \subseteq B$, its preimage $f^{-1}(B')$ always exists. Despite the use of the f^{-1} notation, this has nothing to do with whether or not f has an inverse.

There are four basic results on images and preimages.

Theorem 1.7.24. *Suppose A and B are sets and $f : A \to B$ is a function. Let $A_1, A_2 \subseteq A$ and $B_1, B_2 \subseteq B$. Then*

(*i*) $f(A_1 \cup A_2) = f(A_1) \cup f(A_2)$;

(*ii*) $f(A_1 \cap A_2) \subseteq f(A_1) \cap f(A_2)$;

(*iii*) $f^{-1}(B_1 \cup B_2) = f^{-1}(B_1) \cup f^{-1}(B_2)$;

(*iv*) $f^{-1}(B_1 \cap B_2) = f^{-1}(B_1) \cap f^{-1}(B_2)$.

Proof. The proof is standard stuff. We will prove *iii*. Take $x \in f^{-1}(B_1 \cup B_2)$. Then $f(x) \in B_1 \cup B_2$ so $f(x) \in B_1$ or $f(x) \in B_2$. Hence $x \in f^{-1}(B_1)$ or $x \in f^{-1}(B_2)$. That is, $x \in f^{-1}(B_1) \cup f^{-1}(B_2)$ and so $f^{-1}(B_1 \cup B_2) \subseteq f^{-1}(B_1) \cup f^{-1}(B_2)$. Actually, you can read this argument backwards to show that $f^{-1}(B_1) \cup f^{-1}(B_2) \subseteq f^{-1}(B_1 \cup B_2)$. Thus, finally, the sets are equal. This is terribly boring, but you should do *i* and *iv* to discipline yourself. On the other hand, *ii* is more interesting.

Exercise 1.7.25. *Find an example to show that equality does not necessarily hold in ii.*

Exercise 1.7.26. *Show that equality holds in ii of Theorem* 1.7.24 *if f is an injection. In fact, if equality holds in ii for all subsets $A_1, A_2 \subseteq A$ then f is an injection.*

Exercise 1.7.27. *Let A and B be sets and let $f : A \to B$ be a function. Suppose that $\{A_i\}_{i \in I}$ is a collection of subsets of A and $\{B_j\}_{j \in J}$ is a collection of subsets of B. Show that*

(*i*) $f(\bigcup_{i \in I} A_i) = \bigcup_{i \in I} f(A_i)$;

(*ii*) $f(\bigcap_{i \in I} A_i) \subseteq \bigcap_{i \in I} f(A_i)$;

(*iii*) $f^{-1}(\bigcup_{j \in J} B_j) = \bigcup_{j \in J} f^{-1}(B_j)$;

(*iv*) $f^{-1}(\bigcap_{j \in J} B_j) = \bigcap_{j \in J} f^{-1}(B_j)$.

Note that, in this exercise, the number of sets in the union and intersection is not necessarily finite.

To close this section, we consider two important examples of functions.

Definition 1.7.28. *The* greatest integer function $[\,\cdot\,] : \mathbb{R} \to \mathbb{R}$ *is defined by: $[x]$ equals the largest integer that is less than or equal to x.*

Example 1.7.29. $[n] = n$ *for* $n \in \mathbb{Z}$; $[17.5] = 17$; $[\sqrt{2}] = 1$; $[\pi] = 3$; $[-e] = -3$, *etc.*

Here is the graph of the greatest integer function.

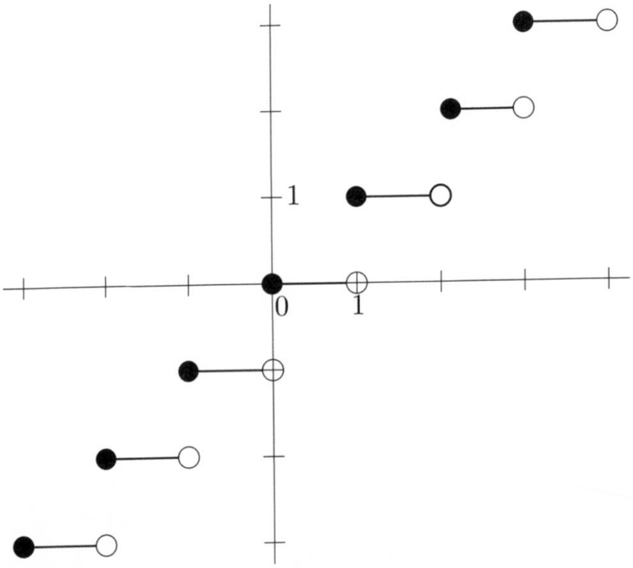

Exercise 1.7.30. *Express the Michelle function (Example 1.7.14) in terms of the greatest integer function. Graph the Michelle function.*

Now we define polynomial functions. Polynomial functions are perfect examples of functions that fit into the "What is my rule?" category. Here is a polynomial function with its rule. Let $p(x)$ be the function given by $p(x) = x^2 + 2x + 1$. You can plug in numbers for x and get values for $p(x)$. For instance, $p(0) = 1$ and $p(1) = 4$, and $p(\sqrt{2}) = 3 + 2\sqrt{2}$. Let's be a little more formal here.

Definition 1.7.31. *A* polynomial function $p : \mathbb{R} \to \mathbb{R}$ *is a function whose rule of correspondence is given by an expression of the form*

$$p(x) = a_n x^n + a_{n-1}x^{n-1} + \cdots + a_1 x + a_0$$

where n is a natural number or zero, and the coefficients $a_n, a_{n-1}, \ldots, a_1, a_0$ *are in $\mathbb{R}$. Note that the function $p(x) = 0$, in which the coefficients $a_0, a_1, \ldots,$ a_n are all zero, is a polynomial function. If $p(x) \neq 0$, then there is a largest power of x (including 0) with a nonzero coefficient. This power is called the* degree *of the polynomial function. We make the convention that the degree of the polynomial function 0 is $-\infty$.*

As an ordered pair, a polynomial function is written $(x, p(x))$. In the above definition, we say that p is a *polynomial function with real coefficients.* Notice that we could restrict the coefficients to be integers or rational numbers. In these cases, we could restrict the domain to be the integers or rational numbers respectively.

Examples 1.7.32.

(i) $p(x) = 0$ *is a polynomial of degree* $-\infty$ *with coefficients in* $\mathbb{Z}$.

(ii) $p(x) = 17x^2 + 2x - 7$ *is a polynomial of degree 2 with coefficients in* $\mathbb{Z}$.

(iii) $p(x) = (\sqrt{2} - 1)x^{83} + \pi x^{17} + \sqrt[3]{2}x^{11} + ex^7 + 6$ *is a polynomial of degree 83 with coefficients in* $\mathbb{R}$.

(iv) $p(x) = 17/4$ *is a polynomial of degree 0 with coefficients in* $\mathbb{Q}$.

You should have experience in adding and multiplying polynomial functions, so we won't go into details. Here are a couple of interesting exercises.

Exercise 1.7.33. *If* p *and* q *are polynomial functions with real coefficients, show that* $\deg(pq) = \deg(p) + \deg(q)$. *To accommodate the zero polynomial, we use the convention* $-\infty + k = -\infty$ *for any* k.

Exercise 1.7.34. *If* p *and* q *are polynomial functions with real coefficients and* $\deg(p) \neq \deg(q)$, *show that* $\deg(p + q) = \max(\deg(p), \deg(q))$. *In any case,* $\deg(p + q) \leq \max(\deg(p), \deg(q))$.

Exercise 1.7.35. *Show that the set of polynomial functions from* $\mathbb{R}$ *to* $\mathbb{R}$ *is an integral domain.*

Another important type of function is that of a sequence. Sequences will occur regularly throughout the remainder of the text.

Definition 1.7.36. *Let* X *be a non-empty set. A* sequence *in* X *is a function* $f : \mathbb{N} \to X$.

Thus, respecting the order in $\mathbb{N}$, we write a sequence

$$f(1), f(2), \ldots, f(n), \ldots$$

or $(x_1, x_2, \ldots, x_n, \ldots)$. We will also adopt the notation $(x_n)_{n\in\mathbb{N}}$.

Remark 1.7.37. *It is also useful to have sequences indexed by the non-negative integers, or even the set of all integers. So, for example, we might have* $(x_0, x_1, \ldots, x_n, \ldots)$ *or* $(x_n)_{n\geq 0}$. *If the index set is* $\mathbb{Z}$, *we write* $(\ldots, x_{-2}, x_{-1}, x_0, x_1, x_2, \ldots)$, *or* $(x_n)_{n\in\mathbb{Z}}$.

Exercise 1.7.38. *If* A_1 *and* A_2 *are subsets of a universal set* X, *show that there is a bijection between the Cartesian product* $A_1 \times A_2$ *and the set of all functions* $f : \{1, 2\} \to X$ *such that* $f(1) \in A_1$ *and* $f(2) \in A_2$. *Do the same for any finite number of subsets of* X.

This exercise is the beginning of our study of the axiom of choice, which comes up later in the chapter.

8. Countability and Other Basic Ideas

Finally, we come to a serious discussion of infinite sets. There are great pitfalls involved in any discussion of set theory, and our basic goal is to avoid these pitfalls while still having appropriate definitions, ideas and facts. In analysis, most of the sets we deal with are infinite. In fact, most of them contain the integers in one way or another. Moreover, any discussion of continuity and change involves infinite sets. So, of course, in our usual perverse manner, we define finite sets first.

Definition 1.8.1. *A set A is* finite *if A is empty or there exists $n \in \mathbb{N}$ such that there is a bijection $f : A \to \{1, 2, \ldots, n\}$, where $\{1, 2, \ldots, n\}$ is the set of all natural numbers less than or equal to n. In this case, we say A has n elements.*

Exercise 1.8.2. *If A is a finite set and B is a subset of A, show that B is a finite set. In addition, show that if B is a proper subset, then the number of elements in B is less than the number of elements in A.*

There is a natural and useful characteristic of finite sets:

Theorem 1.8.3. *If A is a finite set and B is a proper subset of A, then there is no bijection between B and A.*

Proof. Suppose A has n elements and B has m elements with $m < n$. Then the Pigeonhole Principle tells us that, for any function from A to B, there is an element of B that is the image of at least two different elements of A. ☠

Exercise 1.8.4. *Show that the following are finite sets:*

(*i*) *The English alphabet.*

(*ii*) *The set of all possible twelve letter words made up of letters from the English alphabet.*

(*iii*) *The set of all subsets of a finite set.*

This approach to things makes the definition of infinite sets quite simple:

Definition 1.8.5. *An* infinite *set is a set that is not finite.*

The notion of cardinality of a set is very important. Of course, most authors don't define cardinality. Instead, they say what it means for two sets to have the same cardinal number. This will do for our purposes.

Definition 1.8.6. *The* cardinal number *of a non-empty finite set A is the number of elements in A, that is, the cardinal number of A is the natural number n if there is a bijection between A and $\{k \in \mathbb{N} \mid 1 \leq k \leq n\}$. The cardinal number of the empty set is 0.*

Definition 1.8.7. *A set A has* cardinality $\aleph_0$ *(pronounced "aleph null" or "aleph naught") if it can be put in one-to-one correspondence with $\mathbb{N}$, that is there is a bijection between the set and $\mathbb{N}$. In general, two sets have the same cardinality if they can be put in one-to-one correspondence with each other.*

Example 1.8.8. *The set $\mathbb{N}$ has cardinality $\aleph_0$ (this should not come as a surprise).*

Although we will not see one for a while, be assured that there are infinite sets with cardinality other than $\aleph_0$.

Example 1.8.9. *The set $\mathbb{N} \cup \{0\}$ has cardinality $\aleph_0$ because the function $f : \mathbb{N} \cup \{0\} \to \mathbb{N}$ given by $f(n) = n + 1$ is a bijection.*

Example 1.8.10. *The set $\mathbb{Z}$ has cardinality $\aleph_0$ because the function $f : \mathbb{Z} \to \mathbb{N}$ given by*

$$f(z) = \begin{cases} 2z + 2, & \text{if } z \geq 0 \\ -2z - 1, & \text{if } z < 0 \end{cases}$$

is a bijection.

There is a very useful theorem that asserts the existence of a one-to-one correspondence between two sets. This relieves us of the burden of constructing a bijection between two sets to show that they have the same cardinality.

Theorem 1.8.11 (Schröder-Bernstein). *If A and B are sets, and there exist injections $f : A \to B$ and $g : B \to A$, then there exists a bijection between A and B.*

Proof. First, we divide A into three disjoint subsets. For each $x \in A$, consider the list of elements

$$S_x = \{x, g^{-1}(x), f^{-1} \circ g^{-1}(x), g^{-1} \circ f^{-1} \circ g^{-1}(x), \ldots\}.$$

The elements of this sequence are called *predecessors* of x. Notice that in S_x, we start with $x \in A$. Then $g^{-1}(x) \in B$ if $g^{-1}(x)$ exists (x may not be in the image of g). For each $x \in A$, exactly one of the three following possibilities occurs.

(1) The list S_x is infinite.

(2) The last term in the list is an element of A. That is, the last term is $y = x$ or is of the form $y = f^{-1} \circ g^{-1} \circ \cdots \circ g^{-1}(x)$, and $g^{-1}(y)$ does not exist (i.e. y is not in the image of g). In this case, we say that S_x *stops in A*.

(3) The last term in the list is an element of B. That is, the last term is $z = g^{-1}(x)$ or is of the form $z = g^{-1} \circ f^{-1} \circ \cdots \circ g^{-1}(x)$ and $f^{-1}(z)$ does not exist (i.e. z is not in the image of f). In this case, we say that S_x *stops in* B.

Let the corresponding subsets of A be denoted by A_1, A_2, A_3. Similarly, define the corresponding subsets of B. That is:

$$\begin{aligned} B_1 &= \{y \in B \mid y \text{ has infinitely many predecessors}\}, \\ B_2 &= \{y \in B \mid \text{the predecessors of } y \text{ stop in } A\}, \text{ and} \\ B_3 &= \{y \in B \mid \text{the predecessors of } y \text{ stop in } B\}. \end{aligned}$$

Now observe that $f : A_1 \to B_1$, $g : B_1 \to A_1$ are both bijections. Also, $f : A_2 \to B_2$ and $g : B_3 \to A_3$ are bijections.

Exercise 1.8.12. *Suppose A, B, and C are subsets of a set X such that $A \subseteq B \subseteq C$. Show that if A and C have the same cardinality, then A and B have the same cardinality.*

Example 1.8.13. *The set $\mathbb{Q}_+$ has cardinality $\aleph_0$ (recall that $\mathbb{Q}_+$ denotes the positive rational numbers). Here are three proofs:*

(1) *This is a very common and very sloppy proof. However, the underlying idea will stand us in good stead.*

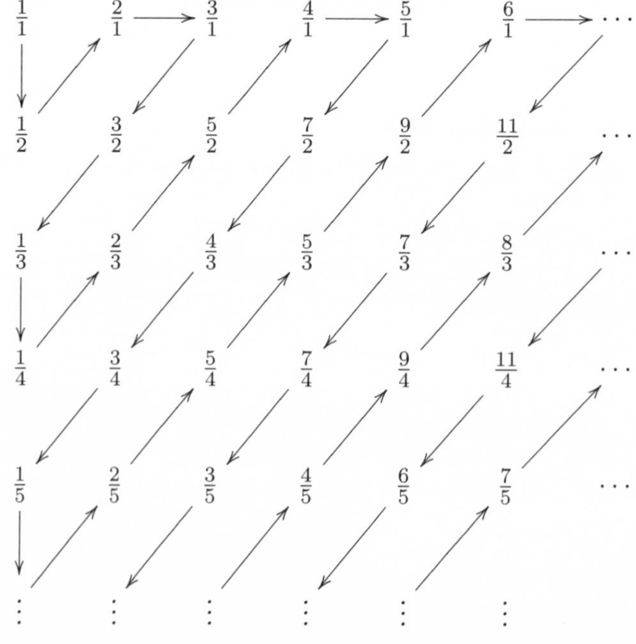

To find a bijection between $\mathbb{N}$ and $\mathbb{Q}_+$, we write all the positive fractions in a grid, with all fractions with denominator 1 in the first row, all fractions with denominator 2 in the second row, all

fractions with denominator 3 in the third row, etc. Now go through row by row and throw out all the fractions that aren't written in lowest terms. Then, starting at the upper left hand corner, trace a path through all the remaining numbers as above.

We can count along the path we drew, assigning a natural number to each fraction. So $\frac{1}{1} \to 1$, $\frac{1}{2} \to 2$, $\frac{2}{1} \to 3$, $\frac{3}{1} \to 4$, $\frac{3}{2} \to 5$, *etc. This is a bijection. Therefore,* $\mathbb{Q}_+$ *has cardinality* $\aleph_0$. *Although this is a very common proof, the formula for the bijection is not at all obvious. It is very difficult to see, for example, which rational number corresponds to* $1,000,000$.

(2) *In this proof, we'll make use of the Schröder-Bernstein Theorem. It is easy to inject* $\mathbb{N}$ *into* $\mathbb{Q}_+$*; simply send* n *to* n. *The injection from* $\mathbb{Q}_+$ *to* $\mathbb{N}$ *will be the one we used in Example* 1.7.14:*iv (where* $\frac{a}{b}$ *is sent to* $adb_{(11)}$*). Each number which is the image of a fraction has one and only one d in it, so it is easy to see which fraction is represented by a given integer. According to Schröder-Bernstein, two injections make a bijection, so* $\mathbb{Q}_+$ *has cardinality* $\aleph_0$.

(3) *Write each positive fraction in lowest terms and factor the numerator and denominator into primes, so that* $\frac{p}{q} = \frac{p_1^{\alpha_1} p_2^{\alpha_2} \cdots p_n^{\alpha_n}}{q_1^{\beta_1} q_2^{\beta_2} \cdots q_m^{\beta_m}}$, *with* $p_i \neq q_j$. *If by chance* p *or* q *is* 1, *and can't be factored, write it as* 1^1. *Then let* $f : \mathbb{Q}_+ \to \mathbb{N}$ *be defined by*

$$f\left(\frac{p_1^{\alpha_1} p_2^{\alpha_2} \cdots p_n^{\alpha_n}}{q_1^{\beta_1} q_2^{\beta_2} \cdots q_m^{\beta_m}}\right) = p_1^{2\alpha_1} p_2^{2\alpha_2} \cdots p_n^{2\alpha_n} q_1^{2\beta_1 - 1} q_2^{2\beta_2 - 1} \cdots q_m^{2\beta_m - 1}.$$

In particular, note that if $a \in \mathbb{Q}_+$ *is an integer, then* $f(a) = a^2$.

Exercise 1.8.14. *Verify that* f *is a bijection.*

Exercise 1.8.15. *Suppose that* $N = 10^k$ *for some integer* k. *Find* $p/q \in \mathbb{Q}_+$ *such that* $f(p/q) = N$.

Exercise 1.8.16. *Use any one of the above three proofs to show that* $\mathbb{Q}$ *has cardinality* $\aleph_0$.

Exercise 1.8.17. *Show that the natural numbers form an infinite set.*

Exercise 1.8.18. *Show that any set that has the same cardinal number as* $\mathbb{N}$ *is an infinite set.*

Note: A set is called *countably infinite* if it has cardinality $\aleph_0$ (that is, if it is in one-to-one correspondence with the natural numbers). The term "countable" (or sometimes "*denumerable*)" is used in several ways. Many people use it to refer to infinite sets that are in one-to-one correspondence with $\mathbb{N}$, while others include finite sets when they say countable. This is not something to get disturbed about. We will say that a set is *countable* if it is finite, or countably infinite.

Exercise 1.8.19. *Show that a subset of a countable set is countable.*

Exercise 1.8.20. *Show that the set of all polynomial functions with integer coefficients is a countable set.*

Theorem 1.8.21. *If A is an infinite set, then A has a countably infinite subset.*

Proof. Take any infinite set A and choose an element a_1 in A. Let $A_1 = A \setminus \{a_1\}$. By the definition of infinite set, A_1 is infinite. So we choose a_2 in A_1 and define $A_2 = A \setminus \{a_1, a_2\}$. Since A is not finite, we can continue to choose elements. Thus, if we have chosen $a_1, \ldots, a_n$, we consider $A_n = A \setminus \{a_1, \ldots, a_n\}$. Since A is infinite, we can choose an element a_{n+1} in A_n. Continuing inductively, we obtain our desired countable subset. Note that this countable set may be all of A.

Remark 1.8.22. *There is some discussion among mathematicians as to whether the preceding proof involves the Axiom of Choice. The Axiom of Choice in its fullest form will be discussed below. However, one can make the argument that it requires some sort of choice mechanism to pick an element from a non-empty set. The technique that we use in the proof of Theorem* 1.8.21 *is sometimes referred to as "the countable Axiom of Choice."*

We could pursue an alternate definition of an infinite set. In fact, we could define infinite sets first and then say that a finite set is a set that is not infinite.

Redefinition 1.8.23. *A set is* infinite *if there is a bijection between the set and one of its proper subsets.*

Redefinition 1.8.24. *A* finite *set is a set that is not infinite.*

To show the equivalence of the two definitions, recall that in Theorem 1.8.3 we showed there is no bijection between a finite set and any of its proper subsets. This means that if a set is infinite by our new definition, it is not finite (hence, infinite) by the old definition too. Next, let's show that any set that is infinite by the old definition is bijective with one of its proper subsets.

Proof. Say A is an infinite set and $B \subseteq A$ is countably infinite. Then we can write $B = \{b_1, b_2, \ldots, b_n, \ldots\}$. Now define $f : A \to A \setminus \{b_1\}$ as follows:

for $a \in A \setminus B$, $f(a) = a$, and for $b_i \in B$, $f(b_i) = b_{i+1}$. Thus f is a bijection between A and $A \setminus \{b_1\}$. Therefore, our definitions are equivalent.

We now turn to operations involving infinite sets.

Facts 1.8.25.

(1) *If A_1 and A_2 are countable sets, then $A_1 \cup A_2$ is a countable set.*

(2) *If A_1, A_2, ..., A_n are countable sets, then $\bigcup_{j=1}^{n} A_j$ is a countable set.*

(3) *Let $\{A_j\}_{j\in\mathbb{N}}$ be a countable collection of countable sets. Then $\bigcup_{j\in\mathbb{N}} A_j$ is a countable set.*

Proof. We prove 3 only. You can prove the other two (or deduce them from 3).

Write $A_j = \{a_{j,1}, a_{j,2}, \ldots, a_{j,n}, \ldots\}$. We use the diagonal process as in Example 1.8.13. Simply write

$$\begin{gathered} A_1 : a_{1,1}, a_{1,2}, \ldots, a_{1,n}, \ldots \\ A_2 : a_{2,1}, a_{2,2}, \ldots, a_{2,n}, \ldots \\ \vdots \\ A_m : a_{m,1}, a_{m,2}, \ldots, a_{m,n}, \ldots \\ \vdots \end{gathered}$$

Now count diagonally, ignoring repetitions.

Now let's take a look at Cartesian products. It is clear from the ideas presented above that if A_1 and A_2 are countable, then $A_1 \times A_2$ is countable.

Exercise 1.8.26.

(*i*) *Show that if A_1, A_2, ..., A_n are countable, then $A_1 \times A_2 \times \cdots \times A_n$ is countable.*

(*ii*) *What can you say about the countable Cartesian product of countable sets?*

Next we look at the power set $\wp(A)$ for any set A.

Theorem 1.8.27. *If A is any set (including the empty set), there is no bijection between A and $\wp(A)$.*

Proof. This is clear if A is the empty set. Suppose that there is a bijection between A and $\wp(A)$. If $a \in A$, let P_a be the subset of A associated with it. Now consider the set $B = \{a \mid a \notin P_a\}$. The set B must be associated to some element of A, which we creatively call b, so that $B = P_b$. Is b in B? For b to be in B, we must have that $b \notin P_b$. But $B = P_b$, so therefore b is not in B. But then $b \in P_b$, which means that b is in B. This is a contradiction. Therefore, there is no bijection between A and $\wp(A)$. ☹

Definition 1.8.28. *If A is a countably infinite set, then the cardinality of $\wp(A)$ is denoted by* $\mathbf{c}$.

Exercise 1.8.29. *Show that the definition of the cardinal number $\mathbf{c}$ does not depend on the choice of the countably infinite set A. That is, if A and B are countably infinite sets, then there is a bijection between $\wp(A)$ and $\wp(B)$.*

Remark 1.8.30. *At this point, we observe that if A is a countably infinite set, $A = \{a_1, a_2, \ldots, a_n, \ldots\}$, then $\wp(A)$ is in one-to-one correspondence with the set of all functions from A to the set $\{0, 1\}$. This correspondence is defined as follows. If B is a subset of A, then we define the map $f_B : A \to \{0, 1\}$ by $f_B(a_j) = 1$ if a_j is in B, 0 if a_j is not in B. In accordance with the notation of Theorem* 1.4.13, *we will write $\mathbf{c} = 2^{\aleph_0}$. Observe that $f_B(a)$ can be viewed as a binary expansion of a real number between* 0 *and* 1.

Exercise 1.8.31. *Suppose that A is a non-empty set. Show that $\wp(A)$ is in one to one correspondence with the set of all functions from A to $\{0, 1\}$.*

One of the most important sets of numbers that we deal with in this book is the collection of real numbers $\mathbb{R}$. In Chapter 3, we will go through the formal construction of the real numbers from the rational numbers. For the present discussion, we can just consider the set of real numbers to be the set of all terminating or infinite decimals with the convention that no decimal expansion can terminate in all 9's. There are two things to show about the reals. The first is the proof due to Cantor that the reals are uncountable, and the second is that the cardinality of the real numbers is in fact $\mathbf{c}$.

Theorem 1.8.32. *The set of all real numbers between* 0 *and* 1 *is not countable.*

Proof. We first note that the decimal expansion of a real number is unique, since it does not end in all nines. In this case, we always round up the digit that occurs before the sequence of nines. To prove that this set is not countable, we assume that it is, and list the real numbers between 0 and 1 vertically.

$$
\begin{aligned}
a_1 &= 0.a_{1,1}a_{1,2}\cdots a_{1,n}\cdots \\
a_2 &= 0.a_{2,1}a_{2,2}\cdots a_{2,n}\cdots \\
&\vdots \\
a_m &= 0.a_{m,1}a_{m,2}\cdots a_{m,n}\cdots \\
&\vdots
\end{aligned}
$$

We now proceed using a process similar to the one used in the proof of Theorem 1.8.27 to produce a real number between 0 and 1 that is not on our list. We construct a number $b = 0.b_1b_2\dots b_n\dots$ by proceeding diagonally down the list as follows: if $a_{1,1} = 1$, take $b_1 = 2$. If $a_{1,1} \neq 1$, take $b_1 = 1$. Next, if $a_{2,2} = 1$, take $b_2 = 2$. If $a_{2,2} \neq 1$, take $b_2 = 1$. Continuing this process, we see that the decimal $b = 0.b_1b_2\dots b_n\dots$ is a real number, since it does not end in all nines, but cannot be on our list, since it differs from each number we list in at least one digit. Consequently, the real numbers between 0 and 1 are not countable. ☠

Theorem 1.8.33. *The cardinality of the real numbers between* 0 *and* 1 *is* $\mathbf{c} = 2^{\aleph_0}$.

Proof. To write down an exact bijection between $\wp(\mathbb{N})$ and the real numbers between 0 and 1 requires some care. The standard way to do this is to write the binary expansions of all real numbers between 0 and 1 in such a way that no expansion terminates in all ones. In considering the corresponding subsets of $\mathbb{N}$, we first remove two specific subsets of $\wp(\mathbb{N})$. We remove the two collections $A_f = \{C \in \wp(\mathbb{N}) \mid C \text{ is finite}\}$ and $A_{cf} = \{D \in \wp(\mathbb{N}) \mid {}^cD \text{ is finite}\}$. The collection $\wp(\mathbb{N}) \setminus (A_f \cup A_{cf})$ is in one-to-one correspondence with all binary expansions which have an infinite number of ones but do not terminate in all ones. We get the required bijection by Remark 1.8.30.

We can place A_f into one-to-one correspondence with the set of all finite binary expansions with 0 in the first place, and A_{cf} into one-to-one correspondence with the set of all finite binary expansions with 1 in the first place. ☠

Exercise 1.8.34. *Write down these last two bijections explicitly.*

Exercise 1.8.35.

(*i*) *Prove that the countable union of sets of cardinality* $\mathbf{c}$ *again has cardinality* $\mathbf{c}$.

(*ii*) *Prove that the set of all real numbers has cardinality* $\mathbf{c}$.

(*iii*) *Prove that the set of irrational numbers in* $\mathbb{R}$ *has cardinality* $\mathbf{c}$.

How big do cardinal numbers get? For instance, the power set of $\mathbb{R}$ is "bigger than" $\mathbb{R}$. In fact, the power set of $\mathbb{R}$ can be identified with the set of all maps from $\mathbb{R}$ into $\{0, 1\}$ just as we did above for the power set of $\mathbb{N}$. Thus, we have $^{\#}(\wp(\mathbb{R})) = 2^{\mathbf{c}}$. We sometimes denote $2^{\mathbf{c}}$ by $\mathbf{f}$.

The following theorem is interesting and useful.

Theorem 1.8.36. *There is a bijection between the unit interval and the unit square.*

Proof. Let $I = [0,1] = \{x \in \mathbb{R} \mid 0 \leq x \leq 1\}$, and $I^2 = [0,1] \times [0,1]$. This seems like a great time to use Schröder-Bernstein. The function $f : I \to I^2$ defined by $f(x) = (x, 0)$ is an injection. Define the function $g : I^2 \to I$ by the rule $g((a_0.a_1a_2 \ldots a_n \ldots, b_0.b_1b_2 \ldots b_n \ldots)) = (0.a_0b_0a_1b_1a_2b_2 \ldots a_nb_n \ldots)$, where $a_0.a_1a_2 \ldots a_n \ldots$ and $b_0.b_1b_2 \ldots b_n \ldots$ are decimal expansions of the coordinates of any point in I^2 (of course, the decimal expansion is prohibited from ending in all 9s). The function $g : I^2 \to I$ is an injection. Therefore, there is a bijection between I and I^2. ☹

9. Axiom of Choice

Definition 1.9.1. *A* partially ordered set *is a set X with a relation $\leq$ that is reflexive, transitive, and anti-symmetric (that means that if $a \leq b$ and $b \leq a$, then $a = b$). A* totally ordered set *is a partially ordered set with the additional property that, for any two elements $a, b \in X$, either $a \leq b$ or $b \leq a$. A* well-ordered set *is a totally ordered set in which any non-empty subset has a least element.*

Example 1.9.2.

(1) *$(\mathbb{N}, \leq)$ is a totally ordered set, as are $(\mathbb{Z}, \leq)$, $(\mathbb{Q}, \leq)$ and $(\mathbb{R}, \leq)$.*

(2) *Let X be a set, and let $\wp(X)$ be the collection of all subsets of X. Then $(\wp(X), \subseteq)$ is a partially ordered set.*

Definition 1.9.3. *Let Y be a subset of a partially ordered set X. An* upper bound *for Y is an element $a \in X$ such that $y \leq a$ for all $y \in Y$. A* least upper bound *for Y is an element $b \in X$ such that b is an upper bound for Y, and if a is an upper bound for Y, then $b \leq a$. The least upper bound is sometimes abbreviated* lub, *and is also denoted as* sup *(supremum). You can figure out what a* lower bound *and* greatest lower bound (glb) *are. The greatest lower bound is also denoted by* inf *(infimum).*

Observe that a subset of a partially ordered set may fail to have an upper bound or a lower bound.

Exercise 1.9.4. *If a subset Y of a partially ordered set X has an upper bound, determine whether or not Y must have a least upper bound. If Y has a least upper bound, determine whether or not this least upper bound is unique.*

Definition 1.9.5. *In a partially ordered set, an element b is* maximal *if $a \geq b$ implies $a = b$.*

We turn now to one of the major topics of this chapter, the axiom of choice, and various logically equivalent statements. For many years, there has been considerable discussion among mathematicians about the use of the axiom of choice and the seemingly contradictory results that come along with it. We find it indispensable in obtaining a number of results in mathematics.

The Axiom of Choice Given a collection $\mathcal{C}$ of sets that does not include the empty set, there exists a function $\phi : \mathcal{C} \to \cup_{C \in \mathcal{C}} C$ with the property that $\forall A \in \mathcal{C}$, $\phi(A) \in A$.

Another way of looking at this is as follows. Suppose $\{A_i\}_{i \in I}$ is a collection of non-empty sets indexed by an index set I. A *choice function* is then defined as a map $\phi : I \to \bigcup_{i \in I} A_i$ such that $\phi(i) \in A_i$. The axiom of choice can then be rephrased.

The Axiom of Choice For every collection of non-empty sets there exists a choice function.

The Axiom of Choice is equivalent to a number of other very useful statements which are not at all obvious. Here they are, in no particular order.

Let X be a partially ordered set. The collection $\wp(X)$ can be partially ordered by inclusion, see Example 1.9.2. This partial ordering on $\wp(X)$ is used in some of the statements below.

Hausdorff Maximality Principle Every partially ordered set X contains a totally ordered subset that is maximal with respect to the ordering on $\wp(X)$.

Zorn's Lemma If a non-empty partially ordered set has the property that every non-empty totally ordered subset has an upper bound, then the partially ordered set has a maximal element.

Well-Ordering Principle Every set can be well-ordered.

This is quite a different statement from the Well-Ordering Principle for the integers.

The following lemma is slightly complicated, but it will allow us to prove the equivalence of the above statements with little trouble.

Lemma 1.9.6. *Suppose that $(X, \leq)$ is a non-empty partially ordered set such that every non-empty totally ordered subset has a least upper bound. If $f : X \to X$ is such that $f(x) \geq x$ for all $x \in X$, then there is some $w \in X$ such that $f(w) = w$.*

Proof. First we reduce to the case when X contains a least element, call it b. In fact, if X is non-empty choose any $b \in X$ and replace X by $X' = \{x \in X \mid x \geq b\}$. It is clear that X' is stable under f (that is

$f(X') \subseteq X')$ and has the same properties as X. We call a subset Y of X "admissible" if

(1) $b \in Y$

(2) $f(Y) \subseteq Y$

(3) Every lub of a totally ordered subset of Y belongs to Y.

X is certainly admissible, and the intersection of any family of admissible sets is admissible. Let W be the intersection of all admissible sets. The set $\{x \in X \mid b \leq x\}$ is admissible, so if $y \in W$, then $b \leq y$.

We will now construct a totally ordered subset of W with the property that its least upper bound is a fixed point of f. Consider the set $P = \{x \in W \mid \text{ if } y \in W \text{ and } y < x \text{ then } f(y) \leq x\}$. Note that P is non-empty since $b \in P$. First we show that any element of P can be compared to any element of W and hence P is totally ordered.

Now fix an $x \in P$ and define $A_x = \{z \in W \mid z \leq x \text{ or } z \geq f(x)\}$. We would like to show that A_x is admissible.

(1) Obviously, $b \in A_x$ since $b \leq x$.

(2) Suppose $z \in A_x$. There are three possibilities. If $z < x$, $f(z) \leq x$ by the conditions of P, so $f(z) \in A_x$. If $z = x$, $f(z) = f(x) \geq f(x)$ so $f(z) \in A_x$. If $z \geq f(x)$, then $f(z) \geq z \geq f(x)$ so $f(z) \in A_x$.

(3) Finally, let Y be a totally ordered non-empty subset of A_x, and let y_0 be the lub of Y in X. Then $y_0 \in W$, since W is admissible. If $z \leq x$ for all $z \in Y$ then $y_0 \leq x$ and hence $y_0 \in A_x$. Otherwise $z \geq f(x)$ for some $z \in Y$, which implies $y_0 \geq f(x)$, so $y_0 \in A_x$.

Thus, A_x is admissible.

Since A_x is an admissible subset of W, $A_x = W$. Put another way, if $x \in P$ and $z \in W$, then either $z \leq x$ or $z \geq f(x) \geq x$, and thus P is totally ordered. Therefore P has a least upper bound, call it x_0. Again $x_0 \in W$ and $f(x_0) \in W$ because W is admissible. We will now show $f(x_0) = x_0$. First we claim $x_0 \in P$. Indeed, if $y \in W$ and $y < x_0$, then there exists $x \in P$ with $y < x \leq x_0$, whence $f(y) \leq x \leq x_0$. Let $y \in W$ and suppose $y < f(x_0)$. As we saw above $A_{x_0} = W$, so we have $y \leq x_0$. If $y = x_0$, then $f(y) = f(x_0) \leq f(x_0)$. If $y < x_0$, then $f(y) \leq x_0 \leq f(x_0)$. In either case, we find $f(x_0) \in P$. Hence $f(x_0) \leq x_0 \leq f(x_0)$.

Whew!

Theorem 1.9.7. *(1) The Axiom of Choice, (2) Hausdorff Maximality Principle, (3) Zorn's Lemma, and (4) Well-Ordering Principle are all equivalent.*

Proof. We will show that (1) implies (2), which implies (3), which implies (4), which implies (1), and then we will be done.

(1) $\Rightarrow$ (2)

Take a non-empty partially ordered set $(E, \leq)$. Make $\mathcal{E}$, the family of totally ordered subsets of E, into a partially ordered set under inclusion. We wish to show that $\mathcal{E}$ has a maximal element (i.e., an element that is not smaller than any other element). So we will assume the opposite and reach a contradiction by applying Lemma 1.9.6. We must first check to see if the lemma is applicable: Suppose $\mathcal{F}$ is a totally ordered subset of $\mathcal{E}$. Then it has a least upper bound, namely $\bigcup_{F \in \mathcal{F}} F$. Now, for a given $e \in \mathcal{E}$, let $S_e = \{x \in \mathcal{E} \mid e \subseteq x, e \neq x\}$. Then S_e can never be the empty set, because that would mean that e is maximal. So we apply the axiom of choice by defining a function $f : \{S_e \mid e \in \mathcal{E}\} \to \mathcal{E}$ with the property that $f(S_e) \in S_e$. Now define $g : \mathcal{E} \to \mathcal{E}$ by $g(e) = f(S_e)$. This gives us that $e \subsetneq g(e)$ for all $e \in \mathcal{E}$, contradicting the lemma.

(2) $\Rightarrow$ (3)

Again, consider a partially ordered set $(E, \leq)$. Now let x be an upper bound for E_0, a maximal totally ordered subset of E. Suppose that there is some $y \in E$ such that $y > x$. Then $E_0 \cup \{y\}$ is a totally ordered set containing E_0, contradicting our assumption of maximality.

Exercise 1.9.8. *Now you finish the proof. Show that Zorn's Lemma implies the Well Ordering Principle, and that the Well Ordering Principle implies the Axiom of Choice.*

10. Independent Projects

10.1. Basic Number Theory.

The following statements present a number of facts about elementary number theory. Prove all of these. If you don't understand some of the words, find a number theory book and look them up. Most of these facts will be used in Chapter 5 when we discuss p-adic numbers. The notation $a \equiv b \pmod{c}$ (pronounced "a is *congruent* to b *modulo* c") means that $c|(a - b)$.

(1) The division algorithm: if $a, b \in \mathbb{Z}$ and $b \neq 0$, then there is a unique pair $q, r \in \mathbb{Z}$ with $a = qb + r$ and $0 \leq r < |b|$.

(2) If M is a subset of $\mathbb{Z}$ which is closed under subtraction and contains a nonzero element, then $M = \{np \mid n \in \mathbb{Z}\}$, where p is the least positive element of M.

(3) If the greatest common divisor of a and b is d, which is denoted by $d = (a, b)$, then there exist $s, t \in \mathbb{Z}$ such that $d = sa + tb$.

(4) Euclid's lemma: If p is prime and $p|ab$, then $p|a$ or $p|b$.

(5) If $(a, c) = 1$ and $c|ab$, then $c|b$.

(6) If $(a, c) = 1$, $a|m$ and $c|m$, then $ac|m$.

(7) If $a > 0$, then $(ab, ac) = a(b, c)$.

(8) The integers $\mathbb{Z}$ have unique factorization, that is, if n is an integer greater than or equal to 2, then there exist unique distinct primes $p_1, p_2, \ldots, p_k$, with $p_1 < p_2 < \ldots < p_k$, and exponents $\alpha_1, \alpha_2, \ldots, \alpha_k$ greater than or equal to one such that $n = p_1^{\alpha_1} p_2^{\alpha_2} \cdots p_k^{\alpha_k}$.

(9) If n is a positive integer greater than or equal to 2 with unique factorization $n = p_1^{\alpha_1} p_2^{\alpha_2} \cdots p_k^{\alpha_k}$, then the number of positive divisors of n is

$$(\alpha_1 + 1)(\alpha_2 + 1) \cdots (\alpha_k + 1).$$

(10) If $a \equiv b \pmod{m}$, then $-a \equiv -b \pmod{m}$, $a + x \equiv b + x \pmod{m}$, and $ax \equiv bx \pmod{m}$ for every $x \in \mathbb{Z}$.

(11) If $(c, m) = 1$ and $ca \equiv cb \pmod{m}$, then $a \equiv b \pmod{m}$.

(12) If $(c, m) = 1$, then $cx \equiv b \pmod{m}$ has a unique solution x modulo m.

(13) If p is prime and $c \not\equiv 0 \pmod{p}$, then $cx \equiv b \pmod{p}$ has a unique solution x modulo p.

(14) If $a \equiv b \pmod{m}$ and $c \equiv d \pmod{m}$, then $a + c \equiv b + d \pmod{m}$ and $ac \equiv bd \pmod{m}$.

(15) If $a, b, c \in \mathbb{Z}$ and $d = (a, b)$, then $ax + by = c$ has a solution in integers x, y if and only if $d|c$.

(16) If $[a, b]$ is the least common multiple of a and b, then $m[a, b] = [ma, mb]$ when $m > 0$.

(17) If $ca \equiv cb \pmod{m}$ and $d = (c, m)$, then $a \equiv b \pmod{\frac{m}{d}}$.

(18) If $m, a, b \in \mathbb{Z}$, the congruence $ax \equiv b \pmod{m}$ is solvable if and only if $(a, m)|b$. There are exactly (a, m) solutions that are distinct modulo m.

(19) If $a, b, s, t \in \mathbb{Z}$ are such that $sa + tb = 1$, then $(a, b) = 1$.

Now suppose that P is the set of integers between 1 and $m - 1$, inclusive, which are relatively prime to m. A *reduced residue system* modulo m is a set of integers such that each of the integers in P is congruent modulo m to exactly one of the elements in this set.

(20) The number of elements in a reduced residue system modulo m is independent of the representatives chosen.

(21) If p is a prime and ϕ denotes Euler's ϕ function (where $\phi(a)$ is the number of integers between 0 and a that are relatively prime to a), then $\phi(p^n) = p^n - p^{n-1} = p^n(1 - \frac{1}{p})$.

(22) The number of elements in a reduced residue system modulo m is $\phi(m)$.

(23) If $a_1, \ldots, a_{\phi(m)}$ is a reduced residue system modulo m and $(\kappa, m) = 1$, then $\kappa a_1, \ldots, \kappa a_{\phi(m)}$ is a reduced residue system modulo m.

(24) If m is a positive integer and $(\kappa, m) = 1$, then $\kappa^{\phi(m)} \equiv 1 \pmod{m}$.

(25) If $d_1, \ldots, d_k$ are the positive divisors of n, then $\sum_{i=1}^{k} \phi(d_i) = n$.

10.2. The Complete Independence of Axiom Systems.

The rules of arithmetic and order which characterize the integers are also known as *axioms*. In general, an axiom is an assumption or rule that we accept without proof. In fact, we made cancellation for multiplication an axiom for an integral domain precisely because we could not prove it from the other axioms of addition and multiplication. Note however, that in the integers we could prove multiplicative cancellation once we stated the axioms for order. A group of axioms is called an *axiom system*.

There are a number of questions we can ask about a given axiom system S. First, is it *consistent*? That is, is there a *model* for S? For instance, the axioms for a field have a model, namely the integers modulo 2.

The next question we could ask is whether any axiom A in S is *independent*. What we mean is, could we replace A with its negation, $\overline{A}$, and still have a consistent system? (Symbolically, we would represent our new axiom system as $(S - A) + \overline{A}$.)

Exercise 1.10.2.1. *What is the negation of "P(b), for all $b \in B$"? What about the negation of "P(b), for some $b \in B$"?*

Consider the axioms for an equivalence relation. Clearly, they are consistent, because the relation of equality on any set is a model. Suppose we remove axiom 1 (reflexivity) and replace it by its negation, $\bar{1}$, by which we mean, $(a, a) \notin R$ for some a in A. Can we come up with a model for $\bar{1}$, 2, and 3? To do this, pick $a \in A$ and do not include $(a, a) \in \mathcal{R}$. For the remaining elements you can fix it up so that 2 and 3 work.

Exercise 1.10.2.2. *State $\bar{2}$ and $\bar{3}$ for the equivalence relation axioms (non-symmetry and non-transitivity). How is non-symmetry different from anti-symmetry?*

The axiom system S is called *independent* if each of its axioms is independent. It is called *completely independent* if, for any subset S_1 of S, the system $(S - S_1) + \overline{S_1}$ is consistent.

Exercise 1.10.2.3. *Show that the axioms for an equivalence relation are completely independent. You can do this by providing models for* $\{1, 2, 3\}$; $\{\bar{1}, 2, 3\}$; $\{1, \bar{2}, 3\}$; $\{1, 2, \bar{3}\}$; $\{\bar{1}, \bar{2}, 3\}$; $\{\bar{1}, 2, \bar{3}\}$; $\{1, \bar{2}, \bar{3}\}$; *and* $\{\bar{1}, \bar{2}, \bar{3}\}$. *Your models can, but need not, be based on relations you've seen before. Or, you could invent a relation on a set which satisfies the necessary axioms. For example, a model for* $\{1, \bar{2}, \bar{3}\}$ *could be the relation on* $\{a, b, c\}$ *defined by* $R = \{(a, a), (b, b), (c, c), (a, b), (b, c)\}$.

The notion of complete independence will arise again when we discuss groups in Project 2.1.

10.3. Ordered Integral Domains.

This project is designed to show that any ordered integral domain contains a copy of the integers. Thus, in particular, any ordered field such as the rationals or real numbers contains a copy of the integers. Let $(R, +, \cdot, <)$ be an ordered integral domain.

Definition 1.10.3.1. *An inductive set in* R *is a subset* S *of* R *such that:*

(a) $1 \in S$;

(b) *if* $x \in S$, *then* $x + 1 \in S$.

Example 1.10.3.2.

(*i*) R *is an inductive subset of* R.

(*ii*) $S = \{x \in R \mid x \geq 1\}$ *is an inductive subset of* R.

Now define N to be the intersection of all the inductive subsets of R. It is clear that N is an inductive subset of R. Of course, N is supposed to be the natural numbers. Since all of the axioms for a commutative ring with 1, as well as the order axioms hold in R, we can use them freely in N. The following facts are easy to prove, so prove them.

Exercise 1.10.3.3.

(*i*) *Suppose that* S *is a non-empty subset of* N *such that* $1 \in S$ *and if* $x \in S$ *then* $x + 1 \in S$. *Show that* $S = N$.

(*ii*) *Show that* N *is closed under addition.*

(*iii*) *Show that* N *is closed under multiplication. Hint: fix* $x \in N$ *and look at the set* $M_x = \{y \in N \mid xy \in N\}$. *Then* $1 \in M_x$. *If* $y \in M_x$, *then* $x(y+1) = xy + x$, *and* xy *is in* N *by the induction hypothesis. Since* N *is closed under addition,* $xy + x \in N$. *Hence* $y + 1 \in M_x$ *and* $M_x = N$.

(*iv*) *Show that the well ordering principle holds in* N.

This is all fine, but where do we get the integers? Well, of course, we just tack on 0 and the negative natural numbers. Before nodding your head and shouting "Hooray!", you must show that this new set $Z = N \cup \{0\} \cup -N$ *is closed under multiplication and addition.*

(*v*) *Show that* Z *is closed under addition.*
This is a little tricky and requires the following fact. If $m, n \in N$ *then* $m - n \in Z$*. In particular, if* $m \in N$*, then* $m - 1 \in Z$*.*

(*vi*) *Show that* Z *is closed under multiplication.*
So we have that Z *is an ordered integral domain in which the positive elements are well ordered.*

(*vii*) *Show that* Z *and the integers,* $\mathbb{Z}$*, are order isomorphic. That is there exists a bijection* $\phi : Z \to \mathbb{Z}$ *such that:*
(a) $\phi(x + y) = \phi(x) + \phi(y)$ *for all* $x, y \in Z$*;*
(b) $\phi(xy) = \phi(x)\phi(y)$ *for all* $x, y \in Z$*;*
(c) *if* $x < y$ *in* Z*, then* $\phi(x) < \phi(y)$ *in* $\mathbb{Z}$*.*

Chapter 2

Linear Algebra

The presentation of the material will perhaps incur the reproach of being too dogmatic in its methods. To this possible objection, we would like to make two answers. Firstly, that what the student may learn here is not designed to help him with problems he has already met but with those he will have to cope with in the future; it is therefore impossible to motivate the definitions and theorems by applications of which the reader does not know the existence as yet. Secondly, that one of the important pedagogical problems which a teacher of beginners in mathematics has to solve is to impart to his students the technique of rigorous mathematical reasoning; this is an exercise in rectitude of thought, of which it would be futile to disguise the austerity.

– *Claude Chevalley,*
Fundamental Concepts of Algebra

This is a book that is tilted toward analysis. However, almost all of the structures that we deal with in analysis have an underlying algebraic component, and an understanding of this algebraic component makes it a lot easier to discuss the analysis. Our approach is more user friendly than Chevalley's. We will find that analysis is mostly about inequalities, while algebra is mostly about equalities. The fundamental algebraic ideas we discuss in this chapter concern vector spaces and linear algebra. Other algebraic structures that play a role in analysis include groups, rings, and fields. Some ideas about these were discussed in Chapter 1. More can be found in the projects at the end of this chapter.

1. Fundamentals of Linear Algebra

The algebraic structures that are really fundamental for analysis are vector spaces (sometimes called linear spaces). Recall that a field has been defined in Definition 1.6.19.

Definition 2.1.1. *Let F be a field. A* vector space *over F is a triple $(V, +, \cdot)$ where $(V, +)$ satisfies the axioms (A1)-(A5) of Chapter 1 and $\cdot$ is a map from $F \times V$ to V satisfying the following properties:*

(a) *if $\alpha \in F$ and $\mathbf{v} \in V$, then $\alpha \cdot \mathbf{v} \in V$;*
(b) *if $\alpha \in F$ and $\mathbf{v}_1, \mathbf{v}_2 \in V$, then $\alpha \cdot (\mathbf{v}_1 + \mathbf{v}_2) = (\alpha \cdot \mathbf{v}_1) + (\alpha \cdot \mathbf{v}_2)$;*
(c) *if $\alpha, \beta \in F$ and $\mathbf{v} \in V$, then $(\alpha + \beta) \cdot \mathbf{v} = (\alpha \cdot \mathbf{v}) + (\beta \cdot \mathbf{v})$;*
(d) *if $\alpha, \beta \in F$ and $\mathbf{v} \in V$, then $(\alpha\beta) \cdot \mathbf{v} = \alpha \cdot (\beta \cdot \mathbf{v})$;*
(e) *if 1 is the multiplicative identity in F and $\mathbf{v} \in V$, then $1 \cdot \mathbf{v} = \mathbf{v}$.*

The function $(\alpha, \mathbf{v}) \mapsto \alpha \cdot \mathbf{v}$ is called *scalar multiplication* and the elements of F are called *scalars*. We frequently suppress the dot $(\cdot)$.

For completeness, we restate axioms (A1)-(A5).

(A1) If $\mathbf{v}_1, \mathbf{v}_2 \in V$, then $\mathbf{v}_1 + \mathbf{v}_2 \in V$.
(A2) If $\mathbf{v}_1, \mathbf{v}_2, \mathbf{v}_3 \in V$, then $\mathbf{v}_1 + (\mathbf{v}_2 + \mathbf{v}_3) = (\mathbf{v}_1 + \mathbf{v}_2) + \mathbf{v}_3$.
(A3) If $\mathbf{v}_1, \mathbf{v}_2 \in V$, then $\mathbf{v}_1 + \mathbf{v}_2 = \mathbf{v}_2 + \mathbf{v}_1$.
(A4) There exists $\mathbf{0} \in V$, such that for all $\mathbf{v} \in V$, $\mathbf{v} + \mathbf{0} = \mathbf{0} + \mathbf{v} = \mathbf{v}$.
(A5) For every $\mathbf{v} \in V$, there exists $-\mathbf{v} \in V$ such that $\mathbf{v} + (-\mathbf{v}) = -\mathbf{v} + \mathbf{v} = \mathbf{0}$.

Any structure satisfying (A1) – (A5) above is called an *abelian group* (see Project 2.6.1). Hence, a vector space is an abelian group with scalar multiplication.

Exercise 2.1.2.

(*i*) *If 0 is the additive identity in F and $\mathbf{0}$ is the additive identity in V, show that $0 \cdot \mathbf{v} = \mathbf{0}$ for any $\mathbf{v} \in V$. Note that this statement actually says something. It says that the additive identity in F has a property for scalar multiplication similar to multiplication by 0 in commutative rings. However, in this case, multiplication by the 0 in F gives $\mathbf{0}$ in V.*

(*ii*) *Determine whether condition e is necessary or follows from the other axioms.*

(*iii*) *Determine which of the statements in the definition are independent.*

(*iv*) *Do the axioms for a vector space form a completely independent system?*

Definition 2.1.3. *Let V be a vector space over a field F, and let $\mathbf{v}_1, \mathbf{v}_2, \ldots, \mathbf{v}_m \in V$. Then a vector of the form*

$$\alpha_1\mathbf{v}_1 + \alpha_2\mathbf{v}_2 + \cdots + \alpha_m\mathbf{v}_m$$

where $\alpha_1, \ldots, \alpha_m \in F$ is called a linear combination *of $\mathbf{v}_1, \ldots, \mathbf{v}_m$.*

Examples 2.1.4.

(1) *If F is a field, $V = \{\mathbf{0}\}$ is a vector space over F.*

(2) *If F is a field, then F is a vector space over F with scalar multiplication being ordinary multiplication in F.*

(3) *Let F be a field and let $F^n = \{(x_1, x_2, \ldots, x_n) \mid x_j \in F, j = 1, 2, \ldots, n\}$. Addition in F^n is defined coordinatewise, that is, if $\mathbf{x} = (x_1, x_2, \ldots, x_n)$ and $\mathbf{y} = (y_1, y_2, \ldots, y_n)$, then $\mathbf{x} + \mathbf{y} = (x_1 + y_1, x_2 + y_2, \ldots, x_n + y_n)$. If $\alpha \in F$ and $\mathbf{x} = (x_1, x_2, \ldots, x_n) \in F^n$, we set $\alpha \cdot \mathbf{x} = (\alpha x_1, \alpha x_2, \ldots, \alpha x_n)$. Then F^n is a vector space over F.*

(4) *Polynomial functions in one variable with real coefficients form a vector space over $\mathbb{R}$. This vector space is denoted by $\mathbb{R}[x]$. We could also consider polynomial functions in one variable with coefficients in $\mathbb{Q}$. This is a vector space over $\mathbb{Q}$ that is denoted by $\mathbb{Q}[x]$.*

(5) *Let X be a non-empty set, let F be a field, and let $V = \mathcal{F}(X, F)$ be the set of all functions from X to F. For $f, g \in V$, define $(f + g)(x) = f(x) + g(x)$ and, for $\alpha \in F$, define $(\alpha f)(x) = \alpha f(x)$.*

(6) *The real numbers $\mathbb{R}$ form a vector space over $\mathbb{Q}$.*

Exercise 2.1.5. *Check that the above examples satisfy the axioms for a vector space.*

Remark 2.1.6. *What is a vector? That's easy to answer. A vector is an element of a vector space. Lots of people describe a vector as a quantity having magnitude and direction. This is not particularly useful in most contexts (for example, see 5 above). However, in this chapter, when we do the geometric interpretation of vectors in n-dimensional Euclidean space, it will be helpful to think of vectors this way.*

Exercise 2.1.7. *Consider the collection $\mathbb{R}[x]$ of all polynomial functions with coefficients in $\mathbb{R}$. Show that $\mathbb{R}[x]$ is a vector space over $\mathbb{R}$ and also over $\mathbb{Q}$.*

There are two fundamental notions that need to be discussed right at the beginning of our treatment of vector spaces. These are linear independence and linear dependence. These notions are the heart and soul of elementary vector space theory.

Definition 2.1.8. *Let V be a vector space over a field F and $\mathbf{v}_1, \ldots, \mathbf{v}_m$ be nonzero vectors in V. We say that the set $\{\mathbf{v}_1, \ldots, \mathbf{v}_m\}$ is a* linearly independent *set if, for any scalars $\alpha_1, \ldots, \alpha_m \in F$ such that*

$$\alpha_1\mathbf{v}_1 + \cdots + \alpha_m\mathbf{v}_m = \mathbf{0},$$

we have $\alpha_1 = \alpha_2 = \cdots = \alpha_m = 0$.

Example 2.1.9. *A set containing a single nonzero vector is linearly independent.*

Exercise 2.1.10. *In the vector space F^n over a field F, set $\mathbf{e}_1 = (1, 0, \ldots, 0)$, $\mathbf{e}_2 = (0, 1, 0, \ldots, 0)$, and generally, $\mathbf{e}_j = (0, 0, \ldots, 1, \ldots, 0)$ where the 1 is in the jth coordinate and 0 is in the other coordinates. Show that, for any k, $1 \leq k \leq n$, the set $\{\mathbf{e}_1, \mathbf{e}_2, \ldots, \mathbf{e}_k\}$ is a linearly independent set.*

Remark 2.1.11. *An infinite set of vectors is said to be* linearly independent *if each finite subset is linearly independent.*

Exercise 2.1.12. *Show that the set $\{1, x, x^2, \ldots, x^n, \ldots\}$ is a linearly independent set in $\mathbb{Q}[x]$.*

Definition 2.1.13. *Let V be a vector space over a field F, and let $\mathbf{v}_1, \ldots, \mathbf{v}_m$ be vectors in V. The set $\{\mathbf{v}_1, \mathbf{v}_2, \ldots, \mathbf{v}_m\}$ is a* linearly dependent *set if there exist scalars $\alpha_1, \ldots, \alpha_m \in F$, not all zero, such that*

$$\alpha_1\mathbf{v}_1 + \alpha_2\mathbf{v}_2 + \cdots + \alpha_m\mathbf{v}_m = \mathbf{0},$$

that is, a set is linearly dependent if it is not linearly independent.

Exercise 2.1.14.

(*i*) *Let $V = F^n$ and let $\mathbf{v}$ be any vector in $V \setminus \{\mathbf{e}_1, \ldots, \mathbf{e}_n\}$. Show that the set $\{\mathbf{e}_1, \mathbf{e}_2, \ldots, \mathbf{e}_n, \mathbf{v}\}$ is a linearly dependent set in V.*

(*ii*) *Show that, if $\{\mathbf{v}_1, \ldots, \mathbf{v}_m\}$ is a set of vectors in a vector space V and one of these vectors is the zero vector, then the set is a linearly dependent set.*

(*iii*) *Let $\mathbf{v}_1$ and $\mathbf{v}_2$ be vectors in a vector space V. Show that the set $\{\mathbf{v}_1, \mathbf{v}_2\}$ is a linearly dependent set iff one of these vectors is a scalar multiple of the other.*

Lemma 2.1.15. *Suppose that $\{\mathbf{v}_1, \ldots, \mathbf{v}_m\}$ is a linearly dependent set of nonzero vectors in a vector space V over a field F. Then there exists k, $1 < k \leq m$, such that $\mathbf{v}_k$ is a linear combination of $\mathbf{v}_1, \ldots, \mathbf{v}_{k-1}$.*

Proof. Let k be the smallest integer such that $\{\mathbf{v}_1, \ldots, \mathbf{v}_{k-1}\}$ is a linearly independent set and $\{\mathbf{v}_1, \ldots, \mathbf{v}_k\}$ is a linearly dependent set. Then there exist scalars $\alpha_1, \ldots, \alpha_k$ such that

$$\alpha_1\mathbf{v}_1 + \cdots + \alpha_k\mathbf{v}_k = \mathbf{0}$$

and $\alpha_k \neq 0$. The integer k gives the desired result. 

There are two additional ideas that are closely related. One is that of a spanning set, and the second is that of a basis.

Definition 2.1.16. *Let V be a vector space over a field F, and let $S = \{\mathbf{v}_1, \ldots, \mathbf{v}_m\}$ be a set of vectors in V. The set S is a* spanning set *for V if every element of V can be written as a linear combination of the vectors $\mathbf{v}_1, \ldots, \mathbf{v}_m$. A spanning set S is a* basis *for V if S is linearly independent.*

Remark 2.1.17. *If $S = \{\mathbf{v}_1, \ldots, \mathbf{v}_m\}$ is a spanning set for V, we say that S* spans *V. It is possible that no finite set spans V. For example, in $\mathbb{Q}[x]$, the collection of monomials $S = \{1, x, x^2, \ldots, x^n, \ldots\}$ has the property that every element in $\mathbb{Q}[x]$ can be written as a finite linear combination of these monomials, but no proper subset of S has this property. We extend the definition of spanning set by saying that a collection S of vectors in V (possibly infinite) is a spanning set if every element of V can be written as a (finite) linear combination of elements of S. We note here that, in the absence of any convergence techniques, infinite sums of vectors do not make any sense. When we get to metric spaces, this situation will change.*

Exercise 2.1.18. *Show that the vector space $\mathbb{Q}[x]$ is a countable set.*

Example 2.1.19. *Let F be a field and let $V = F^n$. The set $\{\mathbf{e}_1, \mathbf{e}_2, \ldots, \mathbf{e}_n\}$ as defined in Exercise* 2.1.10 *is a basis for V. This is called* the standard basis, *or the* canonical basis *for V.*

What we now prove is that if a vector space has a basis with n elements, then all bases have the same number of elements. This will allow us to define the dimension of a vector space as the cardinality of a basis. The following lemma plays a crucial role.

Lemma 2.1.20 (Exchange Lemma). *Suppose that V is a vector space over a field F and that $U = \{\mathbf{u}_1, \ldots, \mathbf{u}_m\}$ is a spanning set for V. If the set $\{\mathbf{v}_1, \ldots, \mathbf{v}_n\}$ is a linearly independent set in V, then $n \leq m$.*

Proof. First, consider the collection $S_1 = \{\mathbf{v}_1, \mathbf{u}_1, \ldots, \mathbf{u}_m\}$. Since U spans V, we have that $\mathbf{v}_1 \in U$ or S_1 is a linearly dependent set. So, according to Lemma 2.1.15, there exists an element $\mathbf{u}_{j_1} \in S_1$ that is a linear combination of $\mathbf{v}_1, \mathbf{u}_1, \ldots, \mathbf{u}_{j_1-1}$. Throw it away. Now define

$$S_2 = \{\mathbf{v}_2, \mathbf{v}_1, \mathbf{u}_1, \ldots, \mathbf{u}_{j_1-1}, \mathbf{u}_{j_1+1}, \ldots, \mathbf{u}_m\}.$$

By similar reasoning, we have that $\mathbf{v}_2 \in U$ or S_2 is linearly dependent. So, proceeding as above, we can take another $\mathbf{u}_{j_2}$ and toss it out and retain the same linear span. We can continue by putting $\mathbf{v}_3, \mathbf{v}_4, \dots$ at the beginning of our list, and each time we do that, we can eliminate an element of U that remains on our list. We will never be able to eliminate one of the $\mathbf{v}$'s since they are linearly independent. So at each stage, we eliminate one of the $\mathbf{u}$'s and are left with a spanning set. If at some point, all the $\mathbf{u}$'s are gone and some $\mathbf{v}$'s have not been used, then a proper subset of the $\mathbf{v}$'s would be a spanning set. This contradicts the linear independence of the $\mathbf{v}$'s. ☠

Now, we assume that our vector space V over F has a finite subset that spans. Such a vector space is called *finite dimensional*. The next corollary proves the existence of a basis for a finite dimensional vector space.

Corollary 2.1.21. *Let V be a nonzero finite dimensional vector space over a field F. Then V has a finite basis.*

Proof. Let $\{\mathbf{v}_1, \dots, \mathbf{v}_m\}$ be a spanning set consisting of nonzero vectors. If $\{\mathbf{v}_1, \dots, \mathbf{v}_m\}$ is linearly dependent, then by Lemma 2.1.15 there exists an integer k such that $\{\mathbf{v}_1, \dots, \mathbf{v}_{k-1}\}$ is a linearly independent set and $\{\mathbf{v}_1, \dots, \mathbf{v}_k\}$ is linearly dependent. Eliminating $\mathbf{v}_k$ from the set $\{\mathbf{v}_1, \dots, \mathbf{v}_m\}$, we still have a spanning set. Continue this process (a finite number of times). This yields a linearly independent set that spans V, that is, a basis. ☠

Now we get to the heart of the matter.

Theorem 2.1.22. *If V is a finite dimensional vector space over a field F, then any two bases of V have the same number of elements.*

Proof. Suppose $\{\mathbf{v}_1, \dots, \mathbf{v}_n\}$ and $\{\mathbf{u}_1, \dots, \mathbf{u}_m\}$ are bases for V. Then by the Exchange Lemma, $n \leq m$ and $m \leq n$. ☠

Now we can talk about an n-dimensional vector space over a field F.

Definition 2.1.23. *Suppose V is a vector space containing a spanning set of n linearly independent vectors, $n \geq 1$. The* dimension *of V, denoted* $\dim V$, *is equal to n, that is* $\dim V = n$. *If $V = \{\mathbf{0}\}$, we set* $\dim V = 0$.

Theorem 2.1.24. *Suppose that V is an n-dimensional vector space over a field F and that $\{\mathbf{v}_1, \dots, \mathbf{v}_m\}$ is a linearly independent set in V. Then $m \leq n$ and there exist vectors $\mathbf{v}_{m+1}, \dots, \mathbf{v}_n$ such that $\{\mathbf{v}_1, \dots, \mathbf{v}_m, \mathbf{v}_{m+1}, \dots, \mathbf{v}_n\}$ is a basis for V.*

Proof. Let $\{\mathbf{u}_1, \dots, \mathbf{u}_n\}$ be a basis for V. If we consider the set $\{\mathbf{v}_1, \dots, \mathbf{v}_m, \mathbf{u}_1, \dots, \mathbf{u}_n\}$, then, again using Lemma 2.1.15 and its proof, the result follows. ☠

Definition 2.1.25. *If V is a vector space over a field F, then a non-empty subset $W \subseteq V$ is a* subspace *if it is closed under addition and scalar multiplication. That is, if $\mathbf{v}, \mathbf{w} \in W$, then $\mathbf{v} + \mathbf{w} \in W$, and if $\mathbf{v} \in W$ and $\alpha \in F$, then $\alpha\mathbf{v} \in W$.*

Theorem 2.1.26. *Let V be a finite dimensional vector space over a field F. Suppose that W is a subspace of V. Then $\dim W \leq \dim V$.*

Proof. Suppose that $\dim V = n$. Now consider a linearly independent set $\{\mathbf{u}_1, \ldots, \mathbf{u}_m\}$ in W. By Theorem 2.1.24, $m \leq n$. Consider the set S of all positive integers that are the cardinalities of linearly independent sets in W. The set S is bounded above by n. Let h be the largest element of S. Let $B = \{\mathbf{w}_1, \ldots, \mathbf{w}_h\}$ be a linearly independent set in W of cardinality h. Then B must be a basis for W. Otherwise, there would be an element $\mathbf{w} \in W$ not in the span of B. Then h would not be maximal since $B \cup \{\mathbf{w}\}$ would be linearly independent. So, $h = \dim W \leq n$. ☠

Exercise 2.1.27.

(i) *Let V be a vector space over a field F. Show that $\{\mathbf{0}\}$ and V are subspaces of V.*

(ii) *When is it true that the only subspaces of V are $\{\mathbf{0}\}$ and V?*

Examples 2.1.28.

(i) *Let $V = \mathbb{Q}[x]$, and let W be the collection of all polynomials in $\mathbb{Q}[x]$ whose degree is less than or equal to a fixed non-negative integer n. Then W is a subspace of $\mathbb{Q}[x]$.*

(ii) *Let $V = F^n$ and for a fixed $m \leq n$, let $W = \{v \in V \mid v = \alpha_1\mathbf{e_1} + \alpha_2\mathbf{e_2} + \cdots + \alpha_m\mathbf{e_m}, \alpha_j \in F, j = 1, \ldots, m\}$. Then W is a subspace of V.*

Exercise 2.1.29. *Find the dimensions of W in the last two examples.*

Most of the vector spaces which arise in analysis are not finite dimensional and thus are called *infinite dimensional*. We will often be dealing with vector spaces of functions whose domain and range are finite dimensional vector spaces over $\mathbb{R}$ (or over the complex numbers $\mathbb{C}$), but the spaces of functions themselves will ordinarily be infinite dimensional spaces. To prove the existence of a basis for an infinite dimensional space, Zorn's Lemma or some other equivalent statement is needed.

Exercise 2.1.30. *Suppose X is a set.*

(i) *If $V = \mathcal{F}(X, F)$, the set of functions from X to F, show that V is finite dimensional if and only if X is finite.*

(ii) *Fix a subset* $A \subseteq X$ *and define* $W(A) = \{f \in V \mid f|_A = 0\}$. *Show that* $W(A)$ *is a subspace of* V.

(iii) *Can you find an infinite set* X *and a field* F *where you can write an explicit basis for* $V = \mathcal{F}(X, F)$?

Theorem 2.1.31. *Let* V *be a nonzero vector space over a field* F. *Then* V *has a basis. That is, there exists a linearly independent subset* B *of* V *such that each element of* V *is a finite linear combination of elements of* B.

Proof. We apply Zorn's Lemma to the collection of linearly independent sets in V. This collection can be partially ordered by inclusion. Given any totally ordered subset, the union of the elements in this subset provides a maximal element. The conclusion of Zorn's Lemma gives a basis for V. ☠

Example 2.1.32. *This last theorem means that there exists a basis* $B = \{\mathbf{v}_i \mid i \in I\}$ *for* $\mathbb{R}$ *considered as a vector space over* $\mathbb{Q}$. *In particular, every real number can be written as a finite linear combination of elements of this basis with coefficients taken from* $\mathbb{Q}$. *The basis is not countable. It is called a* Hamel basis *for* $\mathbb{R}$ *over* $\mathbb{Q}$.

2. Linear Transformations

One of the most important topics in the subject of linear algebra is the study of maps from one vector space over a field F to another vector space over F that preserve addition and scalar multiplication. Such maps are called *linear transformations* and they play a vital role throughout the remainder of this text.

Definition 2.2.1. *Let* V, W *be vector spaces over a field* F. *A map* $T : V \to W$ *is called a* linear transformation *or* linear operator *if*

(a) $T(\mathbf{v}_1 + \mathbf{v}_2) = T(\mathbf{v}_1) + T(\mathbf{v}_2)$ *for all* $\mathbf{v}_1, \mathbf{v}_2 \in V$,

(b) $T(\alpha\mathbf{v}) = \alpha T(\mathbf{v})$ *for all* $\alpha \in F$ *and* $\mathbf{v} \in V$.

Exercise 2.2.2. *Let* V *and* W *be vector spaces over a field* F *and* $T : V \to W$ *a linear transformation. Show that* $T(\mathbf{0}) = \mathbf{0}$ *and* $T(-\mathbf{v}) = -T(\mathbf{v})$ *for all* $\mathbf{v} \in V$.

Exercise 2.2.3. *Let* V *and* W *be vector spaces over a field* F *and* $T : V \to W$ *a linear transformation.*

(i) *Show that* $T(V)$ *is a subspace of* W.

(ii) *If* T *is an injection show that* $T^{-1} : T(V) \to V$ *is a linear operator.*

Example 2.2.4. *Consider* $\mathbb{R}$ *as a vector space over itself and fix* $a \in \mathbb{R}$. *Define* $T_a(x) = ax$ *for* $x \in \mathbb{R}$. *Then* T_a *is a linear operator on* $\mathbb{R}$. *Notice* *that we could also consider* $\mathbb{R}$ *as a vector space over* $\mathbb{Q}$*. Then* T_a *would also be a linear operator from* $\mathbb{R}$ *to* $\mathbb{R}$*, but the underlying field would be different.*

Example 2.2.5. *Let* $V = \mathbb{R}[x]$ *considered as a vector space over* $\mathbb{R}$*. Define* $T : \mathbb{R}[x] \to \mathbb{R}[x]$ *by* $Tp(x) = p'(x)$*, that is, the derivative of the polynomial* p*. It follows from the properties of the derivative that* T *is a linear transformation.*

Exercise 2.2.6. *Show that* $T : \mathbb{R}[x] \to \mathbb{R}[x]$ *as defined in the previous example is surjective but not injective.*

A linear transformation cannot increase the dimension of a vector space. For finite dimensional spaces, this is the content of the following theorem.

Theorem 2.2.7. *Suppose that* V *and* W *are vector spaces over a field* F *and that* $T : V \to W$ *is a linear transformation. If* V *is finite dimensional with* $\dim V = n$*, then* $\dim T(V) \leq n$*.*

Proof. It suffices to show that every subset of $T(V)$ consisting of $n+1$ elements is linearly dependent. Let $\mathbf{w}_1, \mathbf{w}_2, \ldots, \mathbf{w}_{n+1}$ be vectors in $T(V)$. Pick $\mathbf{v}_1, \ldots, \mathbf{v}_{n+1} \in V$ so that $T(\mathbf{v}_j) = \mathbf{w}_j$ for $j = 1, \ldots, n+1$. Then $\{\mathbf{v}_1, \ldots, \mathbf{v}_{n+1}\}$ is a linearly dependent set, so there exist scalars $\alpha_1, \ldots, \alpha_{n+1}$, not all zero, such that $\alpha_1\mathbf{v_1} + \cdots + \alpha_{n+1}\mathbf{v}_{n+1} = \mathbf{0}$. It follows that $T(\alpha_1\mathbf{v}_1 + \cdots + \alpha_{n+1}\mathbf{v}_{n+1}) = \alpha_1\mathbf{w}_1 + \cdots + \alpha_{n+1}\mathbf{w}_{n+1} = \mathbf{0}$. Hence the set $\{\mathbf{w}_1, \mathbf{w}_2, \ldots, \mathbf{w}_{n+1}\}$ is linearly dependent.

Definition 2.2.8. *Let* V *and* W *be vector spaces over a field* F *and* $T : V \to W$ *a linear transformation. The transformation* T *is called a* linear isomorphism *if* T *is a bijection. In this case,* V *and* W *are said to be* linearly isomorphic.

Corollary 2.2.9. *Suppose that* V *and* W *are finite dimensional vector spaces over a field* F*. If* V *and* W *are linearly isomorphic, then* $\dim V = \dim W$*. Moreover, if* $\{\mathbf{v_1}, \ldots, \mathbf{v_n}\}$ *is a basis for* V*, then* $\{T(\mathbf{v_1}), \ldots, T(\mathbf{v_n})\}$ *is a basis for* W*.*

Exercise 2.2.10. *Suppose that* V *and* W *are finite dimensional vector spaces over a field* F *such that* $\dim V = \dim W$*. Show that* V *and* W *are linearly isomorphic.*

In general, if T is a linear transformation from V to W, T is neither injective nor surjective. This leads to an important idea, the kernel of a linear transformation.

Definition 2.2.11. *Let* V *and* W *be vector spaces over a field* F*, and* $T : V \to W$ *a linear transformation. The* kernel of T *is defined by*

$$\ker T = \{\mathbf{v} \in V \mid T(\mathbf{v}) = \mathbf{0}\}.$$

Exercise 2.2.12.

(*i*) *Show that* $\ker T$ *is a subspace of* V.

(*ii*) *Let* $T : \mathbb{R}[x] \to \mathbb{R}[x]$ *be as in Example 2.2.5, that is* $Tp(x) = p'(x)$. *Find* $\ker T$.

Theorem 2.2.13. *Suppose that* V *and* W *are vector spaces over a field* F *and that* $\dim V$ *is finite. Let* $T : V \to W$ *be a linear transformation. Then* $T(V)$ *is a finite dimensional subspace of* W *and* $\dim V = \dim \ker T + \dim T(V)$.

Proof. From above, we know that if $\dim V = n$, then $\dim T(V) \leq n$. Let $\{\mathbf{v}_1, \dots, \mathbf{v}_k\}$ be a basis for $\ker T$. Complete this to a basis $\{\mathbf{v}_1, \dots, \mathbf{v}_k, \dots, \mathbf{v}_n\}$ for V by Theorem 2.1.24. Then $\{T(\mathbf{v}_{k+1}), \dots, T(\mathbf{v}_n)\}$ is a basis for $T(V)$.

Definition 2.2.14. *Let* V *and* W *be vector spaces over a field* F. *If* T, T_1, *and* T_2 *are linear transformations from* V *to* W, *we define*

(a) $(T_1 + T_2)(\mathbf{v}) = T_1(\mathbf{v}) + T_2(\mathbf{v})$, *for* $\mathbf{v} \in V$, *and*

(b) $(\alpha T)(\mathbf{v}) = \alpha T(\mathbf{v})$, *for* $\alpha \in F$.

Theorem 2.2.15. *Let* V *and* W *be vector spaces over a field* F. *Let* $\mathscr{L}(V, W)$ *denote the set of all linear transformations from* V *to* W. *Then, with the above operations,* $\mathscr{L}(V, W)$ *is a vector space over* F.

Proof. Clear.

Exercise 2.2.16. *Show that if* $\dim V = n$ *and* $\dim W = m$, *then* $\mathscr{L}(V, W)$ *is a finite dimensional vector space with* $\dim \mathscr{L}(V, W) = nm$.

The proof of this last exercise is facilitated by the use of bases in V and W. This leads to the notion of matrices representing linear transformations.

3. Linear Transformations and Matrices

Take finite dimensional vector spaces V and W over a field F and $T \in \mathscr{L}(V, W)$. Suppose that $\dim V = n$, $\dim W = m$, and $\{\mathbf{v}_1, \dots, \mathbf{v}_n\}$ and $\{\mathbf{w}_1, \dots, \mathbf{w}_m\}$ are bases for V and W, respectively. For $1 \leq k \leq n$, we can write

$$T(\mathbf{v}_k) = \sum_{j=1}^{m} a_{jk} \mathbf{w}_j,$$

where each $a_{jk} \in F$. Then, if $\mathbf{v} = \sum_{k=1}^{n} \beta_k \mathbf{v}_k$, we have

$$T(\mathbf{v}) = \sum_{k=1}^{n} \beta_k \left(\sum_{j=1}^{m} a_{jk} \mathbf{w}_j \right) = \sum_{j=1}^{m} \left(\sum_{k=1}^{n} \beta_k a_{jk} \right) \mathbf{w}_j.$$

Thus, for any $\mathbf{v} \in V$, we have written $\mathbf{v}$ with respect to the basis $\{\mathbf{v}_1, \ldots, \mathbf{v}_n\}$ and $T(\mathbf{v})$ with respect to the basis $\{\mathbf{w}_1, \ldots, \mathbf{w}_m\}$. The coefficients in the latter expression are written in terms of the coefficients of $\mathbf{v}$ and the coefficients of $T(\mathbf{v}_k)$, $1 \leq k \leq n$. This information is encoded in a rectangular array called a *matrix*. That is, we write

$$A = \begin{pmatrix} a_{11} & a_{12} & \cdots & a_{1n} \\ a_{21} & a_{22} & \cdots & a_{2n} \\ \vdots & \vdots & \ddots & \vdots \\ a_{m1} & a_{m2} & \cdots & a_{mn} \end{pmatrix}.$$

If $\mathbf{v} \in V$ and $\mathbf{v} = \sum_{k=1}^{n} \beta_k \mathbf{v}_k$ as above, the scalars $\beta_1, \beta_2, \ldots, \beta_n$ are called the *coefficients* of $\mathbf{v}$ relative to the basis $\{\mathbf{v}_1, \mathbf{v}_2, \ldots, \mathbf{v}_n\}$. Once we have chosen a basis, it is common to represent the vector $\mathbf{v}$ by writing these coefficients in a column (or row).

Now, we compute $T(\mathbf{v})$ by computing the coefficients of $T(\mathbf{v})$ in the basis $\{\mathbf{w}_1, \ldots, \mathbf{w}_m\}$ as follows,

$$\begin{pmatrix} a_{11} & a_{12} & \cdots & a_{1n} \\ a_{21} & a_{22} & \cdots & a_{2n} \\ \vdots & \vdots & \ddots & \vdots \\ a_{m1} & a_{m2} & \cdots & a_{mn} \end{pmatrix} \begin{pmatrix} \beta_1 \\ \beta_2 \\ \vdots \\ \beta_n \end{pmatrix} = \begin{pmatrix} \sum_{k=1}^{n} a_{1k}\beta_k \\ \sum_{k=1}^{n} a_{2k}\beta_k \\ \vdots \\ \sum_{k=1}^{n} a_{mk}\beta_k \end{pmatrix}.$$

Observe that the matrix A has m rows and n columns (rows are horizontal and columns are vertical). This matrix is called an $m \times n$ *(m by n) matrix over F*. Of course, the coefficients in the matrix depend on the choice of bases in V and W. Incidentally, this might be a good time to formalize the definition of matrix.

Definition 2.3.1. *Let R be a commutative ring with 1. Let a_{ij} be elements of R, where $1 \leq i \leq m$ and $1 \leq j \leq n$. An $m \times n$* matrix over R *is a rectangular array given by*

$$A = \begin{pmatrix} a_{11} & a_{12} & \cdots & a_{1n} \\ a_{21} & a_{22} & \cdots & a_{2n} \\ \vdots & \vdots & \ddots & \vdots \\ a_{m1} & a_{m2} & \cdots & a_{mn} \end{pmatrix}.$$

Exercise 2.3.2. *Let V and W be finite dimensional vector spaces over F of dimensions n and m respectively. Let $M_{mn}(F)$ be the collection of $m \times n$ matrices over F. We use the notation $A = (a_{ij})$ for elements of $M_{mn}(F)$. If $A = (a_{ij})$, $B = (b_{ij})$, we define $A + B = (a_{ij} + b_{ij})$ and for $\alpha \in F$ we define $\alpha A = (\alpha a_{ij})$. Show that $M_{mn}(F)$ is a vector space over F. Find a basis for*

$M_{mn}(F)$. By fixing bases for V and W, give an explicit linear isomorphism between $\mathscr{L}(V,W)$ and $M_{mn}(F)$.

The above development is of particular importance in the case when $V = W$. In this case, we use the notation $\mathscr{L}(V)$ for $\mathscr{L}(V,V)$. If $\dim V = n$, then $\dim \mathscr{L}(V) = n^2$, and each element of $\mathscr{L}(V)$ can be represented by an $n \times n$ matrix relative to a chosen basis. Along with the operations of addition and scalar multiplication in $\mathscr{L}(V)$, we have composition of linear transformations. Suppose that $S, T \in \mathscr{L}(V)$. Then $S \circ T$ is defined in the usual way by $S \circ T(\mathbf{v}) = S(T(\mathbf{v}))$.

Exercise 2.3.3.

(*i*) *If $S, T \in \mathscr{L}(V)$, show that $S \circ T \in \mathscr{L}(V)$.*

(*ii*) *If $R, S, T \in \mathscr{L}(V)$, then $R \circ (S \circ T) = (R \circ S) \circ T$ (this actually follows from the associativity of composition of functions discussed in Chapter 1).*

(*iii*) *If $R, S, T \in \mathscr{L}(V)$, show that $R \circ (S + T) = (R \circ S) + (R \circ T)$ and $(R + S) \circ T = (R \circ T) + (S \circ T)$.*

(*iv*) *Let $I \in \mathscr{L}(V)$ be defined by $I(\mathbf{v}) = \mathbf{v}$ for $\mathbf{v} \in V$. Show that $T \circ I = I \circ T = T$ for all $T \in \mathscr{L}(V)$.*

(*v*) *Show that if $\dim V \geq 2$, then $\mathscr{L}(V)$ is not commutative with respect to the internal law of composition $\circ$. That is, there exist $S, T \in \mathscr{L}(V)$ such that $S \circ T \neq T \circ S$.*

A little vocabulary is in order here. In Chapter 1, we used the terms commutative ring with 1, integral domain, and field. As pointed out there, the word "commutative" referred to the operation of multiplication. Some of the most important algebraic structures that occur in mathematics are called *algebras*.

Definition 2.3.4. *Let F be a field. An* algebra *over F is a set A such that A is a vector space over F and A has an internal law of composition $\circ$ satisfying the associative law, and left and right distributivity. That is, for $a, b, c \in A$ and $\alpha \in F$, we have*

$$\begin{aligned} a \circ (b \circ c) &= (a \circ b) \circ c, \\ a \circ (b + c) &= (a \circ b) + (a \circ c), \\ (a + b) \circ c &= (a \circ c) + (b \circ c) \\ \text{and } (\alpha \cdot a) \circ b &= \alpha \cdot (a \circ b) = a \circ (\alpha \cdot b). \end{aligned}$$

An algebra A is an algebra with identity *cif there is an element $\mathbf{1} \in A$ so that $a \circ \mathbf{1} = \mathbf{1} \circ a = a$ for all $a \in A$. The algebra A is a* commutative algebra *if $a \circ b = b \circ a$ for all $a, b \in A$.*

Example 2.3.5. *If V is a nonzero vector space over a field F, then $\mathscr{L}(V)$ is an algebra with identity which is commutative if and only if* $\dim V = 1$.

Exercise 2.3.6. *Let $\mathbb{R}[x]$ be the vector space of polynomial functions in one variable over $\mathbb{R}$. Define multiplication of polynomials in the usual way. Show that $\mathbb{R}[x]$ is a commutative algebra with identity.*

We have defined "multiplication" in $\mathscr{L}(V)$ as composition of linear transformations. What does this mean when we represent the elements of $\mathscr{L}(V)$ as matrices?

Definition 2.3.7. *Suppose that V is an n-dimensional vector space over a field F and $S, T \in \mathscr{L}(V)$. If $A = (a_{ij})$ and $B = (b_{ij})$ are $n \times n$ matrices over F that represent S and T relative to a given basis for V, we define matrix multiplication by*

$$A \cdot B = C = (c_{ij}) \text{ where } c_{ij} = \sum_{k=1}^{n} a_{ik} b_{kj}.$$

Exercise 2.3.8. *Show that $C = (c_{ij})$ is the matrix of the linear transformation $S \circ T$ relative to the given basis for V. Deduce that multiplication of $n \times n$ matrices over a field F is associative and that*

$$I = \begin{pmatrix} 1 & 0 & \cdots & 0 \\ 0 & 1 & \cdots & 0 \\ \vdots & \vdots & \ddots & \vdots \\ 0 & 0 & \cdots & 1 \end{pmatrix}$$

is an identity for multiplication of matrices. Show further that, for $n \times n$ matrices, multiplication is left and right distributive over addition and the appropriate properties hold for scalar multiplication.

Conclusion: $M_{nn}(F)$ is an algebra with identity over F that is commutative if and only if $n = 1$.

For simplicity we will write $M_n(F)$ for $M_{nn}(F)$. Our next task is to characterize those elements of $M_n(F)$ that are *invertible*, that is those elements that have multiplicative inverses.

4. Determinants

Exercise 2.4.1. *Suppose that $T \in \mathcal{L}(V)$ is a bijection. Then T has an inverse, $T^{-1} : V \to V$. Show that $T^{-1} \in \mathcal{L}(V)$. (See Exercise* 2.2.3.*)*

Of course, $T \circ T^{-1} = T^{-1} \circ T = I$, the identity map. The problem that confronts us is the following: if $A = (a_{ij})$ is the matrix of T relative to a given basis of V, how do we find the matrix of T^{-1} relative to the same basis? We seek a matrix denoted by A^{-1}, such that $A \cdot A^{-1} = A^{-1} \cdot A = I$.

Well, this shouldn't present a great problem. All we do is write the matrix for A^{-1} as (x_{ij}). This leads to n^2 linear equations in n^2 unknowns

$$\begin{array}{rcl} a_{11}x_{11} + a_{12}x_{21} + \cdots + a_{1n}x_{n1} & = & 1 \\ a_{21}x_{11} + a_{22}x_{21} + \cdots + a_{2n}x_{n1} & = & 0 \\ & \vdots & \\ a_{n1}x_{11} + a_{n2}x_{21} + \cdots + a_{nn}x_{n1} & = & 0 \\ a_{11}x_{12} + a_{12}x_{22} + \cdots + a_{1n}x_{n2} & = & 0 \\ & \vdots & \\ a_{n1}x_{1n} + a_{n2}x_{2n} + \cdots + a_{nn}x_{nn} & = & 1. \end{array}$$

This looks somewhat tedious, so maybe at this stage, we should just tell you the answer and consider it further in a project at the end of the chapter. But that would not be true to the nature of this book. So, we are led to the quest for determinants, one of the great discoveries in mathematics.

To begin a discussion of determinants, we must first consider the collection S_n of all self-bijections of the set $\{1, 2, \ldots, n\}$. These bijections are called *permutations of n elements*.

Example 2.4.2. *Let's consider two examples, namely S_2 and S_3. We can represent the elements of S_2 by arrays in which the top row lists the domain and the bottom lists the corresponding elements in the image*

$$I = \begin{pmatrix} 1 & 2 \\ 1 & 2 \end{pmatrix}, r = \begin{pmatrix} 1 & 2 \\ 2 & 1 \end{pmatrix}.$$

Note that these arrays should be thought of not as matrices, but simply as a way to represent permutations as functions. Similarly, we can write S_3 as

$$I = \begin{pmatrix} 1 & 2 & 3 \\ 1 & 2 & 3 \end{pmatrix}, r = \begin{pmatrix} 1 & 2 & 3 \\ 2 & 3 & 1 \end{pmatrix}, r^2 = r \circ r = \begin{pmatrix} 1 & 2 & 3 \\ 3 & 1 & 2 \end{pmatrix}$$

$$f_1 = \begin{pmatrix} 1 & 2 & 3 \\ 1 & 3 & 2 \end{pmatrix}, f_2 = \begin{pmatrix} 1 & 2 & 3 \\ 3 & 2 & 1 \end{pmatrix}, f_3 = \begin{pmatrix} 1 & 2 & 3 \\ 2 & 1 & 3 \end{pmatrix}.$$

Exercise 2.4.3.

(*i*) *Use the basic counting principle to show that the number of elements in S_n is $n!$.*

(*ii*) *Show that the composition of two elements of S_n is also an element of S_n.*

(*iii*) *Show that the elements of S_n satisfy the associative law under composition of functions.*

(*iv*) *Define $I \in S_n$ as in Chapter 1, that is, $I(x) = x$ for all $x \in \{1, 2, \ldots, n\}$. Show that I is an identity for S_n.*

(*v*) *If $\sigma \in S_n$, define σ^{-1} as one does for any bijection. That is $\sigma(x) = y$ iff $\sigma^{-1}(y) = x$. Show that $\sigma \circ \sigma^{-1} = \sigma^{-1} \circ \sigma = I$.*

The collection S_n with the internal law of composition $\circ$ satisfying the above properties is called a *group*. The general theory of groups is discussed in Project 2.1 at the end of the chapter. The group S_n is called *the symmetric group on n objects*.

Definition 2.4.4. *Let σ be an element of S_n. We define the* sign *of σ by*

$$\operatorname{sgn}(\sigma) = \prod_{1 \leq i < j \leq n} \frac{\sigma(j) - \sigma(i)}{j - i}.$$

Exercise 2.4.5. *Show that if $\sigma \in S_n$, then $sgn(\sigma) = \pm 1$.*

Exercise 2.4.6. *Let σ be any map from $\{1, 2, \ldots, n\}$ to $\{1, 2, \ldots, n\}$. We can define* $\operatorname{sgn}(\sigma)$ *as above. Show that* $\operatorname{sgn}(\sigma) = 0$ *if and only if σ is not a bijection.*

Proposition 2.4.7. *For $\sigma, \tau \in S_n$, we have* $\operatorname{sgn}(\sigma \circ \tau) = \operatorname{sgn}(\sigma)\operatorname{sgn}(\tau)$.

Proof. We have $\operatorname{sgn}(\sigma \circ \tau) =$

$$\prod_{1 \leq i < j \leq n} \frac{\sigma(\tau(j)) - \sigma(\tau(i))}{j - i} = \prod_{1 \leq i < j \leq n} \frac{\sigma(\tau(j)) - \sigma(\tau(i))}{\tau(j) - \tau(i)} \frac{\tau(j) - \tau(i)}{j - i}.$$

Exercise 2.4.8. *Find the signs of the permutations in S_2 and S_3.*

Definition 2.4.9. (a) *The permutations σ in S_n for which* $\operatorname{sgn}(\sigma) = 1$ *are called* even permutations. *Those permutations σ for which* $\operatorname{sgn}(\sigma) = -1$ *are called* odd permutations. *The collection of even permutations is denoted by A_n.*

(b) *A permutation that interchanges two distinct elements and leaves the remaining elements fixed is called a* transposition. *The transposition which sends i to j, j to i, and leaves everything else fixed is written $(i\ j)$.*

Exercise 2.4.10.

(*i*) *Show that a transposition is an odd permutation.*

(*ii*) *Show that every element of S_n can be decomposed as a product of transpositions.*

(*iii*) *Show that* $\sigma \in S_n$ *is an even permutation if and only if* σ *can be decomposed into an even number of transpositions. Also show that* $\sigma \in S_n$ *is an odd permutation if and only if* σ *can be decomposed into an odd number of transpositions. The number of transpositions is not unique but the parity is always the same.*

(*iv*) *Show that* A_n *is a group (*A_n *is called the* Alternating Group *on* n *objects).*

(*v*) *Show that the number of elements in* A_n *is* $n!/2$.

(*vi*) *Show that* $\operatorname{sgn}(\sigma)$ *can be defined as simply the sign of the integer* $\prod_{1\leq i<j\leq n}(\sigma(j)-\sigma(i))$.

(*vii*) *Show that* $A_2 = \{I\}$ *and that* $A_3 = \{I, r, r^2\}$.

(*viii*) *Decompose each element in* S_3 *as a product of transpositions.*

(*ix*) *Write explicitly as arrays the elements of* A_4 *and* A_5.

We are now prepared to define the determinant of an $n \times n$ matrix.

Definition 2.4.11. *Let* $A = (a_{ij})$ *be an* $n \times n$ *matrix over a field* F. *The* determinant of A, *denoted by* $\det A$, *is defined by*

$$\det A = \sum_{\sigma \in S_n} \operatorname{sgn}(\sigma) a_{1,\sigma(1)} a_{2,\sigma(2)} \cdots a_{n,\sigma(n)}.$$

Example 2.4.12. *Consider a* 2×2 *matrix*

$$A = \begin{pmatrix} a_{11} & a_{12} \\ a_{21} & a_{22} \end{pmatrix}.$$

Then $\det A = a_{11}a_{22} - a_{12}a_{21}$.

Exercise 2.4.13. *Write out the expression for the determinant of a* 3×3 *matrix*

$$A = \begin{pmatrix} a_{11} & a_{12} & a_{13} \\ a_{21} & a_{22} & a_{23} \\ a_{31} & a_{32} & a_{33} \end{pmatrix}.$$

It should have $3! = 6$ *terms.*

We have two tasks ahead. The first is to illustrate the role of the determinant in computing the inverse of an $n \times n$ matrix. The second is to find some reasonable way to compute the determinant of a matrix.

Definition 2.4.14. *Suppose* $A = (a_{ij})$ *is an* $n \times n$ *matrix over a field* F. *Then* the transpose of A, *denoted* ${}^tA$, *is the matrix obtained by reflecting* A *around the diagonal. That is,*

$${}^tA = (a_{ji}).$$

Thus, if

$$A = \begin{pmatrix} a_{11} & a_{12} \\ a_{21} & a_{22} \end{pmatrix}, \text{ then } \quad {}^tA = \begin{pmatrix} a_{11} & a_{21} \\ a_{12} & a_{22} \end{pmatrix},$$

and, if

$$A = \begin{pmatrix} a_{11} & a_{12} & a_{13} \\ a_{21} & a_{22} & a_{23} \\ a_{31} & a_{32} & a_{33} \end{pmatrix}, \text{ then } \quad {}^tA = \begin{pmatrix} a_{11} & a_{21} & a_{31} \\ a_{12} & a_{22} & a_{32} \\ a_{13} & a_{23} & a_{33} \end{pmatrix}.$$

Exercise 2.4.15. *Let A be an $n \times n$ matrix over a field F. Show that* $\det(A) = \det({}^tA)$.

Exercise 2.4.16. *Let* $A = \begin{pmatrix} a_{11} & a_{12} \\ a_{21} & a_{22} \end{pmatrix}$. *Suppose that* $\det A \neq 0$. *Show that A^{-1} exists, and find it.*

Lemma 2.4.17. *If $A = (a_{ij})$ is an $n \times n$ matrix over a field F such that, for some m, k with $m \neq k$, the m-th row is equal to the k-th row, then* $\det A = 0$.

Proof. For any $\sigma \in S_n$ let $\tilde{\sigma} = \sigma \circ (k\ m)$, where $(k\ m)$ is the transposition defined above. Our assumption implies that

$$a_{1,\sigma(1)} a_{2,\sigma(2)} \cdots a_{n,\sigma(n)} = a_{1,\tilde{\sigma}(1)} a_{2,\tilde{\sigma}(2)} \cdots a_{n,\tilde{\sigma}(n)}.$$

On the other hand, $\mathrm{sgn}(\sigma) = -\mathrm{sgn}(\tilde{\sigma})$. This shows that $\det A = 0$. ☠

Exercise 2.4.18. *Show that, if $A = (a_{ij})$ is an $n \times n$ matrix over a field F such that, for some m, k with $m \neq k$, the m-th column is equal to the k-th column, then* $\det A = 0$.

The following exercise will prove useful in our discussion of the properties of determinants.

Exercise 2.4.19. *Suppose that $A = (a_{ij})$ and $B = (b_{ij})$ are $n \times n$ matrices over a field F. Suppose further that $\sigma : \{1, 2, \ldots, n\} \to \{1, 2, \ldots, n\}$ is not a bijection. Show that*

$$\sum_{\rho \in S_n} \mathrm{sgn}(\rho) a_{1,\sigma(1)} b_{\sigma(1),\rho(1)} a_{2,\sigma(2)} b_{\sigma(2),\rho(2)} \cdots a_{n,\sigma(n)} b_{\sigma(n),\rho(n)} = 0.$$

Definition 2.4.20. *Let $A = (a_{ij})$ be an $n \times n$ matrix over a field F. Let A_{ij} be the $(n-1) \times (n-1)$ matrix obtained by deleting the i-th row and the j-th column of A. The (i, j)* cofactor *of A is the element C_{ij} of F defined by* $C_{ij} = (-1)^{i+j} \det A_{ij}$.

Theorem 2.4.21. *Let $A = (a_{ij})$ be an $n \times n$ matrix over a field F. Then, for any fixed k with $1 \leq k \leq n$,*

$$\det A = a_{k1} C_{k1} + a_{k2} C_{k2} + \cdots + a_{kn} C_{kn}.$$

This is called the expansion of the determinant of A with respect to the k-th row.

Exercise 2.4.22. *Let A be a 3×3 matrix over a field F. Show that the expansion of* $\det A$ *with respect to any row yields the same answer you obtained in Exercise* 2.4.13.

Proof of the theorem. By definition, $\det A$ is the sum of products of the form

$$(*) \qquad \operatorname{sgn}(\sigma) a_{1,\sigma(1)} a_{2,\sigma(2)} \cdots a_{n,\sigma(n)}$$

where σ runs through the elements of S_n. We claim that the sum of all expressions of the form $(*)$ for which $\sigma(k) = j$ is equal to $a_{kj} C_{kj}$. If we show this for every j with $1 \leq j \leq n$, then, summing over all j, we will get the desired result.

We have

$$\sum_{\substack{\sigma \in S_n \\ \sigma(k)=j}} \operatorname{sgn}(\sigma) a_{1,\sigma(1)} a_{2,\sigma(2)} \cdots a_{n,\sigma(n)}$$
$$= a_{kj} \sum_{\substack{\sigma \in S_n \\ \sigma(k)=j}} \operatorname{sgn}(\sigma) a_{1,\sigma(1)} a_{2,\sigma(2)} \cdots \widehat{a_{k,\sigma(k)}} \cdots a_{n,\sigma(n)},$$

where $\widehat{\cdot}$ indicates that the term is removed. Thus, we need to check that

$$(\#) \qquad \sum_{\substack{\sigma \in S_n \\ \sigma(k)=j}} \operatorname{sgn}(\sigma) a_{1,\sigma(1)} \cdots \widehat{a_{k,\sigma(k)}} \cdots a_{n,\sigma(n)} = (-1)^{j+k} \det(A_{kj}).$$

To compute $\det(A_{kj})$, we must first re-index the rows and columns so that the indices go from 1 to $n-1$. For this, define $\phi : \{1, 2, \ldots, n-1\} \to \{1, 2, \ldots, \hat{k}, \ldots, n\}$, by

$$\phi(j) = \begin{cases} j, & \text{for } 1 \leq j \leq k-1 \\ j+1, & \text{for } k \leq j \leq n-1. \end{cases}$$

Similarly, with k replaced by j, define a bijection $\psi : \{1, 2, \ldots, n-1\} \to \{1, 2, \ldots \hat{j}, \ldots, n\}$. Let $\sigma \in S_n$ be such that $\sigma(k) = j$. Then the map $\sigma \circ \phi : \{1, 2, \ldots, n-1\} \to \{1, 2, \ldots n\}$ does not contain j in its image. The map $\psi^{-1} \circ \sigma \circ \phi : \{1, 2, \ldots, n-1\} \to \{1, 2, \ldots, n-1\}$ is well defined. In fact, the map $\{\sigma \in S_n \mid \sigma(k) = j\} \to S_{n-1}$ given by $\sigma \mapsto \psi^{-1} \circ \sigma \circ \phi$ is a bijection.

Now, recalling the definition of $\det A_{kj}$, we see that the proof of $(\#)$ follows immediately from

$$(\#\#) \qquad \operatorname{sgn}(\sigma) = (-1)^{j+k} \operatorname{sgn}(\psi^{-1} \circ \sigma \circ \phi).$$

Note that ϕ and ψ are strictly increasing maps so that $\operatorname{sgn}(\psi^{-1} \circ \sigma \circ \phi)$ coincides with the sign of $\prod_{\substack{1 \leq i < l \leq n \\ i,l \neq k}} (\sigma(l) - \sigma(i))$. Cancelling on both sides of (##), we are left with showing that

$$\operatorname{sign}\left(\prod_{\substack{1 \leq i < l \leq n \\ i=k \text{ or } l=k}} (\sigma(l) - \sigma(i)) \right) = (-1)^{j+k}.$$

Recalling that $\sigma(k) = j$, we see that the last product is

$$\prod_{i=1}^{k-1} (j - \sigma(i)) \cdot \prod_{l=k+1}^{n} (\sigma(l) - j) = (-1)^{k-1} \prod_{l \neq k} (\sigma(l) - j).$$

Moreover, $\operatorname{sign}\left(\prod_{l \neq k}(\sigma(l) - j)\right)$ is clearly $(-1)^{j-1}$. Altogether, we obtain $(-1)^{k-1} \cdot (-1)^{j-1} = (-1)^{j+k}$ as desired. ☠

Exercise 2.4.23. *Suppose that $A = (a_{ij})$ is an $n \times n$ matrix over a field F. Show that the fact that $\det A = \det {}^tA$ allows an expansion of the determinant with respect to the k-th column.*

We can now assert a theorem about inverses.

Theorem 2.4.24. *If A is an $n \times n$ matrix over a field F and $\det A \neq 0$, then A has an inverse. If $\det A \neq 0$, then A^{-1} is the transpose of the cofactor matrix multiplied by the inverse of the determinant of A. That is,*

$$A^{-1} = \frac{1}{\det A} \begin{pmatrix} C_{11} & C_{21} & \cdots & C_{n1} \\ C_{12} & C_{22} & \cdots & C_{n2} \\ \vdots & \vdots & \ddots & \vdots \\ C_{1n} & C_{2n} & \cdots & C_{nn}. \end{pmatrix}.$$

Proof. Let $C = (C_{ij})$ and consider the product ${}^tCA$. Look at the diagonal elements in this product. The j-th diagonal element is $a_{1j}C_{1j} + \cdots + a_{nj}C_{nj} = \det A$. For the off diagonal elements, we take k, m so that $1 \leq k, m \leq n$, $k \neq m$ and consider the (m,k)-th entry of ${}^tCA$. We get $a_{1k}C_{1m} + a_{2k}C_{2m} + \cdots + a_{nk}C_{nm}$. This represents expansion of the determinant of a matrix A' that is equal to A with the exception that the m-th column has been replaced by the k-th column. By the Exercise 2.4.18, this determinant is 0. Thus, if $\det A \neq 0$, then ${}^tC/\det(A)$ is the left inverse of A.

Exercise 2.4.25. *Show that ${}^tC/\det(A)$ is also a right inverse for A.* ☠

We now wish to prove that an $n \times n$ matrix A over a field F has a multiplicative inverse if and only if $\det A \neq 0$. One half of this fact was proved above. That is, if $\det A \neq 0$, then A has an inverse. The other half depends on the following important theorem.

Theorem 2.4.26. *If $A = (a_{ij})$ and $B = (b_{ij})$ are $n \times n$ matrices over a field F, then*

$$\det(AB) = \det(A) \cdot \det(B).$$

Proof. We first expand

$$\det(A) \cdot \det(B) = \sum_{\tau,\sigma \in S_n} \operatorname{sgn}(\sigma)\operatorname{sgn}(\tau) a_{1,\sigma(1)} a_{2,\sigma(2)} \cdots a_{n,\sigma(n)} b_{1,\tau(1)} b_{2,\tau(2)} \cdots b_{n,\tau(n)}.$$

We re-index the product of the b_{jk}'s as follows. It is clear that $b_{1,\tau(1)} \cdots b_{n,\tau(n)} = b_{\sigma(1),\tau(\sigma(1))} \cdots b_{\sigma(n),\tau(\sigma(n))}$. For fixed σ in S_n, we see that, as τ runs through S_n, so does $\tau \circ \sigma$. Moreover, $\operatorname{sgn}(\sigma)\operatorname{sgn}(\tau) = \operatorname{sgn}(\tau \circ \sigma)$. Hence, by letting $\rho = \tau \circ \sigma$, we have

$$\det A \cdot \det B = \sum_{\sigma \in S_n} \sum_{\rho \in S_n} \operatorname{sgn}(\rho) a_{1,\sigma(1)} b_{\sigma(1),\rho(1)} a_{2,\sigma(2)} b_{\sigma(2),\rho(2)} \cdots a_{n,\sigma(n)} b_{\sigma(n),\rho(n)}.$$

By Exercise 2.4.19 this last sum will not change if we allow σ to run over all maps $\sigma : \{1, 2, \dots, n\} \to \{1, 2, \dots, n\}$.

Now we let $C = AB$ and consider $\det(C)$. If $C = (c_{ij})$, then we have

$$\det(C) = \sum_{\rho \in S_n} \operatorname{sgn}(\rho) c_{1,\rho(1)} c_{2,\rho(2)} \cdots c_{n,\rho(n)}.$$

From the definition of C, we know that $c_{j,\rho(j)} = \sum_{k_j=1}^{n} a_{jk_j} b_{k_j,\rho(j)}$. This gives

$$\prod_{j=1}^{n} c_{j,\rho(j)} = \sum_{k_1=1}^{n} \sum_{k_2=1}^{n} \cdots \sum_{k_n=1}^{n} a_{1k_1} b_{k_1,\rho(1)} a_{2k_2} b_{k_2,\rho(2)} \cdots a_{nk_n} b_{k_n,\rho(n)}$$

For each term $(k_1, \dots, k_n)$ in the sum, we can define a map $\sigma : \{1, 2, \dots, n\} \to \{1, 2, \dots, n\}$ by $1 \mapsto k_1, 2 \mapsto k_2, \dots, n \mapsto k_n$. Notice there are exactly n^n such maps. Hence, all maps $\sigma : \{1, 2, \dots, n\} \to \{1, 2, \dots, n\}$ arise in this way. So we can index the sum by σ as we let σ run over all maps. In this way, we get

$$\det(C) = \sum_{\rho \in S_n} \sum_{\sigma} \operatorname{sgn}(\rho) a_{1,\sigma(1)} b_{\sigma(1),\rho(1))} a_{2,\sigma(2)} b_{\sigma(2),\rho(2)} \cdots a_{n,\sigma(n)} b_{\sigma(n),\rho(n)}.$$

Theorem 2.4.27. *Let A be an $n \times n$ matrix over a field F. Then A has a multiplicative inverse if and only if $\det A \neq 0$.*

Proof. Exercise. 

The next exercise illustrates several of the important properties of determinants of $n \times n$ matrices.

Exercise 2.4.28. *Suppose that A is an $n \times n$ matrix over a field F.*

(*i*) *If we multiply a row or column of A by a scalar c, find the determinant of the resulting matrix.*

(*ii*) *Show that if we interchange two rows or two columns of A, then the determinant of the resulting matrix is $-\det A$.*

(*iii*) *Show that if we add a scalar multiple of any row to any other row, or if we add a scalar multiple of any column to any other column, then the determinant remains unchanged.*

Exercise 2.4.29. *Let A be an $n \times n$ matrix over a field F.*

(*i*) *If $\det A \neq 0$, show that the columns of A are linearly independent and hence form a basis for F^n.*

(*ii*) *Do the same for the rows.*

(*iii*) *If the columns of A are linearly independent, show that $\det A \neq 0$. (Hint: consider the image of the linear transformation defined by A.)*

(*iv*) *Do the same for the rows.*

5. Geometric Linear Algebra

We now wish to investigate the geometry of finite dimensional vector spaces over $\mathbb{R}$. The real numbers are constructed carefully in Chapter 3. For the moment, we will use the properties of $\mathbb{R}$ that should be familiar to the reader from previous experience.

A point in $\mathbb{R}^n$ is represented by an n-tuple of elements of $\mathbb{R}$, written $\mathbf{p} = (p_1, \ldots, p_n)$, with each $p_i \in \mathbb{R}$. Geometrically, these are thought of as points in space, where the p_i's give the coordinates of the point $\mathbf{p}$. At the same time, we may consider n-tuples of real numbers as n-dimensional vectors giving the data of a direction and a magnitude, without specifying a base point from which this vector emanates. Thinking this way, we see that such vectors are elements of a vector space, $\mathbb{E}^n$, where elements can be written as $\mathbf{v} = (v_1, \ldots, v_n)$, with each $v_i \in \mathbb{R}$. We will consistently distinguish between the "points" of $\mathbb{R}^n$, and "vectors" in $\mathbb{E}^n$, since geometrically they are quite different. Observe that we are choosing the vectors $\mathbf{e}_1, \mathbf{e}_2, \ldots, \mathbf{e}_n$ of Exercise 2.1.10 as a basis for the vector space $\mathbb{E}^n$ and further that $\mathbf{v} = (v_1, v_2, \ldots, v_n)$ may be written as the linear combination $\mathbf{v} = v_1\mathbf{e}_1 + v_2\mathbf{e}_2 + \cdots + v_n\mathbf{e}_n$. Moreover, the coordinates of a point $\mathbf{p}$ are determined by a collection of mutually perpendicular coordinate axes and a distinguished point called the origin. The idea here is that vectors are free to wander around in space, and points have to stay where they are.

If we want to add two vectors $\mathbf{v}, \mathbf{w} \in \mathbb{E}^n$, we represent $\mathbf{v} + \mathbf{w}$ as the diagonal of a parallelogram as pictured below,

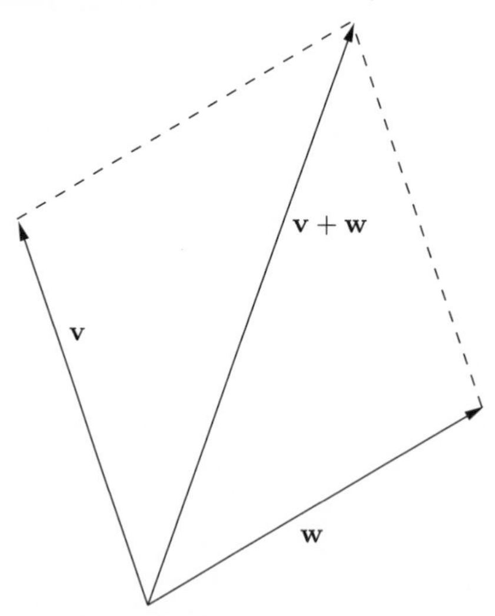

and if $\mathbf{v} = (v_1, \ldots, v_n)$ and $\mathbf{w} = (w_1, \ldots, w_n)$, then $\mathbf{v} + \mathbf{w} = (v_1 + w_1, \ldots, v_n + w_n)$. Continuing this idea, we specify that a direction $\mathbf{v}$ based at a point $\mathbf{p} = (p_1, p_2, \ldots, p_n)$ is given by an element of $\mathbb{R}^n \times \mathbb{E}^n$. We also have a geometric operation on $\mathbb{R}^n \times \mathbb{E}^n$ which is to drag the point $\mathbf{p}$ along $\mathbf{v}$ to get a new point $\mathbf{q} = (q_1, q_2, \ldots, q_n)$. This geometric operation is algebraically encoded in the formula:

$$\mathbb{R}^n \times \mathbb{E}^n \to \mathbb{R}^n$$

$$(\mathbf{p}, \mathbf{v}) \mapsto \mathbf{p} + \mathbf{v} = \mathbf{q}$$

$$((p_1, \ldots, p_n), (v_1, \ldots, v_n)) \mapsto (p_1 + v_1, \ldots, p_n + v_n) = (q_1, \cdots, q_n).$$

With this in mind, we have the statements

$$\text{vector} + \text{vector} = \text{vector},$$

$$\text{point} + \text{vector} = \text{point},$$

so naturally,

$$\text{point} - \text{point} = \text{vector!}$$

To make sense of this formally, given an ordered pair of points $(\mathbf{p}, \mathbf{q}) \in \mathbb{R}^n \times \mathbb{R}^n$, there is a unique vector $\mathbf{v} \in \mathbb{E}^n$ such that $\mathbf{p} + \mathbf{v} = \mathbf{q}$. This $\mathbf{v}$ represents $\mathbf{q} - \mathbf{p}$. Of course, algebraically it is given by nothing more than $\mathbf{v} = (q_1 - p_1, \ldots, q_n - p_n)$.

We are now ready to define some geometric objects in $\mathbb{R}^n$. To describe a *line*, we need a point $\mathbf{p}_0 \in \mathbb{R}^n$ and a (nonzero) direction $\mathbf{v} \in \mathbb{E}^n$.

Definition 2.5.1. *Let* $\mathbf{p}_0$ *be a point in* $\mathbb{R}^n$ *and* $\mathbf{v}$ *be a direction in* $\mathbb{E}^n$*. The* line ℓ through $\mathbf{p}_0$ in the direction $\mathbf{v}$ *is given by*

$$\ell = \{\mathbf{p} \in \mathbb{R}^n \mid \mathbf{p} = \mathbf{p}_0 + t\mathbf{v},\, t \in \mathbb{R}\}.$$

Notice that we are using the formalism of "vector plus point equals point."

Definition 2.5.2. *Suppose that* $\mathbf{p}_0 \in \mathbb{R}^n$ *and* $\mathbf{v}$, $\mathbf{w}$ *are linearly independent vectors in* $\mathbb{E}^n$*. The* plane through $\mathbf{p}_0$, spanned by $\mathbf{v}$ and $\mathbf{w}$, *is*

$$\mathscr{P} = \{\mathbf{p} \in \mathbb{R}^n \mid \mathbf{p} = \mathbf{p}_0 + t\mathbf{v} + s\mathbf{w},\, t, s \in \mathbb{R}.\}$$

More generally, we can use these ideas for other subsets of $\mathbb{R}^n$.

Definition 2.5.3. *If* $\mathbf{v}_1, \ldots, \mathbf{v}_k$ *are linearly independent vectors in* $\mathbb{E}^n$*, then we define the* k-dimensional affine subspace through $\mathbf{p}_0 \in \mathbb{R}^n$, spanned by $\mathbf{v}_1, \ldots, \mathbf{v}_k$*, as*

$$\mathbf{H} = \{\mathbf{p} \in \mathbb{R}^n \mid \mathbf{p} = \mathbf{p}_0 + t_1\mathbf{v}_1 + \ldots + t_k\mathbf{v}_k,\ \textit{where } t_j \in \mathbb{R} \textit{ and } 1 \leq j \leq k\}.$$

Note: The collection of vectors $\{t_1\mathbf{v}_1 + \ldots + t_k\mathbf{v}_k, t_j \in \mathbb{R}\}$ is actually a subspace of $\mathbb{E}^n$. Thus, a k-dimensional affine subspace is constructed by taking a k-dimensional subspace of $\mathbb{E}^n$ and adding it to a point of $\mathbb{R}^n$. When $k = n - 1$, $\mathbf{H}$ is called a *hyperplane* in $\mathbb{R}^n$.

Definition 2.5.4. *If* $\mathbf{v}_1, \ldots, \mathbf{v}_k$ *are linearly independent vectors in* $\mathbb{E}^n$ *with* $k \leq n$ *and* $\mathbf{p}_0 \in \mathbb{R}^n$*, we define the* k-dimensional parallelepiped with vertex $\mathbf{p}_0$ spanned by $\mathbf{v}_1, \mathbf{v}_2, \ldots, \mathbf{v}_k$ *as*

$$\mathbf{P} = \{\mathbf{p} \in \mathbb{R}^n \mid \mathbf{p} = \mathbf{p}_0 + t_1\mathbf{v}_1 + \ldots + t_k\mathbf{v}_k,\ \textit{with } 0 \leq t_j \leq 1\}.$$

Note that if $k = n = 2$, then $\mathbf{P}$ is just a standard parallelogram in $\mathbb{R}^2$.

Much of the geometry that appears in this section will arise in more general contexts throughout mathematics. We introduce only enough here to make the reader feel comfortable in $\mathbb{R}^n$. The rich interplay between $\mathbb{R}^n$ and the vector space $\mathbb{E}^n$ is what makes life interesting.

Definition 2.5.5. *Let* V *be a vector space over a field* F*. A* bilinear form $\langle \cdot, \cdot \rangle$ *on* V *is a map*

$$\langle \cdot, \cdot \rangle : V \times V \to F$$

that satisfies linearity in both variables. That is, for all $\mathbf{v}, \mathbf{w} \in V$*, and all* $\alpha \in F$*,*

$$\langle \mathbf{v}_1 + \mathbf{v}_2, \mathbf{w} \rangle = \langle \mathbf{v}_1, \mathbf{w} \rangle + \langle \mathbf{v}_2, \mathbf{w} \rangle$$
$$\langle \alpha\mathbf{v}, \mathbf{w} \rangle = \alpha\langle \mathbf{v}, \mathbf{w} \rangle$$
$$\langle \mathbf{v}, \mathbf{w}_1 + \mathbf{w}_2 \rangle = \langle \mathbf{v}, \mathbf{w}_1 \rangle + \langle \mathbf{v}, \mathbf{w}_2 \rangle$$
$$\langle \mathbf{v}, \alpha\mathbf{w} \rangle = \alpha\langle \mathbf{v}, \mathbf{w} \rangle.$$

The form $\langle \cdot, \cdot \rangle$ *is said to be* symmetric *if* $\langle \mathbf{v}, \mathbf{w} \rangle = \langle \mathbf{w}, \mathbf{v} \rangle$ *for all* $\mathbf{v}, \mathbf{w} \in V$. *When* $F = \mathbb{R}$, *we say the form is* positive definite *if* $\langle \mathbf{v}, \mathbf{v} \rangle \geq 0$ *for all* $\mathbf{v} \in V$, *and* $\langle \mathbf{v}, \mathbf{v} \rangle = 0$ *if and only if* $\mathbf{v} = \mathbf{0}$. *Henceforth, we assume* $F = \mathbb{R}$.

The main example of a positive definite symmetric bilinear form on $\mathbb{E}^n$ is the scalar product or dot product.

Definition 2.5.6. *Suppose that* $\mathbf{v} = (v_1, \ldots, v_n)$ *and* $\mathbf{w} = (w_1, \ldots, w_n)$ *are vectors in* $\mathbb{E}^n$. *The* scalar product *of* $\mathbf{v}$ *and* $\mathbf{w}$ *is* $\langle \mathbf{v}, \mathbf{w} \rangle = v_1 w_1 + \ldots + v_n w_n$. *The scalar product is sometimes called the* dot product *and is denoted by* $\mathbf{v} \cdot \mathbf{w}$. *We will try our best to be consistent and use* $\langle \, , \, \rangle$.

Exercise 2.5.7. *Prove that the scalar product is a positive definite symmetric bilinear form on* $\mathbb{E}^n$.

There are two concepts that arise immediately with the existence of a positive definite symmetric bilinear form. The first is the length or norm of a vector and the second is orthogonality.

Definition 2.5.8. *If* $\mathbf{v} = (v_1, \ldots, v_n) \in \mathbb{E}^n$, *then the* length *or* norm *of* $\mathbf{v}$ *is defined by*

$$||\mathbf{v}|| = \sqrt{\langle \mathbf{v}, \mathbf{v} \rangle} = (v_1^2 + \cdots + v_n^2)^{1/2}.$$

Exercise 2.5.9. *Prove the following properties of the norm. If* $\mathbf{v}, \mathbf{w} \in \mathbb{E}^n$, *then:*

(*i*) $||\mathbf{v}|| \geq 0$;

(*ii*) $||\mathbf{v}|| = 0$ *iff* $\mathbf{v} = \mathbf{0}$;

(*iii*) $||\alpha \mathbf{v}|| = |\alpha| \, ||\mathbf{v}||, \quad \alpha \in \mathbb{R}$;

(*iv*) $||\mathbf{v} + \mathbf{w}|| \leq ||\mathbf{v}|| + ||\mathbf{w}||$;

(*v*) $\|\mathbf{v} + \mathbf{w}\|^2 + \|\mathbf{v} - \mathbf{w}\|^2 = 2\left(\|\mathbf{v}\|^2 + \|\mathbf{w}\|^2\right)$.

It is time you had the opportunity to use the quadratic formula that was so important in your earlier years.

Theorem 2.5.10 (Cauchy-Schwarz Inequality). *Let* $\mathbf{v}, \mathbf{w} \in \mathbb{E}^n$. *Then*

$$|\langle \mathbf{v}, \mathbf{w} \rangle| \leq \|\mathbf{v}\| \, \|\mathbf{w}\|.$$

Proof. Let λ be a real number. Then

$$\begin{aligned} 0 \leq \langle \mathbf{v} - \lambda \mathbf{w}, \mathbf{v} - \lambda \mathbf{w} \rangle &= \langle \mathbf{v}, \mathbf{v} \rangle - \langle \mathbf{v}, \lambda \mathbf{w} \rangle - \langle \lambda \mathbf{w}, \mathbf{v} \rangle + \langle \lambda \mathbf{w}, \lambda \mathbf{w} \rangle \\ &= ||\mathbf{v}||^2 - 2\lambda \langle \mathbf{v}, \mathbf{w} \rangle + \lambda^2 ||\mathbf{w}||^2. \end{aligned}$$

This is a quadratic polynomial in λ which is always greater than or equal to 0. It follows that, in the usual notation, $B^2 - 4AC \leq 0$. This is the desired inequality.

Exercise 2.5.11. *Prove that equality holds in the Cauchy-Schwarz Inequality iff one of the vectors is a scalar multiple of the other.*

This definition of the norm leads to the usual definition of Euclidean distance between two points in $\mathbb{R}^n$. Thus, if $\mathbf{p}_1, \mathbf{p}_2 \in \mathbb{R}^n$, then $d(\mathbf{p}_1, \mathbf{p}_2) = ||\mathbf{p}_1 - \mathbf{p}_2||$.

This is good enough for now. The general study of distance is carried out in Chapter 4 where we discuss metric spaces.

Since we have a positive definite symmetric bilinear form, the concept of orthogonality (or perpendicularity) in $\mathbb{E}^n$ can be formalized as follows.

Definition 2.5.12. *Let* $\mathbf{v}, \mathbf{w} \in \mathbb{E}^n$. *Then* $\mathbf{v}$ *and* $\mathbf{w}$ *are said to be* orthogonal *(or* perpendicular*) if* $\langle \mathbf{v}, \mathbf{w} \rangle = 0$.

Exercise 2.5.13.

(*i*) *Show that the* $\mathbf{0}$ *vector in* $\mathbb{E}^n$ *is orthogonal to every vector in* $\mathbb{E}^n$.

(*ii*) *Show that the vectors in the set* $\{\mathbf{e}_1, \mathbf{e}_2, \ldots, \mathbf{e}_n\}$ *are pairwise orthogonal, that is* $\langle \mathbf{e}_i, \mathbf{e}_j \rangle = 0$ *if* $i \neq j$, *and further that* $\langle \mathbf{e}_i, \mathbf{e}_i \rangle = 1$.

(*iii*) *If* $\mathbf{v}$ *is a nonzero vector in* $\mathbb{E}^n$, *show that the collection* $W = \{\mathbf{w} \in \mathbb{E}^n \mid \langle \mathbf{w}, \mathbf{v} \rangle = 0\}$ *is an* $(n-1)$*-dimensional subspace of* $\mathbb{E}^n$.

(*iv*) *If* $\mathbf{v}_1, \ldots, \mathbf{v}_k$ *are pairwise orthogonal nonzero vectors in* $\mathbb{E}^n$, *show that they form a linearly independent set in* $\mathbb{E}^n$.

Now, we wish to consider the angle between two nonzero vectors $\mathbf{v}, \mathbf{w}$. If the vectors are linearly dependent, that is $\mathbf{w} = \lambda \mathbf{v}$, then the angle between them is 0 degrees if $\lambda > 0$ and 180 degrees if $\lambda < 0$. If $\mathbf{v}$ and $\mathbf{w}$ are linearly independent, we look at the plane through the origin spanned by $\mathbf{v}$ and $\mathbf{w}$. In this case, there are two angles associated to $\mathbf{v}$ and $\mathbf{w}$. One is less than 180 degrees and one is greater than 180 degrees. We take *the angle between* $\mathbf{v}$ *and* $\mathbf{w}$ to be the angle that is less than 180 degrees.

Theorem 2.5.14. *Let* $\mathbf{v}$ *and* $\mathbf{w}$ *be linearly independent vectors in* $\mathbb{E}^n$. *The angle between* $\mathbf{v}$ *and* $\mathbf{w}$ *is the unique solution* θ *to the equation*

$$\cos\theta = \frac{\langle \mathbf{v}, \mathbf{w} \rangle}{||\mathbf{v}||\,||\mathbf{w}||}, \quad 0 < \theta < 180^\circ.$$

Proof. This is just the law of cosines, which states that $||\mathbf{v} - \mathbf{w}||^2 = ||\mathbf{v}||^2 + ||\mathbf{w}||^2 - 2||\mathbf{v}||\,||\mathbf{w}|| \cos\theta$. ☠

We next define one of the most important operations on vectors in $\mathbb{E}^n$.

Definition 2.5.15. *Let* $\mathbf{v}$ *and* $\mathbf{w}$ *be linearly independent vectors in* $\mathbb{E}^n$. *The* projection of $\mathbf{v}$ onto $\mathbf{w}$ *is defined by*

$$\mathrm{proj}_{\mathbf{w}}(\mathbf{v}) = \frac{\langle \mathbf{v}, \mathbf{w} \rangle}{||\mathbf{w}||} \frac{\mathbf{w}}{||\mathbf{w}||}.$$

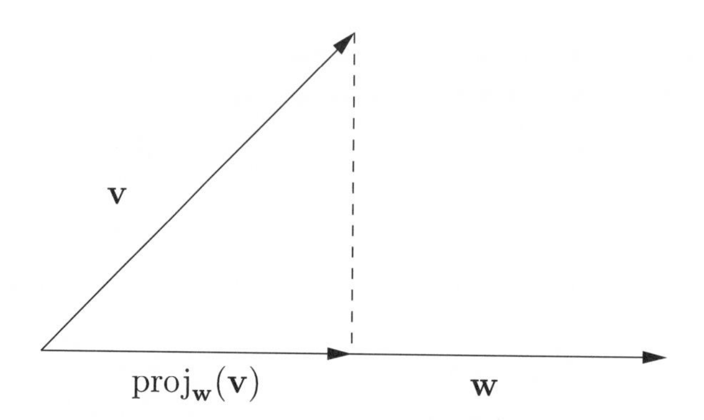

Observe that $\mathbf{w}/\|\mathbf{w}\|$ is a unit vector in the direction of $\mathbf{w}$. Hence, the projection of $\mathbf{v}$ on $\mathbf{w}$ has the same direction as $\mathbf{w}$ if $\langle \mathbf{v}, \mathbf{w} \rangle > 0$, and the direction of $-\mathbf{w}$ if $\langle \mathbf{v}, \mathbf{w} \rangle < 0$. Of course, if $\langle \mathbf{v}, \mathbf{w} \rangle = 0$, then $\mathbf{v}$ and $\mathbf{w}$ are orthogonal and the projection is just the zero vector. Note that the norm of $\operatorname{proj}_{\mathbf{w}}(\mathbf{v})$ is $\|\operatorname{proj}_{\mathbf{w}}(\mathbf{v})\| = \frac{|\langle \mathbf{v}, \mathbf{w} \rangle|}{\|\mathbf{w}\|}$.

Exercise 2.5.16. *Show that* $\mathbf{v} - \operatorname{proj}_{\mathbf{w}}(\mathbf{v})$ *is orthogonal to* $\mathbf{w}$.

Now, given a set of k linearly independent vectors $\mathbf{v}_1, \ldots, \mathbf{v}_k$ in $\mathbb{E}^n$, we want to construct a set $\mathbf{v}_{k+1}, \ldots, \mathbf{v}_n$ of linearly independent vectors such that the set $\{\mathbf{v}_1, \ldots, \mathbf{v}_n\}$ is linearly independent and hence a basis for $\mathbb{E}^n$. In fact, we would like the vectors $\mathbf{v}_{k+1}, \ldots, \mathbf{v}_n$ to be orthogonal to $\mathbf{v}_1, \ldots, \mathbf{v}_k$ and, if there is more than one, to be orthogonal to each other. This can be done in a variety of ways.

First, let's look in 2 and 3 dimensions. Given a vector $\mathbf{v} = (v_1, v_2) \in \mathbb{E}^2$, $\mathbf{v} \neq \mathbf{0}$, we set $\mathbf{v}^\perp = (v_2, -v_1)$. Then, $\langle \mathbf{v}, \mathbf{v}^\perp \rangle = 0$, that is, these vectors are orthogonal. In $\mathbb{E}^3$, we have the usual notion of *cross product*. This is often defined by using determinants. For the moment, given two linearly independent vectors $\mathbf{v} = (v_1, v_2, v_3)$ and $\mathbf{w} = (w_1, w_2, w_3)$ in $\mathbb{E}^3$, we define $\mathbf{v} \times \mathbf{w} = (v_2 w_3 - v_3 w_2, v_3 w_1 - v_1 w_3, v_1 w_2 - v_2 w_1)$.

Exercise 2.5.17.

(*i*) *Show that* $\mathbf{v} \times \mathbf{w} \neq \mathbf{0}$.

(*ii*) *Show that* $\langle \mathbf{v}, \mathbf{v} \times \mathbf{w} \rangle = \langle \mathbf{w}, \mathbf{v} \times \mathbf{w} \rangle = \mathbf{0}$.

(*iii*) *Show that* $\mathbf{w} \times \mathbf{v} = -(\mathbf{v} \times \mathbf{w})$.

Exercise 2.5.18.

(*i*) *Show that* $||\mathbf{v} \times \mathbf{w}|| = ||\mathbf{v}||\,||\mathbf{w}|| \sin\theta$, *where* θ *is the angle between* $\mathbf{v}$ *and* $\mathbf{w}$.

(*ii*) *Show that* $\|\mathbf{v} \times \mathbf{w}\|$ *is the area of the parallelogram spanned by* $\mathbf{v}$ *and* $\mathbf{w}$.

What we have just shown is that given a nonzero vector $\mathbf{v} \in \mathbb{E}^2$, we can find a vector $\mathbf{v}^\perp$ which is nonzero and orthogonal to $\mathbf{v}$. Obviously, the pair $\{\mathbf{v}, \mathbf{v}^\perp\}$ is a basis for $\mathbb{E}^2$. Next, given two linearly independent vectors $\mathbf{v}_1, \mathbf{v}_2 \in \mathbb{E}^3$, we constructed $\mathbf{v}_3 = \mathbf{v}_1 \times \mathbf{v}_2$ orthogonal to both of the original vectors. The set $\{\mathbf{v}_1, \mathbf{v}_2, \mathbf{v}_3\}$ is a basis for $\mathbb{E}^3$. This process can be generalized to $\mathbb{E}^n$.

Determinants can be used in an interesting way in the aforegoing process. For example, given a vector $\mathbf{v} = (v_1, v_2) \in \mathbb{E}^2$, we write the matrix

$$\begin{pmatrix} \mathbf{e}_1 & \mathbf{e}_2 \\ v_1 & v_2 \end{pmatrix}.$$

Without being concerned about vectors in the first row and scalars in the second row, we can take the "determinant" of this matrix by expanding according to the first row and obtain $v_2\mathbf{e}_1 - v_1\mathbf{e}_2$, which is the vector $\mathbf{v}^\perp = (v_2, -v_1)$. Similarly, if we have linearly independent vectors $\mathbf{v} = (v_1, v_2, v_3)$ and $\mathbf{w} = (w_1, w_2, w_3)$ in $\mathbb{E}^3$, we can consider

$$\begin{pmatrix} \mathbf{e}_1 & \mathbf{e}_2 & \mathbf{e}_3 \\ v_1 & v_2 & v_3 \\ w_1 & w_2 & w_3 \end{pmatrix}.$$

Taking the "determinant" of this matrix by expanding according to the first row, we get $(v_2w_3 - v_3w_2)\mathbf{e}_1 + (v_3w_1 - v_1w_3)\mathbf{e}_2 + (v_1w_2 - v_2w_1)\mathbf{e}_3$ which is $\mathbf{v} \times \mathbf{w}$.

Some of the ideas above can be extended to finite dimensional vector spaces over any subfield of the real numbers, in particular the rational numbers. The following is a definition that is somewhat redundant, but emphasizes that the ideas in the definition apply to any subfield of the real numbers.

Definition 2.5.19. *Let F be a subfield of the real numbers, and let $V = F^n$. If $\mathbf{v} = (v_1, \ldots, v_n)$ and $\mathbf{w} = (w_1, \ldots, w_n)$ are elements of V, we say that $\mathbf{v}$ is* orthogonal *(or* perpendicular*) to $\mathbf{w}$ if $\langle \mathbf{v}, \mathbf{w}\rangle = \mathbf{v} \cdot \mathbf{w} = v_1w_1 + v_2w_2 + \ldots + v_nw_n = 0$. We say that $\mathbf{v}$ is a* normalized vector *or* unit vector *if $\langle \mathbf{v}, \mathbf{v}\rangle = v_1^2 + v_2^2 + \ldots + v_n^2 = 1$. An* orthonormal set *in V is a collection $\{\mathbf{v}_1, \mathbf{v}_2, \ldots, \mathbf{v}_k\}$ of vectors in V such that $\langle \mathbf{v}_i, \mathbf{v}_j\rangle = 0$ if $i \neq j$, and $\langle \mathbf{v}_i, \mathbf{v}_i\rangle = 1$ for all $i, j = 1, \ldots, k$. If $k = n$, the orthonormal set $\{\mathbf{v}_1, \mathbf{v}_2, \ldots, \mathbf{v}_n\}$ is called an* orthonormal basis *for V.*

Theorem 2.5.20. *Let F be a subfield of $\mathbb{R}$, and let $V = F^n$. Suppose that $\{\mathbf{v}_1, \mathbf{v}_2, \ldots, \mathbf{v}_{n-1}\}$ is a collection of linearly independent vectors in V, where*

$\mathbf{v}_j = (v_{j1}, v_{j2}, \ldots, v_{jn})$. *Consider the matrix*

$$\begin{pmatrix} \mathbf{e}_1 & \mathbf{e}_2 & \cdots & \mathbf{e}_n \\ v_{11} & v_{12} & \cdots & v_{1n} \\ \vdots & \vdots & \ddots & \vdots \\ v_{(n-1)1} & v_{(n-1)2} & \cdots & v_{(n-1)n} \end{pmatrix}.$$

Let $\mathbf{v}$ *be the vector obtained by taking the "determinant" of this matrix with respect to the first row. Then* $\mathbf{v}$ *is nonzero and is orthogonal to each of the vectors* $\mathbf{v}_1, \mathbf{v}_2, \ldots, \mathbf{v}_{n-1}$. *Moreover, the collection* $\{\mathbf{v}_1, \mathbf{v}_2, \ldots, \mathbf{v}_{n-1}, \mathbf{v}\}$ *is a basis for* V.

Proof. The vector $\mathbf{v}$ obtained by expanding with respect to the first row is simply the vector of cofactors $\mathbf{v} = (C_{11}, C_{12}, \ldots, C_{1n})$. If we replace the first row by $\mathbf{v}$, we obtain the matrix

$$A = \begin{pmatrix} C_{11} & C_{12} & \cdots & C_{1n} \\ v_{11} & v_{12} & \cdots & v_{1n} \\ \vdots & \vdots & \ddots & \vdots \\ v_{(n-1)1} & v_{(n-1)2} & \cdots & v_{(n-1)n} \end{pmatrix}.$$

We prove first that the vector $\mathbf{v}$ is orthogonal to the vectors $\mathbf{v}_1, \ldots, \mathbf{v}_{n-1}$. To see this, choose i with $1 \leq i \leq n-1$. Then $\langle \mathbf{v}_i, \mathbf{v} \rangle = v_{i1}C_{11} + v_{i2}C_{12} + \cdots + v_{in}C_{1n}$. This is the determinant of the matrix obtained by replacing the first row of A by the vector $\mathbf{v}_i$. By Lemma 2.4.17 this determinant is 0. Next, we establish that $\mathbf{v}$ is not the $\mathbf{0}$ vector. To do this, we note that, if $C_{1j} = 0$ for all j, and we replace $\mathbf{v}$ by any vector $\mathbf{w}$ in V, then the determinant of the resulting matrix will be 0. But since $\mathbf{v}_1, \ldots, \mathbf{v}_{n-1}$ form a linearly independent set in V, we can extend this set to a basis in V with a vector $\mathbf{v}_n$. Replacing the vector $\mathbf{v}$ by $\mathbf{v}_n$, we get a matrix whose determinant is not 0. This is a contradiction. ☺

Exercise 2.5.21. *If, as in the previous theorem,* $\{\mathbf{v}_1, \mathbf{v}_2, \ldots, \mathbf{v}_{n-1}\}$ *forms an orthonormal set in* V, *show that* $\{\mathbf{v}_1, \mathbf{v}_2, \ldots, \mathbf{v}_{n-1}, \mathbf{v}\}$ *is an orthonormal basis for* V. *(Hint: Consider* $A^t A$ *and* AA^{-1}.*)*

Exercise 2.5.22. *Suppose that* $\mathbf{v}_1, \mathbf{v}_2, \ldots, \mathbf{v}_{n-1}$ *are linearly independent vectors in* $\mathbb{E}^n$. *Take a point* $\mathbf{p}_0$ *in* $\mathbb{R}^n$ *and consider the hyperplane* $\mathbf{H}$ *through* $\mathbf{p}_0$ *spanned by* $\mathbf{v}_1, \mathbf{v}_2, \ldots, \mathbf{v}_{n-1}$. *If* $\mathbf{v}$ *is the vector determined in Theorem* 2.5.20, *show that* $\mathbf{H} = \{\mathbf{p} \in \mathbb{R}^n \mid \langle \mathbf{p} - \mathbf{p}_0, \mathbf{v} \rangle = 0\}$. *Specialize this to obtain formulas for a line in* $\mathbb{R}^2$ *and for a plane in* $\mathbb{R}^3$.

Exercise 2.5.23. *Let* $\mathbf{v}_1, \mathbf{v}_2, \ldots, \mathbf{v}_{n-1}$ *be linearly independent vectors in* $\mathbb{E}^n$. *Let* $\mathbf{p}_0$ *be a point of* $\mathbb{R}^n$. *Let* $\mathbf{H}$ *be the hyperplane through* $\mathbf{p}_0$ *spanned by* $\mathbf{v}_1, \mathbf{v}_2, \ldots, \mathbf{v}_{n-1}$. *If* $\mathbf{p}$ *is any point in* $\mathbb{R}^n$, *show that the distance from* $\mathbf{p}$ *to* $\mathbf{H}$, *that is* $\inf\{\|\mathbf{p} - \mathbf{q}\| \mid \mathbf{q} \in \mathbf{H}\}$, *is given by the length of the vector*

$\text{proj}_{\mathbf{v}}(\mathbf{p} - \mathbf{p}_0)$ *where* $\mathbf{v}$ *is the vector obtained in Theorem* 2.5.20. *Specialize this to obtain formulas for the distance from a point to a line in* $\mathbb{R}^2$ *and from a point to a plane in* $\mathbb{R}^3$.

Exercise 2.5.24. *Find a formula for the distance from a point to a line in* $\mathbb{R}^n$.

Recall that our goal is to take k linearly independent vectors $\mathbf{v}_1, \mathbf{v}_2, \ldots, \mathbf{v}_k$ in $\mathbb{E}^n$ for $k < n$ and find vectors $\mathbf{v}_{k+1}, \ldots, \mathbf{v}_n$ so that $\{\mathbf{v}_1, \mathbf{v}_2, \ldots, \mathbf{v}_{k-1}, \mathbf{v}_k, \mathbf{v}_{k+1}, \ldots, \mathbf{v}_n\}$ is a basis for $\mathbb{E}^n$. Further, we would like as much orthogonality as possible.

We know that $\mathbf{v}_1, \mathbf{v}_2, \ldots, \mathbf{v}_k$ can be completed to a basis for $\mathbb{E}^n$. In fact, this can be done in a systematic way by considering the collection $\mathbf{v}_1, \mathbf{v}_2, \ldots, \mathbf{v}_k, \mathbf{e}_1, \mathbf{e}_2, \ldots, \mathbf{e}_n$ which is a spanning set. We then proceed as in the Exchange Lemma to obtain a basis for $\mathbb{E}^n$.

Of course, the $\mathbf{e}_j$'s are pairwise orthogonal, but what about the $\mathbf{v}_j$'s? This question leads to the process called *Gram-Schmidt Orthogonalization.*

We begin with a set $\{\mathbf{v}_1, \ldots, \mathbf{v}_k\}$ of linearly independent vectors and proceed as follows. Let $\tilde{\mathbf{v}}_1 = \mathbf{v}_1$. We continue to find vectors $\tilde{\mathbf{v}}_k$ by taking $\mathbf{v}_k$ and subtracting the projections on the vectors already constructed. More explicitly, we let

$$\begin{aligned}
\tilde{\mathbf{v}}_2 &= \mathbf{v}_2 - \text{proj}_{\tilde{\mathbf{v}}_1}(\mathbf{v}_2).\\
\tilde{\mathbf{v}}_3 &= \mathbf{v}_3 - \text{proj}_{\tilde{\mathbf{v}}_1}(\mathbf{v}_3) - \text{proj}_{\tilde{\mathbf{v}}_2}(\mathbf{v}_3).\\
&\vdots\\
\tilde{\mathbf{v}}_k &= \mathbf{v}_k - \sum_{i=1}^{k-1} \text{proj}_{\tilde{\mathbf{v}}_i}(\mathbf{v}_k).
\end{aligned}$$

It is easy to check that this set of vectors is pairwise orthogonal.

Exercise 2.5.25. *Check it, and, in addition, show that* $\tilde{\mathbf{v}}_1, \tilde{\mathbf{v}}_2, \ldots, \tilde{\mathbf{v}}_k$ *span the same subspace as* $\mathbf{v}_1, \mathbf{v}_2, \ldots, \mathbf{v}_k$.

Now, having completed $\mathbf{v}_1, \mathbf{v}_2, \ldots, \mathbf{v}_k$ to a basis $\mathbf{v}_1, \mathbf{v}_2, \ldots, \mathbf{v}_k, \mathbf{v}_{k+1}, \ldots, \mathbf{v}_n$, we can use the Gram-Schmidt process to obtain an orthogonal basis.

Exercise 2.5.26. *Consider the vectors* $\mathbf{v}_1 = (1, 1, -1, 0)$ *and* $\mathbf{v}_2 = (1, 0, 0, -1)$ *in* $\mathbb{E}^4$, *and complete this pair to an orthogonal basis as above.*

The next step is to try to work with vectors whose norms are equal to one. Note that if $\mathbf{v}$ is a nonzero vector in $\mathbb{E}^n$, then $\mathbf{v}$ can be converted to a vector of norm 1, that is, a unit vector, by dividing $\mathbf{v}$ by $\|\mathbf{v}\|$.

Example 2.5.27. *The collection* $\{\mathbf{e}_1, \mathbf{e}_2, \ldots, \mathbf{e}_n\}$ *is an orthonormal basis for* $\mathbb{E}^n$.

Exercise 2.5.28. *Show that, given linearly independent vectors* $\mathbf{v}_1, \ldots, \mathbf{v}_k$ *in* $\mathbb{E}^n$, *we can transform this collection into an orthonormal set* $\{\tilde{\mathbf{v}}_1, \ldots, \tilde{\mathbf{v}}_k\}$ *that spans the same subspace. In addition, the set* $\{\tilde{\mathbf{v}}_1, \ldots, \tilde{\mathbf{v}}_k\}$ *can be completed to an orthonormal basis for* $\mathbb{E}^n$.

6. Independent Projects

6.1. Groups.

In Chapter 1, we introduced commutative rings with 1, integral domains, and fields. In this Chapter, we have introduced vector spaces and algebras over a field, and we have defined groups in the context of the symmetric group. This project gives more details and exercises about groups.

Definition 2.6.1.1. *Let* G *be a set with an ILC (see Definition 1.6.18)* $\circ : G \times G \to G$. *The pair* $(G, \circ)$ *is a* group *if:*

(a) *for all* $a, b, c \in G$, *we have* $(a \circ b) \circ c = a \circ (b \circ c)$ *(Associativity);*

(b) *there is an* identity element $e \in G$ *such that for each* $a \in G$, $e \circ a = a \circ e = a$ *(Identity);*

(c) *for every pair* $a, b \in G$, *there is an element* $c \in G$ *such that* $c \circ a = b$ *and an element* $d \in G$ *such that* $a \circ d = b$ *(Solvability).*

Here is a set of elementary exercises about groups.

Exercise 2.6.1.2. *Suppose that* $(G, \circ)$ *is a group. Prove the following statements.*

(*i*) *Show that the identity is unique.*

(*ii*) *Show that for each* $a \in G$, *there exists an inverse* a^{-1} *for* a *so that* $a \circ a^{-1} = a^{-1} \circ a = e$.

(*iii*) *Show that inverses are unique.*

(*iv*) *If* a, b *are elements of* G, *show that the equations* $a \circ x = b$ *and* $x \circ a = b$ *can be solved uniquely.*

(*v*) *If* $a, b, c \in G$ *and* $a \circ b = a \circ c$, *show that* $b = c$.

(*vi*) *If* $a, b \in G$, *show that* $(a \circ b)^{-1} = b^{-1} \circ a^{-1}$.

Exercise 2.6.1.3. *Show that the axioms for a group are completely independent.*

Examples 2.6.1.4. *The following pairs are groups. If the ILC is addition, denoted by "+", then the identity is normally represented by the symbol "0" and the inverse of an element* a *is denoted by "*$-a$*". Elementary examples* *of groups include:*

(1) *the ordinary integers* $(\mathbb{Z}, +)$*;*

(2) *the integers* $\{1, -1\}$ *under multiplication;*

(3) *the rational numbers* $(\mathbb{Q}, +)$*;*

(4) *the nonzero rational numbers* $(\mathbb{Q}^\times, \cdot)$*; and*

(5) *for an integer* $n \geq 2$, $(\mathbb{Z}_n, +)$.

(6) *The rotations of a regular* n*-gon about the center form a group denoted by* C_n*. Let* r *be a counterclockwise rotation through* $(360/n)^\circ$*, that is* $2\pi/n$ *radians. The rotation group of a regular* n*-gon consists of* I *(the identity rotation),* r*,* r^2 *(the counterclockwise rotation through* $(2 \cdot 360/n)^\circ$*),* r^3*, ...,* r^{n-1}*. Note that* $r^n = I$*.*

Continuing our examples of groups, we have:

(7) *the group* S_n *of permutations of* n *objects;*

(8) *the group* A_n *of even permutations in* S_n*.*

The ILC in these last two examples is composition of functions.

(9) *The set of* $n \times n$ *matrices over a field* F *with addition as the ILC is a group.*

(10) *The set* $GL_2(F) = \{A \in M_2(F) \mid \det A \neq 0\}$ *is a group under multiplication of matrices. The group* $GL_2(F)$ *is called the* 2×2 general linear group *over* F*.*

The first six examples of groups above fit a category of groups that are particularly easy to work with, that is, abelian or commutative groups.

Definition 2.6.1.5. *A group* $(G,\circ)$ *is* abelian *or* commutative *if* $a \circ b = b \circ a$ *for all* $a, b \in G$*.*

In the examples above, the groups S_n for $n \geq 3$, A_n for $n \geq 4$, and $GL_2(F)$ are not abelian.

Remark 2.6.1.6. *It is often convenient to omit the ILC* $\circ$ *when writing a product. Thus, we can write* $a \circ b = ab$*. In particular, if* $(G, \circ)$ *is a group and* k *is a positive integer, we can write* a^k *for* $a \circ a \circ \cdots \circ a$ *(*k*-times). We can also write* $a^{-k} = (a^{-1})^k$*. Given all of this, we occasionally write* $a \circ b$ *when we feel it is useful.*

The simplest groups to analyze are cyclic groups.

Definition 2.6.1.7. *If* G *is a group and there exists an element* $a \in G$ *such that* $G = \{a^k \mid k \in \mathbb{Z}\}$*, then* G *is called the* cyclic group *generated by* a*.*

Note that we do not assume, in the definition of a cyclic group, that the various powers a^k are distinct.

Exercise 2.6.1.8.

(*i*) *If G is a cyclic group of order n generated by a, show that $a^n = e$.*

(*ii*) *Show that a cyclic group of order n generated by a is also generated by a^k when k and n are relatively prime.*

(*iii*) *Show that cyclic groups are abelian and that in a cyclic group of order n, $(a^k)^{-1} = a^{n-k}$ for $1 \leq k \leq n-1$.*

Examples 2.6.1.9.

(1) *The integers, $\mathbb{Z}$, under addition form an infinite cyclic group generated by* 1.

(2) *The even integers, $2\mathbb{Z}$, form an infinite cyclic group under addition generated by* 2.

(3) *Let p be a prime, and let $G = \{p^k \mid k \in \mathbb{Z}\}$. Then, G is an infinite cyclic group under multiplication generated by p.*

(4) *The group C_n of rotations of a regular n-gon is a cyclic group of order n generated by r (see Example* 2.6.1.4(6)*).*

(5) *The group $(\mathbb{Z}_n, +)$ (see Definition 1.6.27) is a cyclic group of order n generated by* 1.

Exercise 2.6.1.10. *Show that the group of rational numbers under addition is not a cyclic group.*

Exercise 2.6.1.11. *Can a cyclic group be uncountable?*

Definition 2.6.1.12. *Suppose that $(G, \circ)$ is a group. If the number of elements in G is finite, we write $|G| = n$ where n is the number of elements of G, and we call n the* order of G. *If G has an infinite number of elements, we say that G is an* infinite group.

Definition 2.6.1.13. *Let G be a group and let $a \in G$. If there exists $m \in \mathbb{N}$ such that $a^m = e$, we say that a has* finite order in G. *If no such m exists, we say that a has* infinite order in G. *If a is of finite order, then $n = \min\{m \in \mathbb{N} \mid a^m = e\}$ is called the* order of a in G.

Note that the order of an element a is 1 if and only if a is the identity element.

Exercise 2.6.1.14.

(*i*) *If G is a finite group show that the order of an element in G is less than or equal to the order of G.*

(*ii*) *Find the orders of the elements in C_{12} and S_4.*

(*iii*) *Does there exist a group with elements of both finite and infinite order?*

We next need the notion of a subgroup.

Definition 2.6.1.15. *Let $(G, \circ)$ be a group. A non-empty subset H of G is a* subgroup *if the pair $(H, \circ)$ is a group. If H is a subgroup of G, with $H \neq G$ and $H \neq \{e\}$, we say that H is a* proper subgroup of G.

Remark 2.6.1.16. *Thus, we require that $\circ$ is an ILC on H, that the identity of the group e is an element of H, and if an element a is in H, then a^{-1} is in H. Observe that associativity is automatic for the elements of H because associativity holds for the elements of G. In this situation, we say that associativity is* inherited *from G.*

Exercise 2.6.1.17. *Show that a subgroup of a cyclic group is a cyclic group. That is, if G is the cyclic group generated by a and H is a subgroup of G, then there exists an element $k \in \mathbb{N}$ such that a^k generates H. This means that for every $h \in H$, there exists $j \in \mathbb{Z}$ such that $(a^k)^j = h$.*

Exercise 2.6.1.18. *Show that every element a generates a cyclic subgroup.*

Examples 2.6.1.19.

(1) *The groups $\{e\}$ and G are subgroups of G.*

(2) *The group $(2\mathbb{Z}, +)$, the even integers, is a subgroup of $(\mathbb{Z}, +)$, the additive group of integers.*

(3) *The group $(n\mathbb{Z}, +)$, the integer multiples of n, is a subgroup of $(\mathbb{Z}, +)$.*

(4) *The group $\{I, r^3, r^6\}$ is a subgroup of C_9, the group of rotations of a regular 9-gon. Note that this is an example of Exercise* 2.6.1.17.

(5) *The groups $\{I, (12)\}$, $\{I, (23)\}$ and $\{I, (13)\}$ are subgroups of S_3.*

(6) *The set $SL_2(\mathbb{Q}) = \{A \in GL_2(\mathbb{Q}) \mid \det(A) = 1\}$ is a subgroup of $GL_2(\mathbb{Q})$. This is called the 2×2* special linear group *over $\mathbb{Q}$.*

(7) *The group A_n is a subgroup of S_n.*

Exercise 2.6.1.20.

(*i*) *Suppose that G is a group and H is a non-empty subset of G. Show that H is a subgroup of G iff for every $a, b \in H$, $a^{-1}b \in H$.*

(*ii*) *Suppose that G is a finite group and H is a non-empty subset of G. Show that H is a subgroup of G iff H is closed under multiplication.*

Definition 2.6.1.21. *Suppose that G_1 and G_2 are groups. A map $\phi : G_1 \to G_2$ is a* homomorphism *if $\phi(ab) = \phi(a)\phi(b)$ for all $a, b \in G_1$. That is, a homomorphism preserves multiplication. In general, a homomorphism of algebraic structures is a map that preserves all the operations of that structure. For example, a homomorphism of rings (or fields) preserves addition* and *multiplication.*

If a homomorphism ϕ is a surjection, then ϕ is called an epimorphism. *If a homomorphism ϕ is an injection, then ϕ is called a* monomorphism. *If a homomorphism ϕ is a bijection, then ϕ is called an* isomorphism.

Of course, group homomorphisms have many of the properties of linear transformations.

Proposition 2.6.1.22. *Let G_1 and G_2 be groups and $\phi : G_1 \to G_2$ a homomorphism.*

(*i*) *If e_1 is the identity in G_1, then $\phi(e_1) = e_2$, the identity in G_2.*

(*ii*) *If $a \in G_1$, then $\phi(a^{-1}) = (\phi(a))^{-1}$.*

Proof. You do it. 

Example 2.6.1.23. *Let $G_1 = G_2 = (\mathbb{Z}, +)$. For $n \in \mathbb{N}$ with $n \geq 2$, define $\phi_n(a) = na$. Then ϕ_n is a homomorphism, and in fact ϕ_n is a monomorphism. If we let $G_2 = (n\mathbb{Z}, +)$ then ϕ_n is an isomorphism.*

Exercise 2.6.1.24.

(*i*) *Let G be a finite cyclic group of order n generated by a. Define $\phi : G \to G$ by $\phi(a^j) = a^{2j}$. Show that ϕ is a homomorphism. Determine those values of n for which ϕ is a monomorphism, epimorphism or homomorphism.*

(*ii*) *Let n be a natural number with $n \geq 2$. Define $\phi : \mathbb{Z} \to \mathbb{Z}_n$ by $\phi(k) = k \mod n$. Show that ϕ is an epimorphism.*

For groups, we have a situation that is analogous to the kernel of a linear transformation in vector spaces.

Definition 2.6.1.25. *Let G_1, G_2 be groups and $\phi : G_1 \to G_2$ a homomorphism. The* kernel of ϕ *is the subset of G defined by*

$$\ker \phi = \{x \in G_1 \mid \phi(x) = e_2, \text{ the identity in } G_2\}.$$

Exercise 2.6.1.26.

(*i*) *Show that* $\ker \phi$ *is a subgroup of G_1.*

(*ii*) *Show that $\phi(G_1)$ is a subgroup of G_2.*

(*iii*) *Find* $\ker \phi$ *in the examples and exercises of homomorphisms above.*

The kernel of a homomorphism $\phi : G_1 \to G_2$ is a subgroup with special properties. In particular, if $a, b \in G_1$ and $b \in \ker \phi$, then $aba^{-1} \in \ker \phi$.

Definition 2.6.1.27. *Let G be a group and H a subgroup of G. The subgroup H is called a* normal subgroup *of G if, for each $a \in G$, we have $aHa^{-1} = \{aba^{-1} \mid b \in H\} = H$.*

Exercise 2.6.1.28.

(i) *Let G_1, G_2 be groups and $\phi : G_1 \to G_2$ be a homomorphism. Show that $\ker \phi$ is a normal subgroup of G_1.*

(ii) *Show that any subgroup of an abelian group is a normal subgroup.*

(iii) *Show that A_n is a normal subgroup of S_n.*

(iv) *Show that, if G is a finite group and H is a subgroup of G, then H is a normal subgroup of G if and only if $aHa^{-1} \subseteq H$.*

Take the collection $M_n(F)$ of $n \times n$ matrices over a field F, and consider $GL_n(F) = \{x \in M_n(F) \mid \det(x) \neq 0\}$.

Exercise 2.6.1.29. *Prove that $GL_n(F)$ is a group with the ILC given by multiplication of matrices. The group $GL_n(F)$ is called the $n \times n$* general linear group over *F.*

Here is a list of some interesting subgroups of $GL_n(F)$.

(1) The $n \times n$ *special linear group over F,*

$$SL_n(F) = \{x \in GL_n(F) \mid \det(x) = 1\}.$$

Exercise 2.6.1.30. *Show that $SL_n(F)$ is a normal subgroup of $GL_n(F)$.*

(2) *The* upper triangular *matrices in $GL_n(F)$,*

$$B = \{(b_{ij}) \in GL_n(F) \mid b_{ij} = 0 \text{ if } i > j\}.$$

(3) *The* upper triangular unipotent *matrices in $GL_n(F)$,*

$$N = \{(b_{ij}) \in B \mid b_{jj} = 1, \ j = 1, \ldots, n\}.$$

(4) *The $n \times n$* diagonal *matrices in $GL_n(F)$,*

$$A = \{(a_{ij}) \in GL_n(F) \mid a_{ij} = 0 \text{ if } i \neq j\}.$$

(5) *The $n \times n$* orthogonal group over *F,*

$$O(n, F) = \{x \in GL_n(F) \mid x^t x = I, \text{ the } n \times n \text{ identity matrix}\}.$$

6.2. Direct Products, Semidirect Products, and Subgroups of the Orthogonal Group.

We now define a class of subgroups of $O(n, F)$. Let $G_n = \{x \in O(n, F) \mid$ there is exactly one 1 in each row and column and zeroes elsewhere$\}$.

Exercise 2.6.2.1. *Show that G_n is actually a subgroup of $O(n, F)$.*

For example,

$$G_3 = \left\{ \begin{pmatrix} 1 & 0 & 0 \\ 0 & 1 & 0 \\ 0 & 0 & 1 \end{pmatrix}, \begin{pmatrix} 1 & 0 & 0 \\ 0 & 0 & 1 \\ 0 & 1 & 0 \end{pmatrix}, \begin{pmatrix} 0 & 1 & 0 \\ 0 & 0 & 1 \\ 1 & 0 & 0 \end{pmatrix}, \right.$$
$$\left. \begin{pmatrix} 0 & 1 & 0 \\ 1 & 0 & 0 \\ 0 & 0 & 1 \end{pmatrix}, \begin{pmatrix} 0 & 0 & 1 \\ 1 & 0 & 0 \\ 0 & 1 & 0 \end{pmatrix}, \begin{pmatrix} 0 & 0 & 1 \\ 0 & 1 & 0 \\ 1 & 0 & 0 \end{pmatrix} \right\}.$$

Exercise 2.6.2.2.

(*i*) *Show that G_n is isomorphic to S_n.*

(*ii*) *If $g \in G_n$ and g corresponds to the permutation $\sigma \in S_n$, then the action of g as a permutation can be written as follows. If $a = (a_1, a_2, \ldots, a_n)$ and*

$$A = \begin{pmatrix} a_1 & 0 & \ldots & 0 \\ 0 & a_2 & \ldots & 0 \\ \vdots & \vdots & \ddots & \vdots \\ 0 & 0 & \ldots & a_n \end{pmatrix},$$

show that

$$gAg^{-1} = \begin{pmatrix} a_{\sigma(1)} & 0 & \ldots & 0 \\ 0 & a_{\sigma(2)} & \ldots & 0 \\ \vdots & \vdots & \ddots & \vdots \\ 0 & 0 & \ldots & a_{\sigma(n)} \end{pmatrix}.$$

The next few definitions involve creating new groups from old groups.

Definition 2.6.2.3. *Let G_1 and G_2 be groups and consider the Cartesian product $G_1 \times G_2$. Define an ILC on $G_1 \times G_2$ as follows. If $(x_1, y_1), (x_2, y_2) \in G_1 \times G_2$, then $(x_1, y_1) \circ (x_2, y_2) = (x_1 \circ x_2, y_1 \circ y_2)$.*

Exercise 2.6.2.4.

(*i*) *Show that $(G_1 \times G_2, \circ)$ is a group.*

(*ii*) *Show that $G_1 \times G_2$ is commutative if and only if both G_1 and G_2 are commutative.*

(*iii*) *Show that $G_1 \times \{e_2\}$ and $\{e_1\} \times G_2$ are subgroups of $G_1 \times G_2$ that are isomorphic to G_1 and G_2, respectively.*

(*iv*) *Show that $G_1 \times \{e_2\}$ and $\{e_1\} \times G_2$ are normal subgroups of $G_1 \times G_2$.*

(*v*) *If H_1 and H_2 are subgroups of G_1 and G_2, respectively, show that $H_1 \times H_2$ is a subgroup of $G_1 \times G_2$.*

(*vi*) *Does every subgroup of $G_1 \times G_2$ have the form given in v?*

Definition 2.6.2.5. *The group* $(G_1 \times G_2, \circ)$ *is called the* direct product *of* G_1 *and* G_2.

It is clear that the idea of direct product can be extended to a finite number of groups.

Examples 2.6.2.6.

(*i*) *The group* $(\mathbb{R}^n, +)$ *is the direct product of* $(\mathbb{R}, +)$ *with itself* n *times.*

(*ii*) *The multiplicative group* $\mathbb{R}^\times$ *of nonzero real numbers has two subgroups of direct interest, namely* $\mathbb{R}^\times_+$ *the multiplicative group of positive real numbers and the group* $\{1, -1\}$. *Clearly,* $\mathbb{R}^\times = \mathbb{R}^\times_+ \times \{1, -1\}$.

Definition 2.6.2.7. *Let* G *be a group and let* H *and* K *be subgroups of* G, *with* H *a normal subgroup. If* $H \cap K = \{e\}$ *and* $HK = \{h \circ k \mid h \in H, k \in K\} = G$, *then* G *is called the* semidirect product *of* H *and* K, *and we write* $G = H \rtimes K$.

Observe that multiplication in the semidirect product is carried out as follows. We drop the circle for the ILC for convenience. If $h_1, h_2 \in H$ and $k_1, k_2 \in K$, then $(h_1k_1)(h_2k_2) = (h_1k_1h_2k_1^{-1})(k_1k_2)$ with $h_1k_1h_2k_1^{-1} \in H$ and $k_1k_2 \in K$.

Examples 2.6.2.8. *We need one more example of groups illustrating the semidirect product. Let* P_n *be the set of* $n \times n$ *matrices that have exactly one 1 or one* -1 *in each row and column and zeroes elsewhere. If* $H = G_n$, *considered as a subgroup of* $O(n, F)$, *and* $\Delta_n = \{(a_{jk}) \mid a_{jj} = \pm 1$ *for* $1 \leq j \leq n$ *and* $a_{jk} = 0$ *for* $j \neq k\}$, *then* $P_n = \Delta_n \rtimes G_n$.

Exercise 2.6.2.9. *Show that* P_n *is a subgroup of* $O(n, F)$ *and that* G_n *and* Δ_n *satisfy the conditions for a semidirect product as subgroups of* P_n.

Example 2.6.2.10. *One of the standard examples of a semidirect product is the group of symmetries of a regular* n*-gon in the plane. The symmetries come in two flavors. First, there are the rotations of the* n*-gon, which form a cyclic group* C_n *of order* n. *Second, there are the reflections about a line of symmetry in the* n*-gon. The lines of symmetries for reflections are different for* n *even or odd. If* n *is odd, the lines of symmetry (or reflection) are those which join a vertex to the midpoint of the opposite side. If* n *is even, the lines of symmetry either connect two opposite vertices or form the bisectors of two opposite sides. The group of symmetries of a regular* n*-gon is made up of the* n *rotations in* C_n *and the* n *reflections just indicated. The symmetry group of a regular* n*-gon is called the* dihedral group of order $2n$ *and is denoted* D_{2n}.

Exercise 2.6.2.11. *Let K be the subgroup of D_{2n} generated by a single reflection. Show that $D_{2n} = C_n \rtimes K$.*

Exercise 2.6.2.12. *Show that D_{2n} is a subgroup of $O(2, \mathbb{R})$.*

Exercise 2.6.2.13.

(*i*) *Let G be a finite group of order $2m$ and let H be a subgroup of G of order m. Show that H is a normal subgroup of G and that, if m is odd, then G is a semidirect product of H with a subgroup of order 2.*

(*ii*) *Show that there is a subgroup K of S_n so that $S_n = A_n \rtimes K$.*

Exercise 2.6.2.14. *Show that in the examples following Exercise* 2.6.1.29, *$B = N \rtimes A$.*

6.3. Orthogonal Transformations in Euclidean Space.

The orthogonal transformations in $\mathbb{R}^n$ play an important role in analysis.

Definition 2.6.3.1. *An* orthogonal transformation *on $\mathbb{R}^n$ is a linear transformation $T : \mathbb{E}^n \to \mathbb{E}^n$ with the property that $\langle T\mathbf{v}, T\mathbf{w}\rangle = \langle \mathbf{v}, \mathbf{w}\rangle$ for all $\mathbf{v}, \mathbf{w} \in \mathbb{E}^n$. We say that T preserves the bilinear form $\langle \cdot, \cdot \rangle$.*

Exercise 2.6.3.2. *Show that an orthogonal linear transformation is distance preserving. That is, for any $\mathbf{v}, \mathbf{w} \in \mathbb{E}^n$, $\|T\mathbf{v} - T\mathbf{w}\| = \|\mathbf{v} - \mathbf{w}\|$. In particular, for any $\mathbf{v} \in \mathbb{E}^n$, we have $\|T\mathbf{v}\| = \|\mathbf{v}\|$.*

Exercise 2.6.3.3. *Let M be the matrix of a linear transformation on $\mathbb{E}^n$ relative to the standard basis. Show that, for any pair of vectors $\mathbf{v}, \mathbf{w} \in \mathbb{E}^n$, we have $\langle M\mathbf{v}, \mathbf{w}\rangle = \langle \mathbf{v}, {}^tM\mathbf{w}\rangle$. Show in particular that, if M is the matrix of an orthogonal linear transformation relative to the standard basis, then $M^tM = {}^tMM = I$. That is, $M \in O(n, \mathbb{R})$.*

Example 2.6.3.4. *Let*

$$M = \begin{pmatrix} a_{11} & a_{12} \\ a_{21} & a_{22} \end{pmatrix}$$

be the matrix of an orthogonal linear transformation on $\mathbb{E}^2$ relative to the standard basis, that is, $M \in O(2, \mathbb{R})$. From the exercise above, it follows that $a_{11}^2 + a_{21}^2 = a_{12}^2 + a_{22}^2 = a_{11}^2 + a_{12}^2 = a_{21}^2 + a_{22}^2 = 1$. Also, $a_{11}a_{12} + a_{21}a_{22} = a_{11}a_{21} + a_{12}a_{22} = 0$. It is now immediate that there is some θ with $0 \le \theta < 2\pi$ such that

$$M = \begin{pmatrix} \cos\theta & -\sin\theta \\ \sin\theta & \cos\theta \end{pmatrix}$$

or

$$M = \begin{pmatrix} \cos\theta & \sin\theta \\ \sin\theta & -\cos\theta \end{pmatrix}.$$

Proposition 2.6.3.5. *If* $M \in O(n, \mathbb{R})$, *then* $\det M = \pm 1$.

Proof. This follows from the fact that $\det {}^tM = \det M$. So that if $M \in O(n, \mathbb{R})$, then $(\det M)^2 = \det M \det {}^tM = \det M^tM = \det I = 1$.

The collection $SO(n, \mathbb{R}) = \{M \in O(n, \mathbb{R}) \mid \det M = 1\}$ is a subgroup of $O(n, \mathbb{R})$ called the *special orthogonal group*. The elements of $SO(n, \mathbb{R})$ are called generalized rotations.

We can write

$$O(n, \mathbb{R}) = SO(n, \mathbb{R}) \cup \begin{pmatrix} -1 & 0 & \dots & 0 & 0 \\ 0 & 1 & \dots & 0 & 0 \\ \vdots & \vdots & \ddots & \vdots & \vdots \\ 0 & 0 & \dots & 1 & 0 \\ 0 & 0 & \dots & 0 & 1 \end{pmatrix} SO(n, \mathbb{R}).$$

The elements of the set

$$\begin{pmatrix} -1 & 0 & \dots & 0 & 0 \\ 0 & 1 & \dots & 0 & 0 \\ \vdots & \vdots & \ddots & \vdots & \vdots \\ 0 & 0 & \dots & 1 & 0 \\ 0 & 0 & \dots & 0 & 1 \end{pmatrix} SO(n, \mathbb{R})$$

are called generalized reflections and have determinant equal to -1.

Exercise 2.6.3.6.

(*i*) *If* $M \in O(2, \mathbb{R})$ *and* $M = \begin{pmatrix} \cos\theta & -\sin\theta \\ \sin\theta & \cos\theta \end{pmatrix}$, *show that* M *is a counter-clockwise rotation around the origin through an angle* θ. *Obviously,* $\det M = 1$.

(*ii*) *If* $M \in O(2, \mathbb{R})$ *and* $M = \begin{pmatrix} -1 & 0 \\ 0 & 1 \end{pmatrix} \begin{pmatrix} \cos\theta & -\sin\theta \\ \sin\theta & \cos\theta \end{pmatrix} = \begin{pmatrix} -\cos\theta & \sin\theta \\ \sin\theta & \cos\theta \end{pmatrix}$, *show that* M *is a reflection across a line through the origin. Here,* $\det M = -1$. *In particular, determine the angle that the line of reflection makes with the positive* x*-axis.*

(*iii*) *Finally, show that* $SO(2, \mathbb{R}) = \left\{ \begin{pmatrix} \cos\theta & -\sin\theta \\ \sin\theta & \cos\theta \end{pmatrix} \,\middle|\, 0 \le \theta < 2\pi \right\}$ *and that* $O(2, \mathbb{R})$ *is the union of the matrices from parts i and ii.*

(*iv*) *Write the dihedral group* D_{2n} *as a subgroup of matrices in* $O(2, \mathbb{R})$.

It is possible to write some "rotations" and "reflections" in $\mathbb{R}^n$ very explicitly. For example, in $O(4,\mathbb{R})$ the matrix

$$M = \begin{pmatrix} \cos\theta & -\sin\theta & 0 & 0 \\ \sin\theta & \cos\theta & 0 & 0 \\ 0 & 0 & \cos\phi & -\sin\phi \\ 0 & 0 & \sin\phi & \cos\phi \end{pmatrix}$$

is the composition of a rotation around the x_1-x_2 plane through the angle ϕ with a rotation around the x_3-x_4 plane through the angle θ. This is an example of a generalized rotation.

As an example of a generalized reflection, if we have $n-1$ pairwise orthogonal nonzero vectors in $\mathbb{R}^n$, we can produce an n-th nonzero vector v, orthogonal to each of the original $n-1$ vectors, by Theorem 2.5.20. In this case reflection through the hyperplane spanned by the original set of $n-1$ orthogonal vectors is given by $T_v(w) = w - 2\frac{\langle v,w\rangle}{\langle v,v\rangle}w$.

Exercise 2.6.3.7.

(*i*) *Show that T_v is an orthogonal transformation that is a generalized reflection on $\mathbb{R}^n$.*

(*ii*) *Find the matrix of T_v relative to the standard basis.*

When $n = 3$, we can be quite precise about the nature of the elements of $O(3,\mathbb{R})$. If T is an element of $SO(3,\mathbb{R})$, then we can find a line through the origin so that T is a rotation around that line. It is then clear that any reflection in $O(3,\mathbb{R})$ can be written as a rotation around a line in $\mathbb{R}^3$ through the origin combined with reflection through the origin, that is, multiplication by $-I$. From this we conclude $O(3,\mathbb{R}) = SO(3,\mathbb{R}) \times \{I, -I\}$.

We conclude this project with the symmetry groups of the regular polyhedra in $\mathbb{R}^3$. The regular polyhedra are the regular tetrahedron, the cube, the regular octahedron, the regular dodecahedron, and the regular icosahedron. Since the octahedron is dual to the cube and the icosahedron is dual to the dodecahedron, we need only work with the tetrahedron, the cube, and the dodecahedron. In each case, we can obtain an upper bound on the number of symmetries by proceeding as follows. Each vertex must be mapped to a vertex and the images of the sides adjacent to a vertex must be adjacent to the image of that vertex, although they can be permuted after the symmetry map is applied. For a tetrahedron, this gives an upper bound of $4 \times 6 = 24$ possible symmetries. In this case, the symmetries are in one to one correspondence with the permutations of the vertices, and the symmetry group is S_4.

Exercise 2.6.3.8.

(*i*) *Write the 24 orthogonal matrices that represent the symmetries of the tetrahedron relative to the standard basis.*

(*ii*) *Show that the rotations in the symmetry group of the tetrahedron form the group A_4.*

(*iii*) *Which of the reflections in the symmetry group of a regular tetrahedron can be realized as reflections through a plane?*

Now consider the symmetry group of the cube with vertices at the eight points $(\pm 1, \pm 1, \pm 1)$. The rotations of this cube can be realized as rotations around the x-axis, rotations around the y-axis, rotations around the z-axis, rotations around the diagonals of the cube, and finally rotations around the lines through the origin and the midpoints of opposite edges.

Exercise 2.6.3.9.

(*i*) *Show that rotations around a coordinate axis have order 2 or 4, rotations around a diagonal have order 3, and rotations around a line through the origin connecting the midpoints of opposite edges have order 2.*

(*ii*) *Write the matrices of the 24 rotational symmetries of the cube.*

For example, the rotations around the z-axis are I, $R = \begin{pmatrix} 0 & -1 & 0 \\ 1 & 0 & 0 \\ 0 & 0 & 1 \end{pmatrix}$,

$R^2 = \begin{pmatrix} -1 & 0 & 0 \\ 0 & -1 & 0 \\ 0 & 0 & 1 \end{pmatrix}$, $R^3 = \begin{pmatrix} 0 & 1 & 0 \\ -1 & 0 & 0 \\ 0 & 0 & 1 \end{pmatrix}$.

If we rotate around the diagonal adjoining $(1, 1, 1)$ and $(-1, -1, -1)$, we obtain the non-identity matrices $R = \begin{pmatrix} 0 & 0 & 1 \\ 1 & 0 & 0 \\ 0 & 1 & 0 \end{pmatrix}$ and $R^2 = \begin{pmatrix} 0 & 1 & 0 \\ 0 & 0 & 1 \\ 1 & 0 & 0 \end{pmatrix}$.

If we rotate around the line connecting $(1, 0, 1)$ and $(-1, 0, -1)$, then we obtain the matrix $R = \begin{pmatrix} 0 & 0 & 1 \\ 0 & -1 & 0 \\ 1 & 0 & 0 \end{pmatrix}$.

We obtain the 24 reflections in the symmetry group of a cube by multiplying the 24 rotations by $-I$.

We conclude from the above discussion that the symmetry group of a cube is isomorphic to $S_4 \times \mathbb{Z}_2$.

Exercise 2.6.3.10.

(*i*) *Show that the group of rotations of a dodecahedron is isomorphic to* A_5 *and the symmetry group of a regular dodecahedron is isomorphic to* $A_5 \times \mathbb{Z}_2$.

(*ii*) *Write the matrices for the* 60 *rotational symmetries of a regular dodecahedron.*

Chapter 3

The Construction of the Real and Complex Numbers

Thus the System of Real Numbers—the definition of irrationals and the extension of the four species to the new numbers—is established. The method has the advantage of simplicity in detail. It is well for the student, after a first study of the method of Dedekind, to work it through in detail. He will then return to the former method with increased power and greater zest.
The method of regular sequences is a middle-of-the-road method. It is an easy way to reach the mountain top. The traveller buys his ticket and takes the funicular. Many people prefer this mode of travel. But some like a stiff climb over rocks and across streams, and such an ascent has its advantages if the heart is good and the muscles are strong.

– *William Fogg Osgood,*
Functions of Real Variables

In Chapter 1, we defined the integers and discussed their properties in some detail. We then constructed the rational numbers from the integers and observed that the rational numbers form an ordered field. Note that any field that contains the integers must also contain the rationals as a subfield.

Exercise 3.0.1. *Prove that any field that contains the integers contains the rationals as a subfield.*

In this chapter, we do several things. First, we introduce the real numbers by adding the Least Upper Bound Property to the axioms for an ordered field. Second, despite Osgood, we construct the real numbers from the rational numbers by the method of Cauchy sequences. Third, we construct the complex numbers from the real numbers and prove a few useful theorems about complex numbers. Intermingled in all of this is a discussion of the fields of algebraic numbers and real algebraic numbers. As a project at the end of the chapter, we lead the reader through a discussion of the construction of the real numbers via Dedekind cuts. In other projects, we study the convergence properties of infinite series and the decimal expansions of real numbers.

1. The Least Upper Bound Property and the Real Numbers

Definition 3.1.1 (see Definition 1.9.3). *Let F be an ordered field. Let A be a non-empty subset of F. We say that A is* bounded above *if there is an element $M \in F$ with the property that if $x \in A$, then $x \leq M$. We call M an* upper bound *for A. Similarly, we say that A is* bounded below *if there is an element $m \in F$ such that if $x \in A$, then $m \leq x$. We call m a* lower bound *for A. We say that A is* bounded *if A is bounded above and A is bounded below.*

Examples 3.1.2.

(*i*) *Consider the subset A of $\mathbb{Q}$:*

$$A = \left\{ 1 + \frac{(-1)^n}{n} \;\middle|\; n \in \mathbb{N} \right\}.$$

Then A is bounded above by $3/2$ and bounded below by 0.

(*ii*) *Let $A = \{x \in \mathbb{Q} \mid 0 < x^3 < 27\}$. Then A is bounded below by 0 and bounded above by 15.*

Exercise 3.1.3. *Let a be a positive rational number. Let $A = \{x \in \mathbb{Q} \mid x^2 < a\}$. Show that A is bounded in $\mathbb{Q}$.*

Definition 3.1.4 (see Definition 1.9.3). *Let F be an ordered field, and let A be a non-empty subset of F that is bounded above. We say that $L \in F$ is a* least upper bound *for A if the following two conditions hold:*

(a) *L is an upper bound for A;*

(b) *if M is any upper bound for A, then $L \leq M$.*

The definition of a greatest lower bound *is the same, with all inequalities reversed.*

Exercise 3.1.5. *Show that the least upper bound of a set is unique, if it exists.*

Up to this point, we have discussed the real numbers in an informal way as a collection of decimal expansions with the property that no expansion ends in all nines. Of course, this is not a formal definition of the real numbers, but it is common practice to work with the real numbers with this particular representation. We now give a formal definition of the real numbers that provides a working basis for proving theorems. Later in this chapter, starting with the rational numbers as an ordered field, we will give a precise construction of the real numbers as an ordered field in which the least upper bound property holds.

Definition 3.1.6. *The* real numbers *are an ordered field in which every non-empty subset that is bounded above has a least upper bound.*

We say that the real numbers are an ordered field with the least upper bound property. In many texts, the real numbers are defined as a *complete ordered field.* This is actually a misuse of the word "complete", which is defined in terms of the convergence of Cauchy sequences. This will be discussed later in this chapter.

Exercise 3.1.7. *Find the least upper bound in* $\mathbb{R}$ *of the set* A *in Exercise* 3.1.3.

Definition 3.1.8. *Suppose that* F *and* F' *are ordered integral domains. We say that* F *and* F' *are* order isomorphic *if there is a bijection* $\phi : F \to F'$ *such that*

(a) $\phi(x + y) = \phi(x) + \phi(y)$ *for all* $x, y \in F$;

(b) $\phi(xy) = \phi(x)\phi(y)$ *for all* $x, y \in F$;

(c) *if* $x, y \in F$ *and* $x < y$ *then* $\phi(x) < \phi(y)$ *in* F'.

Exercise 3.1.9. *Show that any two ordered fields with the least upper bound property are order isomorphic.*

This exercise proves that if the real numbers exist, they are unique up to order isomorphism.

Definition 3.1.10. *An ordered field* F *has the* greatest lower bound property *if every non-empty subset* A *of* F *that is bounded below has a greatest lower bound. That is, there exists an element* ℓ *of* F *such that:*

(a) ℓ *is a lower bound for* A;

(b) *if* m *is any lower bound for* A, *then* $m \leq \ell$.

Exercise 3.1.11. *Prove that an ordered field has the least upper bound property iff it has the greatest lower bound property.*

If L is the least upper bound of a set A, we write $L = \text{lub } A$ or $L = \sup A$ (sup stands for *supremum*). If ℓ is the greatest lower bound of a set A, we write $\ell = \text{glb } A$ or $\ell = \inf A$ (inf stands for *infimum*).

Exercise 3.1.12. *Let n be a positive integer that is not a perfect square. Let $A = \{x \in \mathbb{Q} \mid x^2 < n\}$. Show that A is bounded in $\mathbb{Q}$ but has neither a* glb *nor a* lub *in $\mathbb{Q}$. Conclude that $\sqrt{n}$ exists in $\mathbb{R}$, that is, there exists a real number a such that $a^2 = n$.*

We have observed that the rational numbers are contained in $\mathbb{R}$. A real number is *irrational* if it is not in $\mathbb{Q}$.

Fact 3.1.13. *We can conclude from Exercise* 3.1.12 *that if n is a positive integer that is not a perfect square, then $\sqrt{n}$ exists in $\mathbb{R}$ and is irrational.*

Exercise 3.1.14. *Suppose that A and B are bounded sets in $\mathbb{R}$. Prove or disprove the following:*

(*i*) $\text{lub}(A \cup B) = \max\{\text{lub}(A), \text{lub}(B)\}$.

(*ii*) *If $A + B = \{a + b \mid a \in A, b \in B\}$, then* $\text{lub}(A + B) = \text{lub}(A) + \text{lub}(B)$.

(*iii*) *If the elements of A and B are positive and $A \cdot B = \{ab \mid a \in A, b \in B\}$, then* $\text{lub}(A \cdot B) = \text{lub}(A)\text{lub}(B)$.

(*iv*) *Formulate the analogous problems for the greatest lower bound.*

2. Consequences of the Least Upper Bound Property

We now present some facts that follow from the least upper bound property and the properties of the integers. The first is the *Archimedean property* of the real numbers.

Theorem 3.2.1 (Archimedean property of $\mathbb{R}$). *If a and b are positive real numbers, then there exists a natural number n such that $na > b$.*

Proof. If $a > b$, take $n = 1$. If $a = b$, take $n = 2$. If $a < b$, consider the set $S = \{na \mid n \in \mathbb{N}\}$. The set $S \neq \varnothing$ since $a \in S$. Suppose S is bounded above by b. Let $L = \text{lub } S$. Then, since $a > 0$, there exists an element $n_0 a \in S$ such that $L - a < n_0 a$. But then $L < (n_0 + 1)a$, which is a contradiction. ☠

Corollary 3.2.2. *If ε is a positive real number, there exists a natural number n such that $1/n < \varepsilon$.*

Definition 3.2.3. *Let F be an ordered field. From Chapter 1, we know that $\mathbb{Z} \subseteq F$ and by Exercise 3.0.1, we know $\mathbb{Q} \subseteq F$. We say that F is an* Archimedean ordered field *if, for every $x \in F$, there exists $N \in \mathbb{Z}$ such that $x < N$.*

The fields $\mathbb{Q}$ and $\mathbb{R}$ are Archimedean ordered fields.

Exercise 3.2.4. *Let F be an Archimedean ordered field. Show that F is order isomorphic to a subfield of $\mathbb{R}$.*

Next, we show that every real number lies between two successive integers.

Theorem 3.2.5. *If a is a real number, then there exists an integer N such that $N - 1 \leq a < N$.*

Proof. Let $S = \{n \in \mathbb{Z} \mid n > a\}$. Then by the Archimedean property, $S \neq \varnothing$ and S is bounded below by some large negative integer. By the Well Ordering Principle (applied to an appropriate shift of S), S has a least element. Then $N - 1 \notin S$, so $N - 1 \leq a < N$.

We now show that there is a rational number between any two real numbers.

Theorem 3.2.6. *If a and b are real numbers with $a < b$, there exists a rational number $r = p/q$ such that $a < r < b$.*

Proof. From the Archimedean property of $\mathbb{R}$ (Corollary 3.2.2), there exists $q \in \mathbb{N}$ such that $1/q < b - a$. Now consider the real number qa. By Theorem 3.2.5, there exists an integer p such that $p - 1 \leq qa < p$. It follows that $\frac{p-1}{q} \leq a < \frac{p}{q}$. This implies that $\frac{p}{q} - \frac{1}{q} \leq a$, and hence $a < \frac{p}{q} \leq a + \frac{1}{q} < b$.

Definition 3.2.7. *A subset A of $\mathbb{R}$ is said to be* dense *in $\mathbb{R}$ if for any pair of real numbers a and b with $a < b$, there is an $r \in A$ such that $a < r < b$.*

Corollary 3.2.8. *The rational numbers are dense in the real numbers.*

How do the irrational numbers behave?

Exercise 3.2.9.

(*i*) *Show that any irrational number multiplied by any non-zero rational number is irrational.*

(*ii*) *Show that the product of two irrational numbers may be rational or irrational.*

Next we show that there is an irrational number between any two real numbers.

Corollary 3.2.10. *The irrational numbers are dense in* $\mathbb{R}$.

Proof. Take $a, b \in \mathbb{R}$ such that $a < b$. We know that $\sqrt{2}$ is irrational and greater than 0. But then $\frac{a}{\sqrt{2}} < \frac{b}{\sqrt{2}}$. By Corollary 3.2.8, there exists a rational number p/q, with $p \neq 0$ such that $\frac{a}{\sqrt{2}} < \frac{p}{q} < \frac{b}{\sqrt{2}}$. Thus $a < \sqrt{2}p/q < b$, and $\sqrt{2}p/q$ is irrational. ☺

The real numbers are the union of two disjoint sets, the rational numbers and the irrational numbers, and each of these sets is dense in $\mathbb{R}$. Density implies nothing about cardinality since the rationals are countable and the irrationals are not, as shown in Section 1.8.

3. Rational Approximation

We have just shown that both the rational numbers and the irrational numbers are dense in the real numbers. But, really, how dense are they? It is reasonable to think that proximity for rational numbers can be measured in terms of the size of the denominator. To illustrate this, we ask the question, "How close do two rational numbers have to be in order to be the same rational number?" This is not a trick question – it is designed to illustrate the principle mentioned above. Thus, if $a/b, c/d \in \mathbb{Q}$ and $|a/b - c/d| < 1/bd$, then $a/b = c/d$.

This idea can be encapsulated in the following theorem. Throughout this section, we shall assume that the denominator of a rational number is a positive integer and that the numerator and denominator are relatively prime.

Theorem 3.3.1. *If* a/b *is a fixed rational number and* p/q *is a rational number such that* $0 < |p/q - a/b| < 1/mb$ *for some positive integer* m*, then* $q > m$.

Proof. Easy. ☺

We now present several facts on rational approximation. For α in various subsets of the real numbers, we prove results that measure the degree of accuracy with which α may be approximated. These results take one of the following forms:

(1) positive real numbers $c(\alpha)$ and t exist so that there are infinitely many rational numbers p/q with $|\alpha - p/q| < c(\alpha)/q^t$;

(2) positive real numbers $c(\alpha)$ and t exist so that there are only finitely many rational numbers p/q with $|\alpha - p/q| < c(\alpha)/q^t$;

(3) for $\delta > 0$, there exist real numbers $c(\alpha, \delta)$ and t so that $|\alpha - p/q| \geq c(\alpha, \delta)/q^{t+\delta}$ for all rational numbers p/q.

To begin, we present an exercise that follows easily from the number theory project (Project 1.10.1) at the end of Chapter 1.

Exercise 3.3.2. *Let a and b be relatively prime integers. Show that the equation $ax + by = 1$ has infinitely many solutions $(x, y) = (q, p)$ with q and p relatively prime integers.*

Theorem 3.3.3. *Let $\alpha = a/b$ with a and b relatively prime and $b \neq 1$. Then there exist infinitely many $p/q \in \mathbb{Q}$ such that $|a/b - p/q| < 1/q$.*

Proof. Let $(q, -p)$ be a solution to the equation $ax + by = 1$. Then $q \neq 0$ since $b \neq 1$. We may assume $q > 0$. We then have $|a/b - p/q| = 1/bq < 1/q$. ☺

Remark 3.3.4. *If $b = 1$, then the same result holds with $<$ replaced by $\leq$.*

The next theorem characterizes rational numbers in terms of rational approximation. We first need the following exercise.

Exercise 3.3.5. *Let α be a real number, and let η and t be positive real numbers. Show that there exist only a finite number of rational numbers p/q with $q < \eta$ that satisfy $|\alpha - p/q| < 1/q^t$.*

Theorem 3.3.6. *Let $\alpha = a/b \in \mathbb{Q}$. Then there are only finitely many p/q so that $|\alpha - p/q| \leq 1/q^2$.*

Proof. Suppose there were infinitely many p/q satisfying the inequality. Then by Exercise 3.3.5, q gets arbitrarily large. Thus there exists a p/q with $q > b$ such that $|a/b - p/q| < 1/q^2$. This implies that $|aq - bp| < b/q < 1$, which is a contradiction. ☺

We next consider rational approximation of irrational numbers. The question is: if α is irrational are there any rational numbers p/q satisfying the inequality $|\alpha - p/q| < 1/q^2$? The affirmative answer follows from a theorem of Dirichlet on rational approximation of any real number.

Theorem 3.3.7 (Dirichlet)**.** *Let α be a real number and n a positive integer. Then there is a rational number p/q with $0 < q \leq n$ satisfying the inequality*

$$\left|\alpha - \frac{p}{q}\right| \leq \frac{1}{(n+1)q}.$$

Proof. If $n = 1$ then $p/q = [\alpha]$ or $p/q = [\alpha + 1]$ satisfies $|\alpha - p/q| \leq 1/2$. Suppose that $n \geq 2$. Consider the $n + 2$ numbers

$$0, \alpha - [\alpha], 2\alpha - [2\alpha], \ldots, n\alpha - [n\alpha], 1$$

in the interval $[0, 1]$. Assume that the numbers in our list are distinct, which is the case if α is irrational. By the pigeonhole principle, two of the numbers differ in absolute value by at most $1/(n+1)$. If one of the numbers is 0 and the other is $i\alpha - [i\alpha]$, then $i \le n$, $|i\alpha - [i\alpha]| \le 1/(n+1)$, and

$$\left|\alpha - \frac{[i\alpha]}{i}\right| \le \frac{1}{(n+1)i}.$$

After $[i\alpha]/i$ is reduced to lowest terms p/q, the rational number p/q satisfies the required inequality. Similarly, if the two numbers are $j\alpha - [j\alpha]$ and 1, then $j \le n$ and reducing $([j\alpha]+1)/j$ to lowest terms p/q, we have p/q satisfies the required inequality. Finally, if the two numbers are $i\alpha - [i\alpha]$ and $j\alpha - [j\alpha]$, where $i < j$, then

$$|j\alpha - [j\alpha] - (i\alpha - [i\alpha])| = |(j-i)\alpha - ([j\alpha] - [i\alpha])| \le \frac{1}{n+1}.$$

Then

$$\left|\alpha - \frac{[j\alpha] - [i\alpha]}{j-i}\right| \le \frac{1}{(n+1)(j-i)}.$$

Thus, after $([j\alpha] - [i\alpha])/(j-i)$ is reduced to lowest terms p/q, the rational number p/q satisfies the inequality because $j - i < n$. In the event that the $n+2$ numbers are not distinct, then α itself is a rational number with denominator at most n. For this case, either there exists i with $1 \le i \le n$ so that

$$\alpha = \frac{[i\alpha]}{i}$$

or there exist $1 \le i < j \le n$ so that

$$\alpha = \frac{[j\alpha] - [i\alpha]}{j-i}.$$

Thus, if the numbers are not distinct the required inequality is trivially satisfied by α itself.

Corollary 3.3.8. *Given any real number α, there is a rational number p/q such that $|\alpha - p/q| < 1/q^2$.*

Proof. This follows immediately from the theorem.

Now comes the good news (or bad news depending on how you look at it).

Theorem 3.3.9. *If α is irrational, then there are infinitely many rational numbers p/q such that $|\alpha - p/q| < 1/q^2$.*

Proof. Suppose there are only a finite number of rational numbers p_1/q_1, $p_2/q_2, \ldots, p_k/q_k$ satisfying the inequality. Then, there is a positive integer n

such that $|\alpha - p_i/q_i| > 1/(n+1)q_i$ for $i = 1, 2, \ldots, k$. This contradicts Theorem 3.3.7, which asserts the existence of a rational number p/q satisfying $q \leq n$ and $|\alpha - p/q| \leq 1/(n+1)q < 1/q^2$.

So, there you have it, a real number α is rational if and only if there exist only a finite number of rational numbers p/q such that $|\alpha - p/q| \leq 1/q^2$. And a real number α is irrational if and only if there exist an infinite number of rational numbers p/q such that $|\alpha - p/q| \leq 1/q^2$.

4. Intervals

At this stage, we single out certain subsets of $\mathbb{R}$, which are called intervals.

Definition 3.4.1. *A subset of* $\mathbb{R}$ *is an* interval *if it falls into one of the following categories.*

(a) *For* $a, b \in \mathbb{R}$ *with* $a < b$, *the* open interval (a, b) *is defined by* $(a, b) = \{x \in \mathbb{R} \mid a < x < b\}$.
(b) *For* $a, b \in \mathbb{R}$ *with* $a \leq b$, *the* closed interval $[a, b]$ *is defined by* $[a, b] = \{x \in \mathbb{R} \mid a \leq x \leq b\}$.
(c) *For* $a, b \in \mathbb{R}$ *with* $a < b$, *the* half open interval $[a, b)$ *is defined by* $[a, b) = \{x \in \mathbb{R} \mid a \leq x < b\}$.
(d) *For* $a, b \in \mathbb{R}$ *with* $a < b$, *the* half open interval $(a, b]$ *is defined by* $(a, b] = \{x \in \mathbb{R} \mid a < x \leq b\}$.
(e) *For* $a \in \mathbb{R}$, *the* infinite open interval (a, ∞) *is defined by* $(a, \infty) = \{x \in \mathbb{R} \mid a < x\}$.
(f) *For* $b \in \mathbb{R}$, *the* infinite open interval $(-\infty, b)$ *is defined by* $(-\infty, b) = \{x \in \mathbb{R} \mid x < b\}$.
(g) *For* $a \in \mathbb{R}$, *the* infinite closed interval $[a, \infty)$ *is defined by* $[a, \infty) = \{x \in \mathbb{R} \mid a \leq x\}$.
(h) *For* $b \in \mathbb{R}$, *the* infinite closed interval $(-\infty, b]$ *is defined by* $(-\infty, b] = \{x \in \mathbb{R} \mid x \leq b\}$.
(i) $\mathbb{R} = (-\infty, \infty)$.

Definition 3.4.2. *If* $x \in \mathbb{R}$, *a* neighborhood *of* x *is an open interval containing* x. *For many instances, it is useful to use symmetric neighborhoods. That is, if* $x \in \mathbb{R}$, *a* symmetric neighborhood *of* x *is an interval of the form* $(x - \varepsilon, x + \varepsilon)$, *where* $\varepsilon > 0$.

These intervals, and their counterparts in other spaces, are used extensively throughout mathematics.

Exercise 3.4.3. *Suppose that* I *is a subset of* $\mathbb{R}$. *Show that* I *is an interval if and only if for all* $a, b \in I$, *with* $a \leq b$, *the closed interval* $[a, b] \subseteq I$.

The notion of interval is valid in any ordered field, and we will occasionally find this useful. We end this section with a theorem about intervals in $\mathbb{R}$, which is called the Nested Intervals Theorem.

Theorem 3.4.4 (Nested Intervals Theorem). *Let $([a_n, b_n])_{n\in\mathbb{N}}$ be a nested sequence of closed bounded intervals in $\mathbb{R}$. That is, for any n, we have $[a_{n+1}, b_{n+1}] \subseteq [a_n, b_n]$, or equivalently, $a_n \leq a_{n+1} \leq b_{n+1} \leq b_n$ for all n. Then $\bigcap_{n\in\mathbb{N}}[a_n, b_n] \neq \varnothing$.*

Proof. Let $A = \{a_n \mid n \in \mathbb{N}\}$. Then A is bounded above by b_1. If $a = \text{lub}A$, then $a \in \bigcap_{n\in\mathbb{N}}[a_n, b_n]$.

The nested intervals property is actually not exclusive to the real numbers. In fact, it is really a theorem about a sequence of nested "compact" sets in a metric space. This result will be proved in the next chapter. There is often some confusion about the relationship between the Nested Intervals Theorem in $\mathbb{R}$ and the least upper bound property. Although our proof in $\mathbb{R}$ involves the least upper bound property, it can be proved in alternate ways.

5. The Construction of the Real Numbers

We are now ready to proceed with the construction of the real numbers from the rational numbers using the fact that the rational numbers are the ordered field constructed from $\mathbb{Z}$ in Chapter 1. We have already defined $\mathbb{R}$ as an ordered field in which the least upper bound property holds. We now proceed to build such a field starting from $\mathbb{Q}$ by using Cauchy sequences.

Recall that the *absolute value* on $\mathbb{Q}$ is defined as follows

$$|a| = \begin{cases} a, & \text{if } a \geq 0 \\ -a, & \text{if } a < 0. \end{cases}$$

Also recall that the absolute value on $\mathbb{Q}$ satisfies the following three properties.

(1) For any $a \in \mathbb{Q}$, $|a| \geq 0$, and $|a| = 0$ if and only if $a = 0$.

(2) For any $a, b \in \mathbb{Q}$, $|ab| = |a||b|$.

(3) For any $a, b \in \mathbb{Q}$, $|a + b| \leq |a| + |b|$ (triangle inequality).

Exercise 3.5.1. *Show that, for any $a, b \in \mathbb{Q}$, we have $||a| - |b|| \leq |a - b|$.*

Definition 3.5.2. *A sequence $(a_k)_{k\in\mathbb{N}}$ of rational numbers is a* Cauchy sequence *in $\mathbb{Q}$ if, given any rational number $r > 0$, there exists an integer N such that if $n, m \geq N$, then $|a_n - a_m| < r$.*

Definition 3.5.3. *A sequence $(a_k)_{k\in\mathbb{N}}$* converges in $\mathbb{Q}$ *to $a \in \mathbb{Q}$ if, given any rational number $r > 0$, there exists an integer N such that, if $n \geq N$, then $|a_n - a| < r$. The rational number a is called the* limit *of the sequence*

$(a_k)_{k\in\mathbb{N}}$. *Sometimes, we just say that the sequence* $(a_k)_{k\in\mathbb{N}}$ *converges in* $\mathbb{Q}$ *without mentioning the limit* a.

Exercise 3.5.4. *If a sequence* $(a_k)_{k\in\mathbb{N}}$ *converges in* $\mathbb{Q}$, *show that* $(a_k)_{k\in\mathbb{N}}$ *is a Cauchy sequence in* $\mathbb{Q}$.

Exercise 3.5.5. *Show that the limit of a convergent sequence is unique.*

Definition 3.5.6. *Let* $(a_k)_{k\in\mathbb{N}}$ *be a sequence of rational numbers. We say that* $(a_k)_{k\in\mathbb{N}}$ *is a* bounded sequence *if the set* $\{a_k \mid k \in \mathbb{N}\}$ *is a bounded set in* $\mathbb{Q}$.

Lemma 3.5.7. *Let* $(a_k)_{k\in\mathbb{N}}$ *be a Cauchy sequence of rational numbers. Then* $(a_k)_{k\in\mathbb{N}}$ *is a bounded sequence.*

Proof. Let $(a_k)_{k\in\mathbb{N}}$ be a Cauchy sequence of rational numbers. Pick $N \in \mathbb{N}$ such that $|a_n - a_m| < 1$ for $n, m \geq N$. Then $|a_n - a_N| < 1$ for all $n \geq N$, so that $|a_n| < 1 + |a_N|$ for all $n \geq N$. Let M be the max of $|a_1|, |a_2|, \ldots, |a_{N-1}|, 1 + |a_N|$. Then $(|a_k|)_{k\in\mathbb{N}}$ is bounded by M. ☠

Let $\mathcal{C}$ denote the set of all Cauchy sequences of rational numbers. We define addition and multiplication of Cauchy sequences term-wise, that is $(a_n)_{n\in\mathbb{N}} + (b_n)_{n\in\mathbb{N}} = (a_n + b_n)_{n\in\mathbb{N}}$ and $(a_n)_{n\in\mathbb{N}} \cdot (b_n)_{n\in\mathbb{N}} = (a_n \cdot b_n)_{n\in\mathbb{N}}$.

Exercise 3.5.8. *Show that the sum of two Cauchy sequences in* $\mathbb{Q}$ *is a Cauchy sequence in* $\mathbb{Q}$.

Theorem 3.5.9. *The product of two Cauchy sequences in* $\mathbb{Q}$ *is a Cauchy sequence in* $\mathbb{Q}$.

Proof. Let $(a_k)_{k\in\mathbb{N}}$ and $(b_k)_{k\in\mathbb{N}}$ be Cauchy sequences in $\mathbb{Q}$. Then

$$\begin{aligned} |a_nb_n - a_mb_m| &= |a_nb_n - a_nb_m + a_nb_m - a_mb_m| \\ &\leq |a_n||b_n - b_m| + |b_m||a_n - a_m| \\ &\leq A|b_n - b_m| + B|a_n - a_m|, \end{aligned}$$

where A and B are upper bounds for the sequences $(|a_k|)_{k\in\mathbb{N}}$ and $(|b_k|)_{k\in\mathbb{N}}$. Since $(a_k)_{k\in\mathbb{N}}$ and $(b_k)_{k\in\mathbb{N}}$ are Cauchy sequences, the theorem now follows. ☠

Exercise 3.5.10. *Show that, with addition and multiplication defined as above,* $\mathcal{C}$ *is a commutative ring with* 1.

Definition 3.5.11. *Let* $\mathcal{I}$ *be the set of sequences* $(a_k)_{k\in\mathbb{N}}$ *in* $\mathcal{C}$ *with the property that, given any rational* $r > 0$, *there exists an integer* N *such that if* $n \geq N$, *then* $|a_n| < r$. *The set* $\mathcal{I}$ *consists of Cauchy sequences that converge to* 0.

Lemma 3.5.12. *If $(a_k)_{k\in\mathbb{N}} \in \mathcal{C}\backslash\mathcal{I}$, then there exist a positive rational number r and an integer N so that $|a_k| \geq r$ for all $n \geq N$.*

Proof. Suppose $(a_k)_{k\in\mathbb{N}} \notin \mathcal{I}$. Then there exists a rational number $r > 0$ such that $|a_k| \geq 2r$ infinitely often. Pick $N \in \mathbb{N}$ such that $|a_n - a_m| < r$ for $n, m \geq N$. This implies that

$$|a_n| > |a_m| - r \text{ for } n, m \geq N.$$

Fix an $m \geq N$ for which $|a_m| \geq 2r$. Then for all $n \geq N$, we have

$$|a_n| > r.$$

∎

Exercise 3.5.13. *Show that if a Cauchy sequence does not converge to* 0, *all the terms of the sequence eventually have the same sign.*

Definition 3.5.14. *Let $(a_k)_{k\in\mathbb{N}}$ and $(b_k)_{k\in\mathbb{N}}$ be Cauchy sequences in $\mathbb{Q}$. We say that $(a_k)_{k\in\mathbb{N}}$ is equivalent to $(b_k)_{k\in\mathbb{N}}$, denoted by $(a_k)_{k\in\mathbb{N}} \sim (b_k)_{k\in\mathbb{N}}$, if $(c_k)_{k\in\mathbb{N}} = (a_k - b_k)_{k\in\mathbb{N}}$ is in $\mathcal{I}$.*

Exercise 3.5.15. *Show that $\sim$ defines an equivalence relation on $\mathcal{C}$.*

Denote by $\mathbf{R}$ the set of equivalence classes in $\mathcal{C}$. We claim that, with appropriate definitions of addition and multiplication (already indicated above) and order (to be defined below), $\mathbf{R}$ is an ordered field satisfying the least upper bound property.

If $(a_k)_{k\in\mathbb{N}}$ is a Cauchy sequence, denote its equivalence class by $[a_k]$. As one might expect, the sum and product of equivalence classes are defined as follows: $[a_k] + [b_k] = [a_k + b_k]$ and $[a_k][b_k] = [a_k b_k]$.

Exercise 3.5.16. *Show that addition and multiplication are well-defined on* $\mathbf{R}$.

Exercise 3.5.17. *Show that $\mathbf{R}$ is a commutative ring with 1, with $\mathcal{I}$ as the additive identity and $[a_k]$ such that $a_k = 1$ for all k as the multiplicative identity. This follows easily from Exercise* 3.5.10.

Theorem 3.5.18. $\mathbf{R}$ *is a field.*

Proof. We need only show that multiplicative inverses exist for non-zero elements. So assume that $[a_k] \neq \mathcal{I}$. Then, as we saw in Lemma 3.5.12, $(a_k)_{k\in\mathbb{N}}$ is eventually bounded below in absolute value. Hence, we can pick $M \in \mathbb{N}$ and $c > 0$ such that $|a_k| > c$ for all $k \geq M$. Define a sequence $(b_k)_{k\in\mathbb{N}}$ as follows: $b_k = 1$ for $k \leq M$, and $b_k = 1/a_k$ for $k > M$. Observe that for n, m large enough, $|1/a_n - 1/a_m| = |a_n - a_m|/|a_n a_m| \leq (1/c^2)|a_n - a_m|$. So $(b_k)_{k\in\mathbb{N}}$ is a Cauchy sequence and $[b_k]$ is the multiplicative inverse of $[a_k]$. ∎

The next step is to define order on $\mathbf{R}$. Let $[a_k]$ and $[b_k]$ represent distinct elements of $\mathbf{R}$. Then $[c_k] = [a_k - b_k]$ is not equal to $\mathcal{I}$. Hence, there exists $N \in \mathbb{N}$ such that all the terms of $(c_k)_{k\in\mathbb{N}}$ have the same sign for $k \geq N$. Thus, either $a_k < b_k$ for all $k \geq N$ or $b_k < a_k$ for all $k \geq N$. We use this fact to define an order on $\mathbf{R}$.

Definition 3.5.19. *Let $a = [a_k], b = [b_k]$ be distinct elements of* $\mathbf{R}$. *We define $a < b$ if $a_k < b_k$ eventually and $b < a$ if $b_k < a_k$ eventually.*

Exercise 3.5.20. *Show that the order relation on* $\mathbf{R}$ *defined above is well-defined and makes* $\mathbf{R}$ *an ordered field.*

To finish this off, we must show that $\mathbf{R}$ is an Archimedean ordered field that satisfies the least upper bound property. We will have then reached the mountain top so we can dismount the funicular and ski happily down the slope.

Define a map $i : \mathbb{Q} \to \mathbf{R}$ by sending $r \in \mathbb{Q}$ to the equivalence class of $(r, r, \ldots)$. It is evident that this map is injective and order-preserving, so we may consider $\mathbb{Q} \subseteq \mathbf{R}$ as ordered fields.

Theorem 3.5.21. *The field* $\mathbf{R}$ *is an Archimedean ordered field.*

Proof. Suppose $a \in \mathbf{R}$ and $a > 0$. Let $(a_k)_{k\in\mathbb{N}}$ represent a. By Lemma 3.5.7, and the fact that $\mathbb{Q}$ is an Archimedean ordered field, the Cauchy sequence $(a_k)_{k\in\mathbb{N}}$ is bounded above by some integer N, that is $a_k < N$ for all sufficiently large k. It follows that a is less than the integer $(N, N, \ldots)$ in $\mathbf{R}$ (under the inclusion $\mathbb{Q} \subseteq \mathbf{R}$). ☠

Theorem 3.5.22. *The least upper bound property holds in* $\mathbf{R}$.

Proof. Let A be a non-empty subset of $\mathbf{R}$ that is bounded above by, say, m. Then, by the Archimedean property, we can find $M \in \mathbb{Z}$ with $m \leq M$. Let a be in A and let n be an integer with $n < a$. For $p \in \mathbb{N}$ set $S_p = \{k2^{-p} \mid k \in \mathbb{Z} \text{ and } n \leq k2^{-p} \leq M\}$. Note that $S_p \neq \varnothing$ and is finite. Now let $a_p = \min\{x \mid x \in S_p \text{ and } x \text{ is an upper bound for } A\}$.

Note that if $p < q$, then

$$a_p - 2^{-p} < a_q \leq a_p,$$

since, for example, $a_p - 2^{-p}$ is not an upper bound for A, while a_q is an upper bound. But this implies that

$$|a_p - a_q| \leq 2^{-p} \text{ for all } p < q$$

from which it follows that $(a_k)_{k\in\mathbb{N}}$ is a Cauchy sequence. Let $L = [a_k]$.

We claim that L is a least upper bound for A. Suppose $x \in A$ and $x > L$. Choose p such that $2^{-p} < (x - L)$ (using the Archimedean property). Since

$a_p - 2^{-p} < a_q$ for $p < q$ and $(a_p)_{p\in\mathbb{N}}$ is a decreasing Cauchy sequence, it follows that $a_p - 2^{-p} \leq L \leq a_p$. In particular if we add $2^{-p} < x - L$ and $a_p - 2^{-p} \leq L$ we obtain $a_p < x$ which is a contradiction. Therefore L is an upper bound for A.

Suppose that H is an upper bound for A and $H < L$. Choose p such that $2^{-p} < L - H$. Take $x \in A$ such that $a_p - 2^{-p} < x$. Then $a_p - 2^{-p} < H$. Adding, we get $a_p < L$. But, as noted above, $L \leq a_p$ for all $p \in \mathbb{N}$, so this is a contradiction.

Exercise 3.5.23. *Prove that* $\mathbf{R}$ *is order isomorphic to* $\mathbb{R}$. *(Hint: you have already done this.)*

6. Convergence in $\mathbb{R}$

We define the absolute value on $\mathbb{R}$ in exactly the same manner as on $\mathbb{Q}$. In fact, the absolute value on $\mathbb{R}$ was used extensively in Chapter 2, and we simply recall the idea here.

Definition 3.6.1. *Suppose* $x \in \mathbb{R}$. *The* absolute value *of* x *is defined by*

$$|x| = \begin{cases} x, & \text{if } x \geq 0, \\ -x, & \text{if } x < 0. \end{cases}$$

The following are the essential properties of the absolute value.

Theorem 3.6.2. *(Properties of absolute value on* $\mathbb{R}$*)*

(1) *For any* $x \in \mathbb{R}$, $|x| \geq 0$, *and* $|x| = 0$ *iff* $x = 0$.

(2) *For any* $x, y \in \mathbb{R}$, $|xy| = |x||y|$.

(3) *For any* $x, y \in \mathbb{R}$, $|x + y| \leq |x| + |y|$ *(triangle inequality).*

Exercise 3.6.3. *Prove the properties of the absolute value.*

With absolute value defined, we can talk about Cauchy and convergent sequences in $\mathbb{R}$.

Definition 3.6.4. *A sequence* $(a_k)_{k\in\mathbb{N}}$ *of real numbers is* convergent *if there exists an element* $a \in \mathbb{R}$ *such that given any* $\varepsilon > 0$, *there exists* $N_\varepsilon \in \mathbb{N}$ *such that* $k \geq N_\varepsilon$ *implies that* $|a_k - a| < \varepsilon$. *We say that* $(a_k)_{k\in\mathbb{N}}$ converges to a, *and* a *is called the* limit *of the sequence* $(a_k)_{k\in\mathbb{N}}$. *Symbolically, we write*

$$\lim_{k\to\infty} a_k = a.$$

We will often say that a sequence of real numbers is convergent without specific reference to the limit a. Note that N_ε depends on ε.

Exercise 3.6.5. *Show that the limit of a convergent sequence is unique.*

Definition 3.6.6. *A sequence $(a_k)_{k\in\mathbb{N}}$ of real numbers is* monotonic increasing *if $a_k \le a_{k+1}$ for all $k \in \mathbb{N}$. A sequence $(a_k)_{k\in\mathbb{N}}$ of real numbers is* strictly monotonic increasing *if $a_k < a_{k+1}$ for all $k \in \mathbb{N}$. Similar definitions hold for monotonic decreasing and strictly monotonic decreasing sequences.*

Exercise 3.6.7. *Define the notion of a bounded sequence in $\mathbb{R}$.*

The following lemma is one of the more useful lemmas in discussing convergence in $\mathbb{R}$ (and $\mathbb{R}^n$).

Lemma 3.6.8. *Let $(a_k)_{k\in\mathbb{N}}$ be a sequence in $\mathbb{R}$. Then $(a_k)_{k\in\mathbb{N}}$ has a monotonic subsequence.*

Proof. Suppose $(a_k)_{k\in\mathbb{N}}$ does not have a monotonic increasing subsequence. Then, there exists $n_1 \in \mathbb{N}$ such that $a_{n_1} > a_k$ for all $k > n_1$. Again, since $(a_k)_{k>n_1}$ does not have a monotonic increasing subsequence, there exists $n_2 > n_1$ such that $a_{n_2} > a_k$ for all $k > n_2$. Moreover $a_{n_1} > a_{n_2}$. Continuing in this way, we obtain a monotonic strictly decreasing subsequence. ☠

Lemma 3.6.9. *Every bounded monotonic sequence in $\mathbb{R}$ converges to an element of $\mathbb{R}$.*

Proof. Suppose $(a_k)_{k\in\mathbb{N}}$ is monotonic increasing and bounded. Let a be the least upper bound of the set $\{a_1, a_2, \ldots\}$. For all $\varepsilon > 0$, there exists an N such that $a - \varepsilon < a_N \le a$. Since $(a_k)_{k\in\mathbb{N}}$ is increasing, if $k > N$, we have $a \ge a_k \ge a_N > a - \varepsilon$. So $\lim_{k\to\infty} a_k = a$. ☠

The next lemma is basic for analysis on $\mathbb{R}$.

Lemma 3.6.10. *Every bounded sequence in $\mathbb{R}$ has a convergent subsequence.*

Exercise 3.6.11. *Prove Lemma* 3.6.10*. This shouldn't take long.*

Definition 3.6.12. *(See Definition* 3.5.2*) A sequence $(a_k)_{k\in\mathbb{N}}$ in $\mathbb{R}$ is a* Cauchy sequence *if, given any $\varepsilon > 0$, there exists $N_\varepsilon \in \mathbb{N}$ such that $n, m \ge N_\varepsilon$ implies $|a_m - a_n| < \varepsilon$.*

Exercise 3.6.13.

(*i*) *Prove that every Cauchy sequence in $\mathbb{R}$ is bounded.*

(*ii*) *If $(a_k)_{k\in\mathbb{N}}$ is a Cauchy seqence in $\mathbb{R}$, show that, for any $\varepsilon > 0$, there exists a subsequence $(a_{k_j})_{j\in\mathbb{N}}$ so that $|a_{k_j} - a_{k_{j+1}}| < \varepsilon/2^{j+1}$ for $j \in \mathbb{N}$.*

Theorem 3.6.14 (Cauchy Criterion). *A sequence $(a_k)_{k\in\mathbb{N}}$ of real numbers is convergent if and only if it is a Cauchy sequence.*

Proof. We already did half of this in $\mathbb{Q}$ (see Exercise 3.5.4), but we will do it again. First, we prove that if $(a_k)_{k\in\mathbb{N}}$ is convergent, then it is Cauchy.

Suppose $\lim_{k\to\infty} a_k = a$. Then, since the sequence converges, given $\varepsilon > 0$, there exists $N_\varepsilon \in \mathbb{N}$ such that $|a_n - a| < \frac{\varepsilon}{2}$ for all $n \geq N_\varepsilon$. Thus, if $n, m \geq N_\varepsilon$, we have

$$|a_n - a_m| \leq |a_n - a| + |a_m - a| < \frac{\varepsilon}{2} + \frac{\varepsilon}{2} = \varepsilon$$

and so $(a_k)_{k\in\mathbb{N}}$ is a Cauchy sequence.

Suppose now that $(a_k)_{k\in\mathbb{N}}$ is a Cauchy sequence in $\mathbb{R}$. Then, by Exercise 3.6.13, $(a_k)_{k\in\mathbb{N}}$ is a bounded sequence, and hence by Lemma 3.6.10 has a convergent subsequence. Call the limit of this subsequence a. Then, since $(a_k)_{k\in\mathbb{N}}$ is Cauchy, it is clear that $\lim_{k\to\infty} a_k = a$.

Exercise 3.6.15. *Show that, if $(a_n)_{n\in\mathbb{N}}$ and $(b_n)_{n\in\mathbb{N}}$ are Cauchy sequences in $\mathbb{R}$, then $(a_n + b_n)_{n\in\mathbb{N}}$ and $(a_n \cdot b_n)_{n\in\mathbb{N}}$ are Cauchy sequences in $\mathbb{R}$.*

Definition 3.6.16. *Let S be a subset of $\mathbb{R}$. Then $x \in \mathbb{R}$ is an* accumulation point *of S if, for all $\varepsilon > 0$, we have $((x - \varepsilon, x + \varepsilon) \setminus \{x\}) \cap S \neq \varnothing$.*

Remark 3.6.17. *Thus, x is an accumulation point of S if every interval around x contains points of S other than x. Of course, x does not have to be an element of S in order to be an accumulation point of S.*

Exercise 3.6.18. *Find the accumulation points of the following sets in $\mathbb{R}$:*

(i) $S = (0, 1)$;

(ii) $S = \{(-1)^n + \frac{1}{n} \mid n \in \mathbb{N}\}$;

(iii) $S = \mathbb{Q}$;

(iv) $S = \mathbb{Z}$;

(v) *S is the set of rational numbers whose denominators are prime.*

Lemma 3.6.19. *Let S be a subset of $\mathbb{R}$. Then $x \in \mathbb{R}$ is an accumulation point of S iff every neighborhood of x contains infinitely many points of x.*

Proof. Let x be an accumulation point of S. Given $\varepsilon > 0$, there is a point $x_1 \in (x - \varepsilon, x + \varepsilon) \cap S$ such that $x_1 \neq x$. Let $\varepsilon_1 = |x - x_1|$. Then, there is a point $x_2 \in (x - \varepsilon_1, x + \varepsilon_1) \cap S$ such that $x_2 \neq x$. Iterating this procedure, we get an infinite set of elements in S that is contained in $(x - \varepsilon, x + \varepsilon)$.

Exercise. *You prove the converse.*

Now here is a Big Time Theorem.

Theorem 3.6.20. *(Bolzano-Weierstrass) Let S be a bounded, infinite subset of $\mathbb{R}$. Then S has an accumulation point in $\mathbb{R}$.*

Proof. Pick an infinite sequence $(a_k)_{k\in\mathbb{N}}$ of distinct elements of S. Then, by Lemma 3.6.10, $(a_k)_{k\in\mathbb{N}}$ has a convergent subsequence, $(b_j)_{j\in\mathbb{N}}$. If $\lim_{j\to\infty} b_j = b$, then b is an accumulation point of S.

Exercise 3.6.21.

(*i*) *Find an infinite subset of* $\mathbb{R}$ *that does not have an accumulation point in* $\mathbb{R}$.

(*ii*) *Find a bounded subset of* $\mathbb{R}$ *that does not have an accumulation point in* $\mathbb{R}$.

(*iii*) *Find a bounded infinite subset of* $\mathbb{Q}$ *that does not have an accumulation point in* $\mathbb{Q}$.

Definition 3.6.22. *Let S be a subset of $\mathbb{R}$. We say that S is an* open set *in $\mathbb{R}$ if, for each point $x \in S$, there is an $\varepsilon > 0$ (depending on x) such that $(x-\varepsilon, x+\varepsilon) \subseteq S$.*

Definition 3.6.23. *Let $S \subseteq \mathbb{R}$. We say S is a* closed set *in $\mathbb{R}$ if the complement of S is an open set in $\mathbb{R}$.*

Note that the empty set and $\mathbb{R}$ are both open and closed subsets of $\mathbb{R}$.

Exercise 3.6.24.

(*i*) *Show that $\varnothing$ and $\mathbb{R}$ are the only subsets of $\mathbb{R}$ that are both open and closed in $\mathbb{R}$.*

(*ii*) *Show that every non-empty open set in $\mathbb{R}$ can be written as a countable union of pairwise disjoint open intervals.*

(*iii*) *Show that an arbitrary union of open sets in $\mathbb{R}$ is open in $\mathbb{R}$.*

(*iv*) *Show that a finite intersection of open sets in $\mathbb{R}$ is open in $\mathbb{R}$.*

(*v*) *Show, by example, that an infinite intersection of open sets is not necessarily open.*

(*vi*) *Show that an arbitrary intersection of closed sets in $\mathbb{R}$ is a closed set in $\mathbb{R}$.*

(*vii*) *Show that a finite union of closed sets in $\mathbb{R}$ is a closed set in $\mathbb{R}$.*

(*viii*) *Show, by example, that an infinite union of closed sets in $\mathbb{R}$ is not necessarily a closed set in $\mathbb{R}$.*

Exercise 3.6.25. *Show that a subset of $\mathbb{R}$ is closed iff it contains all its accumulation points.*

Exercise 3.6.26. *We now define the Cantor set to be a subset of the closed interval $[0,1]$. First, remove the open interval $(1/3, 2/3)$ from $[0,1]$. Next, remove the open intervals $(1/9, 2/9)$ and $(7/9, 8/9)$. At each step, remove the middle third of the remaining closed intervals. Repeating this process a* *countable number of times, we are left with a subset of the closed interval* $[0,1]$ *called the* Cantor set. *Show that:*

(*i*) *the Cantor set is closed;*

(*ii*) *the Cantor set is uncountable;*

(*iii*) *the Cantor set consists of all numbers in the closed interval* $[0,1]$ *whose ternary expansion consists of only* 0's *and* 2's *and may end in infinitely many* 2's;

(*iv*) *every point of the Cantor set is an accumulation point of the Cantor set;*

(*v*) *the set* $[0,1] \setminus$ *Cantor set is a dense subset of* $[0,1]$.

The next theorem, the Heine-Borel theorem for $\mathbb{R}$, is the second of the two basic topological theorems for the real numbers, the other is the Bolzano-Weierstrass theorem. We shall see more details about these two theorems in Chapter 4.

Theorem 3.6.27 (Heine-Borel). *Let S be a closed and bounded subset of $\mathbb{R}$. Given a collection $\{U_i\}_{i\in I}$ of open sets such that $S \subseteq \bigcup_{i\in I} U_i$, there exists a finite subcollection $U_1, \ldots, U_n$ of $\{U_i\}_{i\in I}$ such that $S \subseteq U_1 \cup \ldots \cup U_n$.*

Proof. Suppose that S is a non-empty, closed, bounded subset of $\mathbb{R}$. If $a = \text{glb}(S)$ and $b = \text{lub}(S)$, then, since S is closed, a and b are in S, and $S \subseteq [a,b]$. Let $\{U_i\}_{i\in I}$ be a collection of open sets such that $S \subseteq \bigcup U_i$. By adjoining the complement of S (if necessary), we obtain a collection $\mathcal{U}$ of open sets whose union contains $[a,b]$.

Now let $B = \{x \in [a,b] \mid [a,x]$ is covered by a finite number of open sets in $\mathcal{U}\}$. Then B is non-empty since $a \in B$, and B is bounded above by b. Let $c = \text{lub}(B)$.

Exercise. *Prove that $c \in B$. (Hint: Prove that B is closed.)*

If $c = b$, we're done. Otherwise, let $\mathcal{U}'$ be a finite subcollection of $\mathcal{U}$ that covers $[a,c]$. There exists y such that $c < y < b$ and $[c,y]$ in an open set in $\mathcal{U}'$ that contains c. Thus $[a,y]$ is covered by $\mathcal{U}'$. This is a contradiction, and hence b must equal c. Thus $[a,b]$ is covered by a finite number of open sets from $\mathcal{U}$, and by throwing away the complement of S (if necessary), S is covered by a finite number of open sets from the original collection. ☺

Definition 3.6.28. *Let A be a subset of $\mathbb{R}$. An* open covering *of A is a collection of open sets $(U_i)_{i\in I}$ such that $A \subseteq \bigcup_{i\in I} U_i$.*

Definition 3.6.29. *Let A be a subset of $\mathbb{R}$. We say that A is a* compact set *if every open covering of A has a finite subcovering. That is, if $(U_i)_{i\in I}$*

is an open covering of A, there is a finite subcollection $U_1, U_2, \ldots, U_n$ of the collection $(U_i)_{i \in I}$ so that $A \subseteq U_1 \cup U_2 \cup \cdots \cup U_n$.

Definition 3.6.30. *A subset A of $\mathbb{R}$ is* sequentially compact *if every infinite sequence in A has a subsequence that converges to an element of A.*

Exercise 3.6.31. *Show that a subset of $\mathbb{R}$ is compact if and only if it is closed and bounded.*

The following fact can be proved easily using the Bolzano-Weierstrass and Heine-Borel theorems in $\mathbb{R}$. We will see in Chapter 4 that the same theorem is true in metric spaces. In Section 8, we give an indication of how this works in $\mathbb{C}$.

Exercise 3.6.32. *A subset of $\mathbb{R}$ is compact if and only if it is sequentially compact.*

7. Automorphisms of Fields

Suppose that we have a map f from $\mathbb{Q}$ to $\mathbb{Q}$ or from $\mathbb{R}$ to $\mathbb{R}$ that satisfies the additive condition of a linear transformation. That is, if $f(x+y) = f(x) + f(y)$ for all x and y, what can we say about f? Recall that we also discussed linear transformations of $\mathbb{R}$ as a vector space over $\mathbb{Q}$ (see Section 2.2).

First consider the problem for the rational numbers. We have $f(x) = f(x+0) = f(x)+f(0)$, so $f(0) = 0$. By induction, we have that $f(n) = nf(1)$ for $n \in \mathbb{N}$. Since $f(0) = f(n) + f(-n)$, we have that $f(-n) = -nf(1)$ for $n \in \mathbb{N}$. Thus, $f(n) = nf(1)$ for $n \in \mathbb{Z}$. By induction again, we have that $nf(m/n) = f(m)$ for $m \in \mathbb{Z}$ and $n \in \mathbb{N}$, so $f(r) = rf(1)$ for $r \in \mathbb{Q}$.

Let's see what happens for $\mathbb{R}$. We assume that $f(1) \neq 0$. We have $f(r) = rf(1)$ for all $r \in \mathbb{Q}$. However, as we pointed out after the definition of Hamel basis in Chapter 2, things go completely awry unless we impose further properties. So let's assume that f preserves multiplication, that is, $f(xy) = f(x)f(y)$ for all $x, y \in \mathbb{R}$. Then, it follows immediately that $f(1) = 1$, and $f(a^{-1}) = f(a)^{-1}$ if $a \neq 0$. The next thing to note here is that if $a \in \mathbb{R}$ and $a \neq 0$, then $a^2 > 0$ and $f(a^2) = (f(a))^2$, so $f(a^2) > 0$. Since every positive real number has a unique positive square root (by Exercise 4.5.34) we can conclude that if $c > 0$, then $f(c) > 0$. Thus, if $a < b$, then $f(a) < f(b)$ since $b - a > 0$. Now take any real number c. If $c \in \mathbb{Q}$, then $f(c) = c$. If $c \notin \mathbb{Q}$ and $f(c) \neq c$, then there are two possibilities. If $c < f(c)$, choose a rational number r so that $c < r < f(c)$. Then $f(c) < f(r) = r$, which is a contradiction. If $f(c) < c$, we run into the same problem.

So we conclude that any non-trivial map $f : \mathbb{R} \to \mathbb{R}$ that preserves addition and multiplication must be the identity map.

Definition 3.7.1. *Let F be a field. An* automorphism *of F is a bijection, $\phi : F \to F$, such that*

(a) $\phi(x + y) = \phi(x) + \phi(y)$ *for all $x, y \in F$,*

(b) $\phi(xy) = \phi(x)\phi(y)$ *for all $x, y \in F$.*

Exercise 3.7.2. *If F is a field, show that the automorphisms of F form a group under composition of functions. This group is called* the automorphism group of the field F *and is denoted by* $\mathrm{Aut}(F)$.

Theorem 3.7.3. *The groups* $\mathrm{Aut}(\mathbb{Q})$ *and* $\mathrm{Aut}(\mathbb{R})$ *consist only of the identity map.*

Exercise 3.7.4. *Find a field F such that* $\mathrm{Aut}(F) \neq \{I\}$.

Exercise 3.7.5.

(*i*) *Let F be a field and let ϕ be an element of* $\mathrm{Aut}(F)$. *Define* $H_\phi = \{x \in F \mid \phi(x) = x\}$. *Show that H_ϕ is a subfield of F.*

(*ii*) *Suppose that F is a field and that $\mathbb{Q}$ is a subfield of F. If* $\phi \in \mathrm{Aut}(F)$, *show that $\mathbb{Q}$ is a subfield of H_ϕ.*

Exercise 3.7.6.

(*i*) *Find* $\mathrm{Aut}(\mathbb{Z}_p)$ *where p is a prime and $\mathbb{Z}_p$ is the finite field with p elements.*

(*ii*) *Let* $F = \{a + b\sqrt{2} \mid a, b \in \mathbb{Q}\}$. *Show that F is a field and find* $\mathrm{Aut}(F)$. *This is the beginning of the subject called Galois theory, in which one of the goals is to determine* $\mathrm{Aut}(F)$ *when F is a so-called "algebraic extension" of $\mathbb{Q}$.*

8. Construction of the Complex Numbers

To start this section, we give a somewhat inexact definition of the complex numbers. This is often used as a definition of the complex numbers, but it does contain some ambiguity which we will rectify immediately.

Definition 3.8.1. *(Rural Definition) The set of* complex numbers, $\mathbb{C}$, *is the collection of expressions of the form $z = a + bi$ where $a, b \in \mathbb{R}$, and i is a symbol that satisfies $i^2 = -1$. If $z = a + bi$ and $w = c + di$ are in $\mathbb{C}$, then we define $z + w = (a + c) + (b + d)i$, and $zw = (ac - bd) + (bc + ad)i$.*

Actually, one can go a long way with this definition if the symbol i with the property that $i^2 = -1$ doesn't cause insomnia. In fact, once you assert that $i^2 = -1$, you must accept the fact that $(-i)^2 = -1$, and hence there is some ambiguity in the choice of the square root of -1. This difficulty is avoided in the following construction.

We consider the Cartesian product $\mathbb{R} \times \mathbb{R}$ with addition defined by $(a, b) + (c, d) = (a + c, b + d)$ and multiplication defined by $(a, b)(c, d) = (ac - bd, bc + ad)$.

Exercise 3.8.2. *Show that $\mathbb{R} \times \mathbb{R}$ with addition and multiplication as defined above is a field, with $(0, 0)$ as the additive identity, $(1, 0)$ as the multiplicative identity, $-(a, b) = (-a, -b)$, and $(a, b)^{-1} = (a/(a^2 + b^2), -b/(a^2 + b^2))$ if $(a, b) \neq (0, 0)$.*

So $\mathbb{R} \times \mathbb{R}$ with these operations forms a field, which we denote by $\mathbb{C}$ and call *the field of complex numbers*. Note that $\mathbb{R}$ is isomorphic to the subfield of $\mathbb{C}$ given by $\{(a, 0) \mid a \in \mathbb{R}\}$. If we set $i = (0, 1)$, then $i^2 = (-1, 0)$. Finally, to fix things up real nice, we write $(a, b) = (a, 0) + (b, 0)(0, 1)$, or, returning to our original rural definition, $(a, b) = a + bi$.

The first observation to make is that $\mathbb{C}$ cannot be made into an ordered field. That is, it cannot satisfy the order axioms given in Section 5. This is immediate because in any ordered field, if $a \neq 0$ then $a^2 > 0$. This would imply that $i^2 = -1 > 0$, but $1^2 = 1 > 0$ and this is a contradiction.

Definition 3.8.3. *If $z = a + bi$ with a, $b \in \mathbb{R}$, we call a the* real part *of z and b the* imaginary part *of z. We write $a = \text{Re } z$ and $b = \text{Im } z$. The complex number z is called* pure imaginary *if $a = \text{Re } z = 0$.*

Definition 3.8.4. *If $z = a + bi$ with a, $b \in \mathbb{R}$, the* complex conjugate *of z, denoted $\bar{z}$, is $\bar{z} = a - bi$. The* absolute value *of z is*

$$|z| = (z\bar{z})^{\frac{1}{2}} = (a^2 + b^2)^{\frac{1}{2}},$$

where, of course, we mean the non-negative square root in $\mathbb{R}$.

If z and w are complex numbers, then $|z|, |w| \in \mathbb{R}$ and hence it makes sense to say that $|z| < |w|$. However, it makes no sense to say that $z < w$.

Exercise 3.8.5. *Show that if we identify $z = a + bi$ with the point $(a, b) \in \mathbb{R}^2$, then the absolute value of z is equal to the distance of the point (a, b) from $(0, 0)$.*

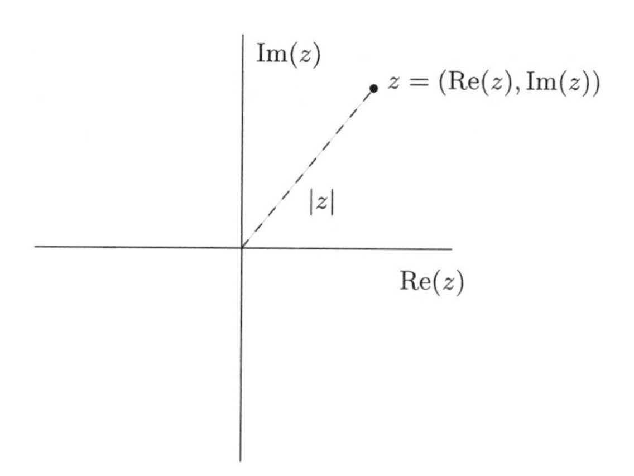

Exercise 3.8.6. *Show that the absolute value on $\mathbb{C}$ satisfies all the properties of the absolute value on $\mathbb{R}$.*

(1) *For any $z \in \mathbb{C}$, we have $|z| \geq 0$, and $|z| = 0$ iff $z = 0$.*
(2) *For any $z, w \in \mathbb{C}$, we have $|zw| = |z||w|$.*
(3) *For any $z, w \in \mathbb{C}$, we have $|z + w| \leq |z| + |w|$ (triangle inequality).*

Exercise 3.8.7. *Show that the field of complex numbers is not isomorphic to the field of real numbers.*

9. Convergence in $\mathbb{C}$

Now that we have an absolute value on $\mathbb{C}$, we can define the notions of Cauchy sequence and convergent sequence in $\mathbb{C}$.

Definition 3.9.1. *A sequence $(z_k)_{k \in \mathbb{N}}$ of complex numbers is* convergent *if there exists an element $z \in \mathbb{C}$ such that given any $\varepsilon > 0$, there exists $N_\varepsilon \in \mathbb{N}$ such that $k \geq N_\varepsilon$ implies that $|z_k - z| < \varepsilon$. We say that $(z_k)_{k \in \mathbb{N}}$* converges to *z, and z is called the* limit *of the sequence $(z_k)_{k \in \mathbb{N}}$. Symbolically, we write*

$$\lim_{k \to \infty} z_k = z.$$

We will often say that a sequence of complex numbers is convergent without specific reference to the limit z. Note that N_ε depends on ε. As usual, the limit of a convergent sequence is unique.

Definition 3.9.2. *Let r be a positive real number, and let $z_0 \in \mathbb{C}$. The* open ball *of radius r with center at z_0 is*

(1) $$B_r(z_0) = \{z \in \mathbb{C} \mid |z - z_0| < r\}.$$

The closed ball *of radius r with center z_0 is*

(2) $$\bar{B}_r(z_0) = \{z \in \mathbb{C} \mid |z - z_0| \leq r\}.$$

The open balls and closed balls in $\mathbb{C}$ are the analogs of open and closed intervals in $\mathbb{R}$. We can define open and closed sets in $\mathbb{C}$ in a fashion similar to the definitions in $\mathbb{R}$ (Definitions 3.6.22 and 3.6.23).

Definition 3.9.3. *Let S be a subset of $\mathbb{C}$. We say that S is an* open set *in $\mathbb{C}$ if, for each point $z \in S$, there is an $\varepsilon > 0$ (depending on z) such that $B_\varepsilon(z) \subseteq S$.*

Definition 3.9.4. *Let $S \subseteq \mathbb{C}$. We say that S is a* closed set *in $\mathbb{C}$ if the complement of S is an open set in $\mathbb{C}$.*

Note that the empty set and $\mathbb{C}$ are both open and closed subsets of $\mathbb{C}$.

Exercise 3.9.5.

(i) *Show that $\varnothing$ and $\mathbb{C}$ are the only subsets of $\mathbb{C}$ that are both open and closed in $\mathbb{C}$.*

(ii) *Show that every open set in $\mathbb{C}$ can be written as a countable union of open balls.*

(iii) *Show, by example, that there are open sets in $\mathbb{C}$ for which the open balls in ii cannot be made pairwise disjoint.*

(iv) *Show that an arbitrary union of open sets in $\mathbb{C}$ is an open set in $\mathbb{C}$.*

(v) *Show that a finite intersection of open sets in $\mathbb{C}$ is an open set in $\mathbb{C}$.*

(vi) *Show, by example, that an infinite intersection of open sets in $\mathbb{C}$ need not be an open set in $\mathbb{C}$.*

(vii) *Show that an arbitrary intersection of closed sets in $\mathbb{C}$ is a closed set in $\mathbb{C}$.*

(viii) *Show that a finite union of closed sets in $\mathbb{C}$ is a closed set in $\mathbb{C}$.*

(ix) *Show, by example, that an infinite union of closed sets in $\mathbb{C}$ is not necessarily a closed set in $\mathbb{C}$.*

Exercise 3.9.6. *Consider the collection of open balls $\{B_r(z)\}$ in $\mathbb{C}$ where $r \in \mathbb{Q}$ and $\mathrm{Re}(z), \mathrm{Im}(z) \in \mathbb{Q}$. Show that any open set in $\mathbb{C}$ can be written as a finite or countable union from this collection of sets.*

Definition 3.9.7. *Let $A \subseteq \mathbb{C}$. The set A is bounded if there exists $r > 0$ such that $A \subseteq B_r(0)$.*

Exercise 3.9.8. *Define the notion of a bounded sequence in $\mathbb{C}$.*

Definition 3.9.9. *(See Definition 3.6.12) A sequence $(z_k)_{k\in\mathbb{N}}$ in $\mathbb{C}$ is a* Cauchy sequence *if, given any $\varepsilon > 0$, there exists $N \in \mathbb{N}$ such that $n, m \geq N$ implies $|z_m - z_n| < \varepsilon$.*

Exercise 3.9.10. *Prove that every Cauchy sequence in $\mathbb{C}$ is bounded.*

Theorem 3.9.11 (Cauchy Criterion). *A sequence $(z_k)_{k\in\mathbb{N}}$ of complex numbers is convergent if and only if it is a Cauchy sequence.*

Proof. The first half of the proof is identical to the proof of Theorem 3.6.14.

Suppose now that $(z_k)_{k\in\mathbb{N}}$ is a Cauchy sequence in $\mathbb{C}$. Let $z_k = a_k + b_k i$, where $a_k, b_k \in \mathbb{R}$. Then $|z_m - z_n|^2 = (a_m - a_n)^2 + (b_m - b_n)^2$. It follows immediately that $(a_k)_{k\in\mathbb{N}}$ is a Cauchy sequence in $\mathbb{R}$ and $(b_k)_{k\in\mathbb{N}}$ is a Cauchy sequence in $\mathbb{R}$. If $\lim_{k\to\infty} a_k = a$ and $\lim_{k\to\infty} b_k = b$ (see Theorem 3.6.14), then $\lim_{k\to\infty} z_k = z$ where $z = a + bi$.

Exercise 3.9.12. *Show that every bounded sequence in $\mathbb{C}$ has a convergent subsequence.*

Definition 3.9.13. *Let S be a subset of $\mathbb{C}$. Then z is an* accumulation point *of S if, for all $\varepsilon > 0$, we have $(B_\varepsilon(z) \setminus \{z\}) \cap S \neq \varnothing$.*

Remark 3.9.14. *Thus, z is an accumulation point of S if every open ball around z contains points of S other than z. Of course, z does not have to be an element of S in order to be an accumulation point of S.*

Exercise 3.9.15. *Find the accumulation points of the following sets:*

(*i*) $\mathbb{T} = \{z \in \mathbb{C} \mid |z| = 1\}$ *(this is the* unit circle in $\mathbb{C}$*);*

(*ii*) $S = \{z \in \mathbb{C} \mid \mathrm{Re}\ z > \mathrm{Im}\ z\}$*;*

(*iii*) $S = \{a + bi \mid a, b \in \mathbb{Q}\}$*;*

(*iv*) $S = \{a + bi \mid a, b \in \mathbb{Z}\}$*.*

(*v*) $S = \{\frac{1}{n} + \frac{1}{m} i \mid n, m \in \mathbb{N}\}$*.*

Exercise 3.9.16.

(*i*) *Let S be a subset of $\mathbb{C}$. Show that every neighborhood of an accumulation point of S contains infinitely many points of S.*

(*ii*) *(Bolzano-Weierstrass Theorem for $\mathbb{C}$) Prove that any bounded infinite set in $\mathbb{C}$ has an accumulation point in $\mathbb{C}$.*

Definition 3.9.17. *Let S be a subset of $\mathbb{C}$. We say that S is a* compact set *if every open covering of S has a finite subcovering. That is, if $(U_i)_{i\in I}$ is an open covering of S, there is a finite subcollection $U_1, U_2, \ldots, U_n$ of the collection $(U_i)_{i\in I}$ so that $S \subseteq U_1 \cup U_2 \cup \cdots \cup U_n$.*

Theorem 3.9.18 (Heine-Borel). *If S is a closed and bounded subset of $\mathbb{C}$, then S is compact.*

Proof. For the purposes of this proof, we treat $\mathbb{C}$ as $\mathbb{R}^2$. We prove it for $S = [a, b] \times [c, d]$ where $a, b, c, d \in \mathbb{R}$ and $a < b$ and $c < d$ and leave the general case for an exercise.

Take a point $x_0 \in [a,b]$ and consider the set $\{x_0\} \times [c,d]$. We take an open set $N \subseteq \mathbb{C}$ containing $\{x_0\} \times [c,d]$. We claim that there exists an open interval I of x_0 such that $I \times [c,d] \subseteq N$. For each point in $(x_0, y) \in \{x_0\} \times [c,d]$, choose $r_y > 0$ such that the open square $(x_0 - r_y, x_0 + r_y) \times (y - r_y, y + r_y) \subseteq N$. By intersecting these squares with $\{x_0\} \times \mathbb{R}$ and projecting on the second coordinate, we get a collection of open intervals of the form $(y - r_y, y + r_y)$ that cover $[c,d]$. By the Heine-Borel theorem in $\mathbb{R}$, there exists a finite subcollection of these open intervals that covers the interval $[c,d]$. Hence the corresponding collection of open squares also covers $\{x_0\} \times [c,d]$. Let r be the minimum of the r_y from this finite collection. Then $I = (x_0 - r, x_0 + r)$ is the interval we sought.

Now let $\{U_j\}_{j \in J}$ be an open covering of S. For each $x \in [a,b]$, the collection $\{U_j\}_{j \in J}$ covers $\{x\} \times [c,d]$. As we did above, we choose a finite subcollection $U_1, \ldots, U_n$ that covers $\{x\} \times [c,d]$. The open set $N_x = U_1 \cup \cdots \cup U_n$ contains a set of the form $I_x \times [c,d]$ by the preceding discussion, where I_x is an open interval containing x. The collection $\{I_x\}_{x \in [a,b]}$ covers $[a,b]$, and hence by the Heine-Borel theorem for $\mathbb{R}$, there exists a finite subcollection $I_{x_1}, \ldots, I_{x_m}$ that covers $[a,b]$. We take our finite subcollection of the original open cover $\{U_j\}_{j \in J}$ to be $\{U \mid \text{for some } x_i \text{ the set } U \text{ is one of the elements in the union that defines } N_{x_i}\}$.

Exercise 3.9.19. *Prove the general case of the Heine-Borel theorem in $\mathbb{C}$. (Hint: Take a closed bounded set in $\mathbb{C}$ and put it inside the product of two closed bounded intervals. Then use the procedure in Theorem 3.6.27.)*

Exercise 3.9.20. *Show that a subset of $\mathbb{C}$ is closed iff it contains all its accumulation points.*

Exercise 3.9.21. *Define the notion of sequentially compact for a subset of $\mathbb{C}$, and show that a subset of $\mathbb{C}$ is sequentially compact if and only if it is closed and bounded.*

Definition 3.9.22. *If $z = x + iy \in \mathbb{C}$, $z \neq 0$, and $r = |z|$, then the* polar form *of z is $z = r(\cos\theta + i\sin\theta)$ where θ is the unique solution to the equations*

$$x = r\cos\theta$$

$$y = r\sin\theta$$

in the interval $[0, 2\pi)$. The angle θ is called the principal branch of the argument of *z and is denoted* $\operatorname{Arg}(z)$. *For z as above, we often write $z = re^{i\theta}$ where $e^{i\theta}$ is defined to be* $\cos\theta + i\sin\theta$. *(In fact, $\cos\theta + i\sin\theta$ is the value of the complex exponential function $f(z) = e^z$, defined by the power series $e^z = \sum_{n=0}^{\infty} z^n/n!$, when $z = i\theta$. See Project 3.10.2.)*

Exercise 3.9.23. *Suppose that $n \in \mathbb{N}$. Prove that, if $z = e^{\frac{2k\pi i}{n}}$, for $k \in \mathbb{Z}$ and $0 \leq k \leq n-1$, then $z^n = 1$. Such a z is called an* n-th root of unity. *Note that these n roots of unity are all distinct.*

The n-th roots of unity form a cyclic group of order n under multiplication. An n-th root of unity is *primitive* if it is a generator of this group.

Exercise 3.9.24. *Show that the primitive n-th roots of unity are of the form $e^{2\pi ik/n}$ where k and n are relatively prime.*

Proposition 3.9.25. *If $n > 1$, the sum of the n distinct n-th roots of unity is 0.*

Proof. For any $z \in \mathbb{C}$,

$$(1 - z^n) = (1 - z)(1 + z + z^2 + \ldots + z^{n-1}).$$

Now let z be a primitive n-th root of unity. ☠

Exercise 3.9.26. *Suppose z is a nonzero complex number, and write $z = re^{i\theta}$. Show that z has exactly n distinct complex n-th roots given by $r^{1/n}e^{i(2\pi k+\theta)/n}$ for $0 \leq k \leq n-1$.*

In Chapter 1, we discussed polynomial functions with real coefficients. We denoted this set of polynomials by $\mathbb{R}[x]$ and observed in Exercise 1.7.35 that with the ordinary addition and multiplication of polynomials, $\mathbb{R}[x]$ is a commutative ring with 1. Of course, we could just as well have considered the sets $\mathbb{Z}[x]$ and $\mathbb{Q}[x]$. For current purposes, it is useful to consider the elements of $\mathbb{Z}[x]$ and $\mathbb{Q}[x]$ as polynomial functions from $\mathbb{R}$ to $\mathbb{R}$. In the case of $\mathbb{C}[x]$, we will consider these as functions from $\mathbb{C}$ to $\mathbb{C}$, and we will ordinarily write $\mathbb{C}[z]$ for the ring of polynomials with complex coefficients.

Exercise 3.9.27. *Show that $\mathbb{Z}[x]$, $\mathbb{Q}[x]$, $\mathbb{R}[x]$, and $\mathbb{C}[z]$ are integral domains. In each of these domains determine those elements that have multiplicative inverses.*

Definition 3.9.28. *Let F be a field. We say that F is* algebraically closed *if every non-constant polynomial in $F[x]$ has a root in F. That is, F is algebraically closed if, for every non-constant $p(x) \in F[x]$, there is an element $r \in F$ such that $p(r) = 0$.*

The most important example of an algebraically closed field is supplied by the Fundamental Theorem of Algebra, which states that the field of complex numbers is algebraically closed. There is a semi-infinite number of proofs of this theorem. We will present one of these in Project 4.6.2 using the properties of continuous functions developed in Chapter 4.

Exercise 3.9.29. *Let F be a field and suppose that $p(x) \in F[x]$. Show that r is a root of $p(x)$ if and only if $(x - r)$ is a factor of $p(x)$. That is, we can write $p(x) = (x - r)q(x)$ for some $q(x) \in F[x]$.*

Definition 3.9.30. *Let $\mathbb{A}$ be the collection of all roots of non-0 polynomials in $\mathbb{Z}[x]$, $\mathbb{A}$ is called* the set of algebraic numbers *in $\mathbb{C}$. The set $\mathbb{A}_{\mathbb{R}} = \mathbb{A} \cap \mathbb{R}$ is called* the set of real algebraic numbers. *A real number which is not a real algebraic number is called* transcendental.

Example 3.9.31. *Among the more famous algebraic numbers are i and $-i$. For real algebraic numbers, the most famous one is probably $\sqrt{2}$. The most famous transcendental numbers are π and e.*

Exercise 3.9.32. *Show that $\mathbb{A}$ and $\mathbb{A}_{\mathbb{R}}$ are fields.*

Exercise 3.9.33. *Show that the field $\mathbb{A}$ of algebraic numbers is countable.*

Remark 3.9.34. *It follows from the exercise above that the field $\mathbb{A}_{\mathbb{R}}$ of real algebraic numbers is countable and hence the set of transcendental numbers is uncountable.*

10. Independent Projects

10.1. Another Construction of $\mathbb{R}$: Dedekind Cuts.

Definition 3.10.1.1. *A subset α of $\mathbb{Q}$ is said to be a* cut *(or a* Dedekind cut*) if it satisfies the following:*

(a) *the set $\alpha \neq \varnothing$ and $\alpha \neq \mathbb{Q}$;*

(b) *if $r \in \alpha$ and $s \in \mathbb{Q}$ satisfies $s < r$, then $s \in \alpha$;*

(c) *if $r \in \alpha$, then there exists $s \in \mathbb{Q}$ with $s > r$ and $s \in \alpha$.*

Let R denote the collection of all cuts.

Definition 3.10.1.2. *For $\alpha, \beta \in R$, we define $\alpha + \beta = \{r + s \mid r \in \alpha \text{ and } s \in \beta\}$. Let $\mathbf{0} = \{r \in \mathbb{Q} \mid r < 0\}$.*

Exercise 3.10.1.3. *If α and β are cuts, show that $\alpha + \beta$ is a cut, and also show that $\mathbf{0}$ is a cut.*

Exercise 3.10.1.4. *Show that with this addition $(R, +)$ is an abelian group with $\mathbf{0}$ as the identity element.*

We now define an order on R.

Definition 3.10.1.5. *If $\alpha, \beta \in R$, we say that $\alpha < \beta$ if α is a proper subset of β.*

Exercise 3.10.1.6. *Show that the relation $<$ satisfies the following properties:*

(1) *if $\alpha, \beta \in R$, then one and only one of the following holds: $\alpha < \beta$, $\alpha = \beta$, or $\beta < \alpha$ (Trichotomy);*
(2) *if $\alpha, \beta, \gamma \in R$ with $\alpha < \beta$ and $\beta < \gamma$, then $\alpha < \gamma$ (Transitivity);*
(3) *if $\alpha, \beta, \gamma \in R$ with $\alpha < \beta$, then $\alpha + \gamma < \beta + \gamma$ (Additivity) .*

It is now possible to define the notions of bounded above, bounded below, bounded, upper bound, least upper bound, lower bound, and greatest lower bound in R just as we did earlier in this chapter (see Definitions 3.1.1 and 3.1.4).

Exercise 3.10.1.7. *Show that the least upper bound property holds in R, that is, if A is a non-empty subset of R which is bounded above, then A has a least upper bound in R.*

Next, we must define multiplication in R.

Definition 3.10.1.8. *If $\alpha, \beta \in R$ with $\alpha, \beta > 0$, then*

$$\alpha\beta = \{p \in \mathbb{Q} \mid \text{there are positive elements } r \in \alpha \text{ and } s \in \beta \text{ so that } p \leq rs\}.$$

The next step is multiplication by $\mathbf{0}$ which is exactly as it should be, namely for any $\alpha \in R$, we define $\alpha\mathbf{0} = \mathbf{0}$.

Exercise 3.10.1.9. *If $\alpha < 0$ or $\beta < 0$, or both, replace any negative element by its additive inverse and use the multiplication of positive elements to define multiplication accordingly. For example, if $\alpha < 0$ and $\beta > 0$, $\alpha\beta = -[(-\alpha)(\beta)]$. Show that R with addition, multiplication, and order as defined above is an ordered field.*

Exercise 3.10.1.10. *Put it all together and show that R is an Archimedean ordered field in which the least upper bound property holds (see Exercise 3.1.9).*

10.2. Infinite Series. An important topic in analysis is the study of infinite series. This theory will be used in the remaining chapters of this book.

We assume that the reader has had at least an elementary introduction to infinite series and their convergence properties. In fact, the theory of infinite series actually reduces to the convergence of sequences, which we have covered thoroughly in this chapter. An infinite series is expressed as a sum of an infinite number of elements from some place or other. These elements could be numbers, functions or what have you. We begin with one-sided series of numbers.

An infinite series is an expression of the form $\sum_{n=1}^{\infty} a_n$, where the elements a_n come from a number system in which addition makes sense. So that we don't wander around aimlessly, let's fix our number system to be the complex numbers, that is $a_n \in \mathbb{C}$, with the possibility of restricting to the real numbers or even the rational numbers. In the definition we have chosen to use the natural numbers as the index set, but in considering infinite series we could start the summation with any integer and write $\sum_{n=n_0}^{\infty} a_n$. If these expressions are going to have any meaning at all, we must look at the partial sums.

Definition 3.10.2.1. *If $\sum_{n=1}^{\infty} a_n$ is an infinite series of complex numbers, the* N-th partial sum *of the series is $S_N = \sum_{n=1}^{N} a_n$.*

Examples 3.10.2.2.

(i) *Let $a_n = 1$ for all n. Then $S_N = N$.*

(ii) *Let $a_n = 1/n$. Then $S_N = 1 + 1/2 + \cdots + 1/N$.*

(iii) *Let $a_n = 1/2^n$. Then $S_N = 1 - 1/2^N$.*

(iv) *Let $a_n = (-1)^{n+1}$. In this case, $S_N = 1$ if N is odd and 0 if N is even.*

(v) *Let $a_n = (-i)^{n+1}/(n^2+1)$. Then $S_N = -1/2 + i/5 + \cdots + (-i)^{N+1}/(N^2+1)$.*

(vi) *Fix θ, with $0 < \theta < 2\pi$, and let $a_n = e^{in\theta}/n$. Then $S_N = \sum_{n=1}^{N} e^{in\theta}/n$, which is the best we can do without more information about θ.*

(vii) *Let $a_n = \sin n\pi/n^2$. In this case, $S_N = \sum_{n=1}^{N} sin(n\pi)/n^2$.*

Notice that it is often difficult to compute a closed form for the partial sums of a series.

Definition 3.10.2.3. *Let $\sum_{n=1}^{\infty} a_n$ be an infinite series of complex numbers. If $N \in \mathbb{N}$, we let $S_N = \sum_{n=1}^{N} a_n$. The sequence $(S_N)_{N\in\mathbb{N}}$ is called* the sequence of partial sums. *We say that the series $\sum_{n=1}^{\infty} a_n$* converges *if the sequence of partial sums $(S_N)_{N\in\mathbb{N}}$ converges, say to L, in which case we write $\sum_{n=1}^{\infty} a_n = L$. If the sequence $(S_N)_{N\in\mathbb{N}}$ does not converge we say that $\sum_{n=1}^{\infty} a_n$* diverges.

Of course, since we are working in $\mathbb{C}$, the series converges if and only if the sequence $(S_N)_{N\in\mathbb{N}}$ is a Cauchy sequence. That is, given $\varepsilon > 0$, there is an $N_\varepsilon \in \mathbb{N}$ so that if $n, m > N_\varepsilon$ (assuming $n > m$), then $|\sum_{k=m+1}^{n} a_n| < \varepsilon$.

Exercise 3.10.2.4. *Determine which of the series in Example* 3.10.2.2 *converge.*

Exercise 3.10.2.5. *Suppose that a series* $\sum_{n=1}^{\infty} a_n$ *converges. Show that* $\lim_{n\to\infty} a_n = 0$.

We are faced with two problems. The first is, "How do we tell if a series converges?" The second is, "If a series does converge, how do we find the explicit sum?" There is extensive literature about these two questions, but the fact is that the second question presents many more difficulties than the first.

The most helpful series in all of this discussion is a geometric series.

Definition 3.10.2.6. *Let* z *be a complex number. The geometric series defined by* z *is* $\sum_{n=0}^{\infty} z^n$.

Exercise 3.10.2.7.

(*i*) *If* $N \in \mathbb{N}$ *and* $z \neq 1$, *show that* $S_N = \sum_{n=0}^{N} z^n = \frac{1-z^{N+1}}{1-z}$.

(*ii*) *If* $|z| < 1$, *show that* $\lim_{n\to\infty} z^n = 0$.

(*iii*) *If* $|z| > 1$, *show that* $\lim_{n\to\infty} z^n$ *does not exist.*

Theorem 3.10.2.8. *Consider the geometric series defined by a complex number* z. *If* $|z| < 1$, *then the series converges to* $\frac{1}{1-z}$. *If* $|z| > 1$, *then the series diverges.*

Proof. This follows from the Exercise above. 

Exercise 3.10.2.9. *What can you say if* $|z| = 1$*?*

We saw earlier that the terms of a convergent series must go to zero. However, the property that $\lim_{n\to\infty} a_n = 0$ does not ensure that the series $\sum_{n=1}^{\infty} a_n$ converges. The most useful example is where $a_n = 1/n$ (see Example 3.10.2.2(ii)). In this case, it is easy to check that $S_{2^n} > n$ for $n \in \mathbb{N}$, and hence the series $\sum_{n=1}^{\infty} 1/n$ diverges.

Exercise 3.10.2.10. *The series* $\sum_{n=1}^{\infty} 1/n$ *is often called the* harmonic series. *We have just proved that this series diverges. Show that, by suitably eliminating an infinite number of terms, the remaining subseries can be made to converge to any positive real number.*

Exercise 3.10.2.11.

(*i*) *If* $p \in \mathbb{R}$ *and* $p > 1$, *show that* $\sum_{n=1}^{\infty} 1/n^p$ *converges.*

(*ii*) *If* $p \in \mathbb{R}$ *and* $p < 1$, *show that* $\sum_{n=1}^{\infty} 1/n^p$ *diverges.*

Definition 3.10.2.12. *A series* $\sum_{n=1}^{\infty} a_n$ *of complex numbers* converges absolutely *if the series* $\sum_{n=1}^{\infty} |a_n|$ *converges.*

Proposition 3.10.2.13. *If $\sum_{n=1}^{\infty} a_n$ converges absolutely, then $\sum_{n=1}^{\infty} a_n$ converges.*

Proof. This follows from the fact that $|\sum_{k=m+1}^{n} a_k| \leq \sum_{k=m+1}^{n} |a_k|$.

The converse to Proposition 3.10.2.13 is false, as is shown by the example $\sum_{n=1}^{\infty}(-1)^{n+1}/n$. This series converges since $|\sum_{k=m+1}^{n}(-1)^{k+1}/k| < 1/m$. However, as we have seen above the series does not converge absolutely.

There are various tests to determine if a series converges. These include the Comparison Test, the Ratio Test, and the Root Test.

The Comparison Test is often very useful, but its use depends on knowing ahead of time a series that converges.

Theorem 3.10.2.14 (Comparison Test). *Suppose $a_n > 0$ for $n \in \mathbb{N}$ and $\sum_{n=1}^{\infty} a_n$ converges. If $b_n \in \mathbb{C}$ satisfies $|b_n| \leq a_n$ for all n, then the series $\sum_{n=1}^{\infty} b_n$ converges absolutely and hence converges.*

Exercise 3.10.2.15.

(i) *Prove the Comparison Test.*

(ii) *If the series $\sum_{n=1}^{\infty} a_n$ converges to s and c is any constant, show that the series $\sum_{n=1}^{\infty} ca_n$ converges to cs.*

(iii) *Suppose that $\sum_{n=1}^{\infty} a_n$ and $\sum_{n=1}^{\infty} b_n$ are infinite series. Suppose that $a_n > 0$ and $b_n > 0$ for $n \in \mathbb{N}$ and $\lim_{n\to\infty} a_n/b_n = c > 0$. Show that $\sum_{n=1}^{\infty} a_n$ converges if and only if $\sum_{n=1}^{\infty} b_n$ converges.*

The most useful series for comparison is the geometric series defined by a real number r, with $0 < r < 1$.

Theorem 3.10.2.16 (Ratio Test). *Suppose that $\sum_{n=1}^{\infty} a_n$ is a series of nonzero complex numbers. If $r = \lim_{n\to\infty} |a_{n+1}/a_n|$ exists, then the series converges absolutely if $r < 1$, and the series diverges if $r > 1$.*

Proof. Suppose $\lim_{n\to\infty} |a_{n+1}/a_n| = r < 1$. If ρ satisfies $r < \rho < 1$, then there exists $N \in \mathbb{N}$ such that $|a_{n+1}|/|a_n| < \rho$ for all $n \geq N$. Consequently, $|a_n| \leq |a_N|\rho^{n-N}$ for all $n \geq N$. The result follows from the Comparison Test. The result is obvious for $r > 1$.

Exercise 3.10.2.17. *Give examples to show that if $r = 1$, anything may happen.*

Our final test for convergence is called the Root Test. This can be quite effective when the Comparison Test and Ratio Test fail. We need one simple definition to state the test. Let $(x_n)_{n\in\mathbb{N}}$ be a sequence of non-negative real numbers. We define $\limsup_{n\to\infty} x_n$ to be the least upper bound of the set of limits of convergent subsequences of $(x_n)_{n\in\mathbb{N}}$. If $(x_n)_{n\in\mathbb{N}}$ is not bounded above, we define $\limsup_{n\to\infty} x_n$ to be $+\infty$.

Exercise 3.10.2.18. *Let $(x_n)_{n\in\mathbb{N}}$ be a bounded sequence of non-negative real numbers and let $x_0 = \limsup_{n\to\infty} x_n$. For any $\varepsilon > 0$, show that there are only finitely many terms of the sequence greater than $x_0 + \varepsilon$, whereas there are infinitely many terms less than $x_0 + \varepsilon$.*

Theorem 3.10.2.19 (Root Test). *Suppose that $\sum_{n=1}^{\infty} a_n$ is a series of complex numbers. Let $r = \limsup_{n\to\infty} |a_n|^{1/n}$. If $r < 1$, then the series converges absolutely. If $r > 1$, then the series diverges.*

Proof. Suppose that $\limsup_{n\to\infty} |a_n|^{1/n} = r < 1$. Pick ρ so that $r < \rho < 1$. Then, there exists $N \in \mathbb{N}$ such that $|a_n| \leq \rho^n$ for all $n \geq N$. The convergence of the series now follows from the comparison test. The second half of the theorem is left as an exercise.

Exercise 3.10.2.20. *Give examples to show that if $r = 1$, anything may happen.*

Exercise 3.10.2.21. *Suppose that the Ratio Test applies to $\sum_{n=1}^{\infty} a_n$; that is, that $\lim_{n\to\infty} |a_{n+1}|/|a_n|$ exists. Write r for the limit. Show that $\limsup_{n\to\infty} |a_n|^{1/n} = r$.*

Definition 3.10.2.22. *Let z_0 be a fixed complex number. A* complex power series *around z_0 is a series of the form $\sum_{n=0}^{\infty} a_n(z - z_0)^n$, where the coefficients $a_n \in \mathbb{C}$. This series defines a function of the complex variable z on the set where it converges.*

Exercise 3.10.2.23. *Show that if a complex power series around z_0 converges absolutely for a complex number z then it also converges for a any complex number w such that $|w - z_0| \leq |z - z_0|$, that is, the series converges on the disk $\{w \in \mathbb{C} \mid |w - z_0| \leq |z - z_0|\}$.*

Consider a complex power series around z_0. Put $r = \sup\{|w - z_0| |$ the power series converges absolutely at $w\}$. Note that r could be 0 or ∞. From the exercise, it follows that the power series converges absolutely on $B_r(z_0)$. It is possible that the series converges for some points z such that $|z - z_0| = r$, but to determine this requires additional analysis.

To determine the radius of convergence for a complex power series we use the convergence tests developed above, in particular the Root Test.

Theorem 3.10.2.24. *Suppose that $\limsup_{n\to\infty} |a_n|^{1/n} = r$. Then the power series $\sum_{n=0}^{\infty} a_n(z-z_0)^n$ has a radius of convergence $1/r$. If the number $r = 0$, then we say that the radius of convergence is infinity. If $r = \infty$, then we say that the radius of convergence is 0.*

Examples 3.10.2.25.

(i) *Consider the series* $\sum_{n=0}^{\infty} n(z-z_0)^n$. *Then* $\lim_{n\to\infty} n^{1/n} = 1$, *so the radius of convergence is* 1*—that is, the power series converges absolutely for* z *with* $|z-z_0| < 1$.

(ii) *Consider the series* $\sum_{n=1}^{\infty} n^n(z-z_0)^n$. *Then* $\lim_{n\to\infty}(n^n)^{1/n} = \infty$, *so the radius of convergence is* 0 *and the series converges only for* $z = z_0$.

Exercise 3.10.2.26. *Determine the radii of convergence of the following power series:*

(i)
$$\sum_{n=0}^{\infty} \frac{z^n}{n!};$$

(ii)
$$\sum_{n=2}^{\infty} \frac{z^n}{ln(n)};$$

(iii)
$$\sum_{n=1}^{\infty} \frac{n^n}{n!} z^n.$$

10.3. Decimal Expansions of Real Numbers.

In Chapter 1, we used the decimal representation of the real numbers to show that the real numbers between 0 and 1 form an uncountable set. In this project, we actually prove that every real number between 0 and 1 has a unique decimal expansion that does not terminate in all 9's. In addition, we discuss the fact that rational numbers fall into three classes: those with a terminating decimal expansion; those that can be written with a denominator that is relatively prime to 10; and the rest.

Since we know every real number lies between two consecutive integers (see Theorem 3.2.5), we start with a real number x so that $0 < x < 1$. Let $S = \{0,1,2,3,4,5,6,7,8,9\}$. Assume first that x is irrational. The construction proceeds as follows. Let a_1 be the largest element of S which is less then $10x$. Then $0 < x - a_1/10 < 1/10$. Let a_2 be the largest integer in S less then $100x - 10a_1$. Proceeding as before we get $0 < x - a_1/10 - a_2/10^2 < 1/10^2$. Continuing this process, we obtain a monotonic increasing sequence $S_n = a_1/10 + a_2/10^2 + \ldots + a_n/10^n$, where each $a_j \in S$ and $0 < x - S_n < 1/10^n$. So we conclude that S_n converges to x and we get $x = a_1/10 + a_2/10^2 + \cdots + a_n/10^n + \cdots = \sum_{n=1}^{\infty} a_n/10^n$. We call $0.a_1a_2\ldots$ the *decimal expansion* of x.

Exercise 3.10.3.1. *Let x be an irrational number between 0 and 1. Show that the decimal expansion of x is unique.*

We now turn to rational numbers between 0 and 1. We can apply the above procedure to rational numbers but with the possibility of equality in any of the inequalities.

We say that x has a *terminating decimal expansion* if there exists N so that $a_n = 0$ for all $n > N$ and $a_N \neq 0$. In this case, we can write $x = a_1/10 + a_2/10^2 + \cdots + a_N/10^N$.

Exercise 3.10.3.2.

(i) *Show that if r is a rational number in $(0, 1)$, then the decimal expansion of r terminates if and only if the denominator of r has the form $2^a 5^b$ where a, b are non-negative integers.*

(ii) *With r as above show that the last nonzero digit of r is in the m-th place after the decimal point where $m = max(a, b)$.*

Note that rational numbers with terminating decimal expansions are the only real numbers between 0 and 1 for which equality can occur in the initial procedure.

Next consider a rational number $r = p/q$ in $(0, 1)$ for which q is relatively prime to 10. From Exercise 1.10.1.24, q divides $10^{\phi(q)} - 1$. Let n be the smallest natural number so that q divides $10^n - 1$. Then $(p/q)(10^n - 1)$ is an integer, which we denote by m. That is,

$$m = \frac{p}{q}(10^n - 1) \text{ or } \frac{p}{q} = \frac{m}{10^n - 1}.$$

Using results about geometric series from Project 3.2, we can now write

$$\begin{aligned} \frac{p}{q} = \frac{m}{10^n - 1} = \frac{m}{10^n}(1 - 10^{-n})^{-1} &= \frac{m}{10^n}(1 + 10^{-n} + 10^{-2n} + \cdots) \\ &= m/10^n + m/10^{2n} + \cdots . \end{aligned}$$

As $0 < p/q < 1$ we have $m < 10^n$. Thus the right hand side of the equation above gives us a periodic decimal expansion of p/q whose period has length at most n.

Exercise. *Prove that the period is exactly n.*

Exercise 3.10.3.3. *Let p/q be a rational number between 0 and 1. If q and 10 are relatively prime, show that p/q has a unique periodic decimal expansion with the length of the period equal to the order of 10 mod q, that is the smallest power of 10 that is congruent to 1 mod q.*

We now present the remaining case as an exercise.

Exercise 3.10.3.4. *Let p/q be a rational number in $(0,1)$ with $q = 2^a 5^b r$ where r is relatively prime to 10. Let $k = max(a,b)$ and let n be the smallest positive integer such that r divides $10^n - 1$. Show that after k digits the decimal expansion of p/q is periodic of length n.*

We ask finally whether decimal expansions are unique. The answer is contained in the following exercise.

Exercise 3.10.3.5.

(i) *Consider the decimal $0.9999\ldots = \sum_{n=1}^{\infty} 9/10^n$. Show that this geometric series converges to 1. That is, $0.99999\ldots = 1$.*

(ii) *Show that every number that has a decimal expansion that terminates in all nines can be written as a terminating decimal.*

(iii) *Show that this is the only non-uniqueness that can occur.*

Chapter 4

Metric and Euclidean Spaces

...la notion d'espace métrique fut introduite en 1906 par M. Fréchet, et développée quelques années plus tard par F. Hausdorff dans sa Mengenlehre. Elle acquit une grande importance aprés 1920, d'une part à la suite des travaux fondamentaux de S. Banach et de son école sur les espaces normés et leurs applications à l'Analyse fonctionnelle, de l'autre en raison de l'intérêt que présente la notion de valeur absolue en Arithmétique et en Géométrie algébrique (où notamment la complétion par rapport à une valeur absolue se montre très féconde).

– *N. Bourbaki,*
Topologie Générale, Book 3

1. Introduction

We have already encountered the notion of distance in n-dimensional Euclidean space. All that this involves is the repeated use of the Pythagorean theorem. If $x = (x_1, \ldots, x_n)$ and $y = (y_1, \ldots, y_n)$ are elements in $\mathbb{R}^n$, then in Chapter 2 we defined

$$d(x,y) = ((x_1 - y_1)^2 + \cdots + (x_n - y_n)^2)^{1/2}.$$

Thus, if $\|x\| = (\sum_{j=1}^n x_j^2)^{1/2}$, then $d(x,y) = \|x - y\|$ (see Definition 2.5.8).

In this chapter, we introduce the notion of a metric on a set. The word "metric" is simply a synonym for distance. As we shall see below, a metric on a set comes with a list of names attached to different subsets of the ambient space such as open set, closed set, etc. The open sets have some particular properties – so do the closed sets. These properties of subsets of metric spaces are special cases of similar properties for subsets of "topological spaces". The basic theory of topological spaces is developed in a project at the end of this chapter (Project 4.6.1).

Remark 4.1.1. *Note that the metric d on $\mathbb{R}^n$ given above is called the* usual metric on $\mathbb{R}^n$.

It should be mentioned that this is not the only way to define the distance between two points in $\mathbb{R}^n$. For example, in $\mathbb{R}^2$, we could define $d_1(x, y) = |x_1 - y_1| + |x_2 - y_2|$. This is sometimes called the taxicab metric. This is what happens when you are driving on city streets and are not allowed to drive across people's lawns. The distance is illustrated below.

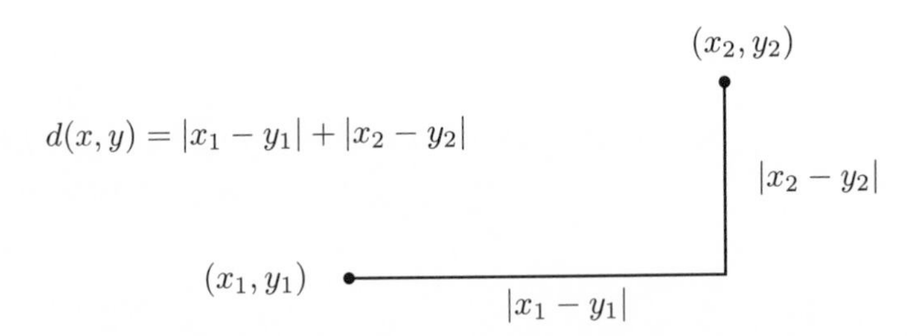

2. Definition and Basic Properties of Metric Spaces

Definition 4.2.1. *A* metric space *is a pair (X, d) where X is a set and $d : X \times X \to \mathbb{R}$ is a map satisfying the following properties.*

(a) *For $x_1, x_2 \in X$, $d(x_1, x_2) \geq 0$, and $d(x_1, x_2) = 0$ if and only if $x_1 = x_2$, (positive definite).*

(b) *For any $x_1, x_2 \in X$, we have $d(x_1, x_2) = d(x_2, x_1)$, (symmetric).*

(c) *For any $x_1, x_2, x_3 \in X$, we have*

$$d(x_1, x_2) \leq d(x_1, x_3) + d(x_3, x_2),$$

(triangle inequality).

Exercise 4.2.2.

(i) *Draw a triangle and figure out why the triangle inequality is so named.*

(ii) *Replace the triangle inequality by the inequality*

$$d(x_1, x_2) \leq d(x_1, x_3) + d(x_2, x_3)$$

for any $x_1, x_2, x_3 \in X$. Show that symmetry follows from this version of the triangle inequality and property 4.2.1(a).

Example 4.2.3. *Observe that we proved in Exercise* 2.5.9 *that the usual metric on $\mathbb{R}^n$ satisfies this definition.*

Exercise 4.2.4. *On $\mathbb{C}^n = \{z = (z_1, z_2, \ldots, z_n) \mid z_j \in \mathbb{C}\}$, we define*

$$\|z\| = \left(\sum_{j=1}^{n} |z_j|^2\right)^{1/2}$$

and, for $z, w \in \mathbb{C}^n$, we define $d(z, w) = \|z - w\|$. Show that d is a metric on $\mathbb{C}^n$.

Exercise 4.2.5. *Let X be any nonempty set and, for $x_1, x_2 \in X$, define*

$$d(x_1, x_2) = \begin{cases} 0 & \text{if } x_1 = x_2 \\ 1, & \text{if } x_1 \neq x_2. \end{cases}$$

Show that d is a metric on X. This is called the discrete metric. *It is designed to disabuse people of the notion that every metric looks like the usual metric on $\mathbb{R}^n$. The discrete metric is very handy for producing counterexamples.*

Example 4.2.6. *Expanding on Remark* 4.1.1, *we introduce an important collection of metrics on $\mathbb{R}^n$.*

Let p be a real number such that $p \geq 1$. For $x = (x_1, x_2, \ldots, x_n) \in \mathbb{R}^n$, we define

$$\|x\|_p = \left(\sum_{j=1}^{n} |x_j|^p\right)^{1/p}.$$

PAY ATTENTION! This is a key example for future developments.

As usual, if $x = (x_1, x_2, \ldots, x_n) \in \mathbb{R}^n$ and $y = (y_1, y_2, \ldots, y_n) \in \mathbb{R}^n$, we define $d_p(x, y) = \|x - y\|_p$. To show that d_p is a metric on $\mathbb{R}^n$, we need the following inequality.

Theorem 4.2.7. *(Hölder's Inequality) Suppose p, q are real numbers greater than* 1 *such that $1/p + 1/q = 1$. Suppose $x = (x_1, x_2, \ldots, x_n) \in \mathbb{R}^n$ and $y = (y_1, y_2, \ldots, y_n) \in \mathbb{R}^n$. Then*

$$\sum_{k=1}^{n} |x_k y_k| \leq \left(\sum_{k=1}^{n} |x_k|^p\right)^{1/p} \left(\sum_{k=1}^{n} |y_k|^q\right)^{1/q}.$$

Proof. The proof is based on the following inequality. Suppose a and b are positive real numbers and p, q are as in the hypothesis of the theorem. Then $ab \le \frac{a^p}{p} + \frac{b^q}{q}$. This is proved with elementary calculus. Consider the function $y = x^{p-1}$, for $x \ge 0$. Then the inverse function is $x = y^{q-1}$, for $y \ge 0$. We have $\int_0^a x^{p-1}dx + \int_0^b y^{q-1}dy = \frac{a^p}{p} + \frac{b^q}{q}$. A look at the graph of the functions reveals immediately that this sum is greater than or equal to ab where equality holds if and only if $a = b$.

Using this inequality, we get

$$\sum_{k=1}^{n} \frac{|x_k|}{||x||_p}\frac{|y_k|}{||y||_q} \le \sum_{k=1}^{n} \frac{|x_k|^p}{p||x||_p^p} + \sum_{k=1}^{n} \frac{|y_k|^q}{q||y||_q^q} = 1/p + 1/q = 1.$$

☹

Exercise 4.2.8. *Now prove that d_p is a metric on $\mathbb{R}^n$.* Hint: *The triangle inequality is the only hard part. The proof of the triangle inequality depends on Hölder's Inequality. To begin, observe that*

$$||x+y||_p^p = \sum_i |x_i + y_i|^p \le \sum_i |x_i + y_i|^{p-1}|x_i| + \sum_i |x_i + y_i|^{p-1}|y_i|.$$

Now apply Hölder.

Exercise 4.2.9. *Note that Hölder's inequality works only for $p, q > 1$. Prove the triangle inequality for the d_1 metric.*

We also define a metric for $p = \infty$. If $x = (x_1, x_2, \dots, x_n)$, we set $||x||_\infty = \max_{1\le j\le n} |x_j|$, and define $d_\infty(x, y) = \max_{1\le j\le n} |x_j - y_j| = ||x - y||_\infty$. It is easy to prove that d_∞ defines a metric on $\mathbb{R}^n$. The space $(\mathbb{R}^n, d_p)$ or alternatively $(\mathbb{R}^n, ||\cdot||_p)$, $1 \le p \le \infty$, is denoted by $\ell_n^p(\mathbb{R})$. Note that, in our present notation, the norm symbol $||\cdot||$ on $\mathbb{R}^n$ should be relabeled $||\cdot||_2$.

Exercise 4.2.10. *Show that everything we have just done for $\mathbb{R}^n$ can also be done for $\mathbb{C}^n$. This yields a collection of spaces $\ell_n^p(\mathbb{C})$.*

There is a lengthy menu attached to the study of metric spaces. For example, we need to deal with such concepts as open sets, closed sets, compact sets, accumulation points, isolated points, boundary points, interior, closure, and other things. To understand metric spaces fully, the reader must deal not only with these ideas, but with the relationships among them. Most of these ideas have a setting in the context of general topological spaces.

3. Topology of Metric Spaces

A fundamental notion in the study of metric spaces is that of an open ball.

Definition 4.3.1. *Suppose that (X, d) is a metric space and $x_0 \in X$. If $r \in \mathbb{R}$, with $r > 0$, the* open ball of radius r around x_0 *is the subset of X defined by $B_r(x_0) = \{x \in X \mid d(x, x_0) < r\}$. The* closed ball of radius r around x_0 *is the subset of X defined by $\overline{B}_r(x_0) = \{x \in X \mid d(x, x_0) \leq r\}$.*

Example 4.3.2. *In $\mathbb{R}^2$, with the usual metric, a ball of radius $3/2$ around the point $(3, 4)$ looks like this:*

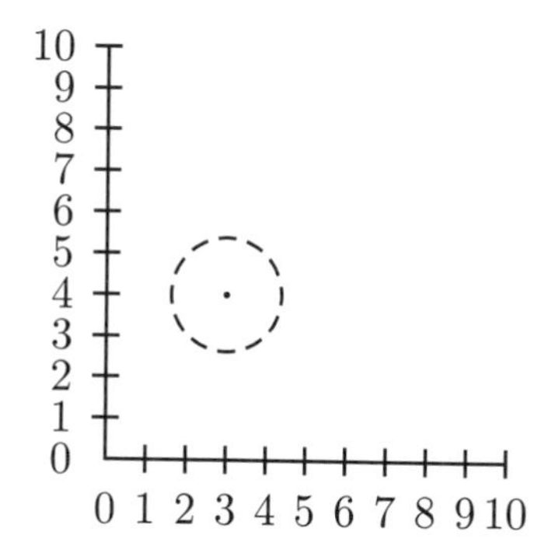

Example 4.3.3. *In $\mathbb{R}^2$, a ball of radius $3/2$ around the point $(3, 4)$ in the d_1 metric looks like this:*

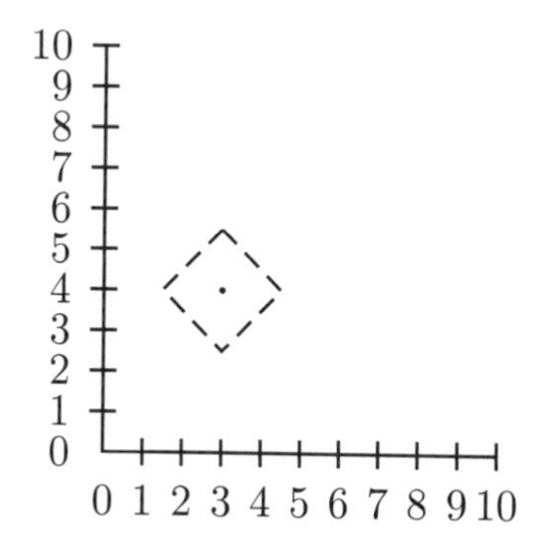

Definition 4.3.4. *Suppose that V is a vector space with a metric d. The* unit ball in V *is the ball of radius 1 with center at $\mathbf{0}$, that is $B_1(\mathbf{0})$. This definition is usually only interesting when the metric arises from a "norm" (as in Exercise 4.2.4 and Example 4.2.6).*

We want to analyze the nature of the *unit ball* in $\ell_n^p(\mathbb{R})$, that is, the set of all points $x \in \mathbb{R}^n$ such that $\|x\|_p < 1$. For the moment, let's take $n = 2$

and consider the cases of $\ell_2^1(\mathbb{R})$, $\ell_2^2(\mathbb{R})$, and $\ell_2^\infty(\mathbb{R})$. The pictures of the unit balls in these spaces are shown below. This leads to an interesting diagram.

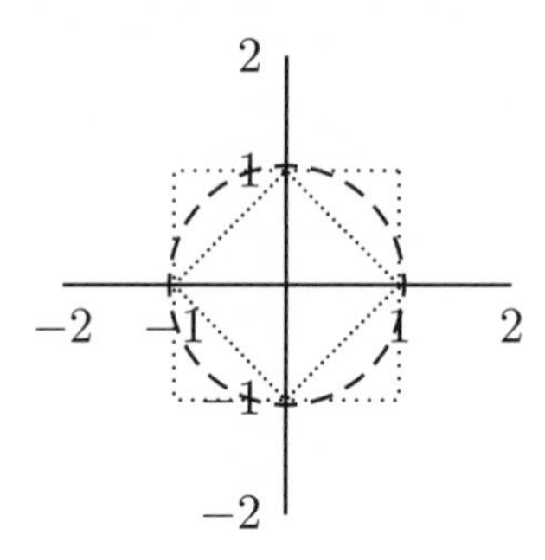

Exercise 4.3.5. *If $1 \leq p < q$, show that the unit ball in $\ell_n^p(\mathbb{R})$ is contained in the unit ball in $\ell_n^q(\mathbb{R})$.*

Exercise 4.3.6. *Consider the set of all points in $\mathbb{R}^2$ that lie outside the unit ball in $\ell_2^1(\mathbb{R})$ and inside the unit ball in $\ell_2^\infty(\mathbb{R})$. Does every point in this region lie on the boundary (see Definition 4.3.18 below) of the unit ball in $\ell_2^p(\mathbb{R})$ for some p between 1 and ∞? Do the same problem for $\ell_n^p(\mathbb{R})$.*

Next, we look at open sets.

Definition 4.3.7. *Let (X, d) be a metric space and suppose that $A \subseteq X$. The set A is an* open set *in X if, for each $a \in A$, there is an $r > 0$ such that $B_r(a) \subseteq A$.*

Notice that the radius r depends on the point a. Also, observe that the empty set $\varnothing$ and the whole space X are both open sets.

Exercise 4.3.8. *Prove that, for any $x_0 \in X$ and any $r > 0$, the "open ball" $B_r(x_0)$ is open. So now we can legitimately call an "open" ball an open set.*

Exercise 4.3.9. *Prove that the following are open sets:*

(*i*) *the "first quadrant," $\{(x, y) \in \mathbb{R}^2 \mid x > 0$ and $y > 0\}$, in the usual metric;*

(*ii*) *any subset of a discrete metric space.*

Open sets behave nicely under certain set-theoretic operations.

Theorem 4.3.10.

(*i*) *If $\{A_j\}_{j\in J}$ is a family of open sets in a metric space (X, d), then*

$$\bigcup_{j\in J} A_j$$

is an open set in X;

(*ii*) *if* $A_1, A_2, \ldots, A_n$ *are open sets in a metric space* (X, d), *then*

$$\bigcap_{j=1}^{n} A_j$$

is an open set in X.

Proof.

(*i*) Suppose that $x \in \bigcup_{j\in J} A_j$. Then $x \in A_k$ for some $k \in J$. Since A_k is open, there is a real number $r > 0$ such that $B_r(x) \subseteq A_k$. But then, $B_r(x) \subseteq \bigcup_{j\in J} A_j$.

(*ii*) Suppose $x \in \bigcap_{j=1}^{n} A_j$. Then $x \in A_j$ for each $j = 1, 2, \ldots, n$. Since A_j is open, for each j, there exists a radius r_j such that $B_{r_j}(x) \subseteq A_j$. Let $r = \min_{1\leq j\leq n}\{r_j\}$. Then $r > 0$ and $B_r(x) \subseteq \bigcap_{j=1}^{n} A_j$.

We can now say that open sets are closed under arbitrary union and finite intersection.

Exercise 4.3.11.

(*i*) *There can be problems with infinite intersections. For example, let* $A_n = B_{1/n}((0, 0))$ *in* $\mathbb{R}^2$ *with the usual metric. Show that*

$$\bigcap_{n=1}^{\infty} A_n$$

is not open.

(*ii*) *Find an infinite collection of distinct open sets in* $\mathbb{R}^2$ *with the usual metric whose intersection is a nonempty open set.*

Thus infinite intersections of open sets may or may not be open.

If there are open sets in a metric space, can closed sets be far behind?

Definition 4.3.12. *Let* (X, d) *be a metric space and suppose that* $A \subseteq X$. *We say that* A *is a* closed set *in* X *if* ${}^cA$ *is open in* X. *(Recall that* ${}^cA = X \setminus A$ *is the complement of* A *in* X.*)*

Exercise 4.3.13. *Show that the following are closed sets:*

(*i*) *the* x*-axis in* $\mathbb{R}^2$ *with the usual metric;*

(*ii*) *the whole space* X *in any metric space;*

(*iii*) *the empty set in any metric space;*

(*iv*) *a single point in any metric space;*

(*v*) *any subset of a discrete metric space.*

Exercise 4.3.14. *Show that $\mathbb{Q}$ as a subset of $\mathbb{R}$ with the usual metric is neither open nor closed in $\mathbb{R}$. Of course, if the metric space is simply $\mathbb{Q}$ with the usual metric, then $\mathbb{Q}$ is both open and closed in $\mathbb{Q}$.*

Here is a basic theorem about closed sets.

Theorem 4.3.15.

(i) *Suppose that (X, d) is a metric space and that $\{A_j\}_{j \in J}$ is a collection of closed sets in X. Then*

$$\bigcap_{j \in J} A_j$$

is a closed set in X;

(ii) *if $A_1, A_2, \ldots, A_n$ are closed sets in X, then*

$$\bigcup_{j=1}^{n} A_j$$

is a closed set in X.

Proof. Use Theorem 4.3.10 and DeMorgan's laws.

So, a set is closed iff its complement is open, and a set is open iff its complement is closed. However, most of time, most sets in a metric space are neither open or closed. There is a different way to characterize closed sets. First, we need the notion of an accumulation point. From here on, we shall simply refer to a metric space X and suppress the notation d for the metric.

Definition 4.3.16. *Suppose that A is a subset of a metric space X. A point $x_0 \in X$ is an* accumulation point *of A if, for every $r > 0$, we have $(B_r(x_0) \setminus \{x_0\}) \cap A \neq \varnothing$.*

Thus, if x_0 is an accumulation point of A, there are points of A (other than x_0) that are arbitrarily close to x_0. Note that x_0 may or may not be an element of A. For example, for $\mathbb{R}$ with the usual metric, 1 and 0 are accumulation points of the open interval $(0, 1)$ as well as all of the points in the interval itself.

Definition 4.3.17. *Suppose that A is a subset of a metric space X. A point $x_0 \in A$ is an* isolated point *of A if there is an $r > 0$ such that $B_r(x_0) \cap A = \{x_0\}$.*

Definition 4.3.18. *Suppose that A is a subset of a metric space X. A point $x_0 \in X$ is a* boundary point *of A if, for every $r > 0$, $B_r(x_0) \cap A \neq \varnothing$ and $B_r(x_0) \cap {}^cA \neq \varnothing$. The* boundary *of A is the set of boundary points of A, and is denoted by ∂A.*

We need some examples.

Examples 4.3.19. (*i*) *Let* $A = \{(x, y, z) \in \mathbb{R}^3 \mid x^2 + y^2 + z^2 < 1\}$. *We take the usual metric on* $\mathbb{R}^3$. *The set of accumulation points of* A *is* $B^3 = \{(x, y, z) \mid x^2 + y^2 + z^2 \leq 1\}$ *and is called* the closed unit ball *in* $\mathbb{R}^3$ *with respect to the usual metric. The set* A *has no isolated points, and* $\partial A = S^2 = \{(x, y, z) \mid x^2 + y^2 + z^2 = 1\}$. *The set* S^2 *is called the* 2-sphere *in* $\mathbb{R}^3$ *with respect to the usual metric.*

(*ii*) *Let* $A = \{(x_1, x_2, \ldots, x_n) \in \mathbb{R}^n \mid x_1^2 + x_2^2 + \ldots + x_n^2 < 1\}$. *We take the usual metric in* $\mathbb{R}^n$. *The set of accumulation points of* A *is* $B^n = \{(x_1, x_2, \ldots, x_n) \mid x_1^2 + x_2^2 + \ldots + x_n^2 \leq 1\}$. *The set* A *is called* the open unit ball *with respect to the usual metric and the set* B^n *is called* the closed unit ball *in* $\mathbb{R}^n$ *with respect to the usual metric. The set* A *has no isolated points and* $\partial A = S^{n-1} = \{(x_1, x_2, \ldots, x_n) \mid x_1^2 + x_2^2 + \ldots + x_n^2 = 1\}$. *The set* S^{n-1} *is called the* $(n-1)$-sphere *in* $\mathbb{R}^n$ *with respect to the usual metric.*

(*iii*) *Let* $A = \mathbb{Q} \subseteq \mathbb{R}$ *with the usual metric. Then every point in* $\mathbb{R}$ *is an accumulation point of* A, *the set* A *has no isolated points, and* $\partial A = \mathbb{R}$.

(*iv*) *If* A *is any subset of a discrete metric space* X, *then* A *has no accumulation points. Every point in* A *is an isolated point, and* $\partial A = \varnothing$.

(*v*) *Let* $A = \{\frac{1}{n} \mid n \in \mathbb{N}\} \subseteq \mathbb{R}$ *with the usual metric. Then every point of* A *is an isolated point and a boundary point, the point* 0 *is the only accumulation point of the set, and the set* A *is neither open nor closed.*

Now, we have another means of identifying closed sets, that is, accumulation points.

Theorem 4.3.20. *Suppose* A *is a subset of a metric space* X. *Then* A *is closed iff* A *contains all its accumulation points.*

Proof. If A is the empty set, then A has no accumulation points. Suppose that A is a non-empty closed set and that x_0 is an accumulation point of A. If $x_0 \notin A$, then $x_0 \in {}^cA$, which is open. Hence, there is an $r > 0$ such that $B_r(x_0) \subseteq {}^cA$, and this contradicts the definition of accumulation point. Conversely, suppose that A contains all its accumulation points. Take $x_0 \in {}^cA$. Then x_0 is not an accumulation point of A, and hence there exists $r > 0$ such that $B_r(x_0) \cap A = \varnothing$. This means that ${}^cA$ is open, and so A is closed. ☠

In a discrete metric space any subset is both open and closed. This is not generally the case. For example, in the case of $\ell_n^p(\mathbb{R})$ and $\ell_n^p(\mathbb{C})$, most subsets are neither open nor closed.

Exercise 4.3.21. *Find an uncountable number of subsets of $\ell_n^p(\mathbb{R})$ and $\ell_n^p(\mathbb{C})$ that are neither open nor closed.*

If a set A in a metric space X is not closed, and we wish that it were, then we can do something about it.

Definition 4.3.22. *Suppose that A is a nonempty subset of a metric space X. The* closure *of A is the intersection of all the closed sets that contain A.*

The closure of any set A exists since there are always closed sets that contain A, for example X. The closure of A is a closed set since it is the intersection of closed sets. So the closure of A is the "smallest" closed set that contains A. We denote the closure of a set A by $\overline{A}$. Obviously, $A \subseteq \overline{A}$ and $A = \overline{A}$ iff A is closed.

Examples 4.3.23.

(*i*) *Let $A = \{(x, y, z) \in \mathbb{R}^3 \mid x > 0, y > 0, z > 0\}$. If $\mathbb{R}^3$ has the usual metric, then $\overline{A} = \{(x, y, z) \in \mathbb{R}^3 \mid x \geq 0, y \geq 0, z \geq 0\}$.*

(*ii*) *Let $\mathbb{Q}^n = \{(x_1, x_2, \ldots, x_n) \in \mathbb{R}^n \mid x_j \in \mathbb{Q}$ for $1 \leq j \leq n\}$. If $\mathbb{R}^n$ has the usual metric, then $\overline{\mathbb{Q}^n} = \mathbb{R}^n$.*

(*iii*) *Let X be a discrete metric space and let A be any subset of X. Then $\overline{A} = A$.*

It should not come as a surprise that the notions of closure and accumulation point are intimately related.

Exercise 4.3.24. *Suppose that A is a subset of a metric space X. Show that $\overline{A} = A \cup \{$accumulation points of $A\}$.*

Exercise 4.3.25. *Suppose A is a subset of a metric space X. Prove or disprove: $\overline{A} = A \cup \partial A$.*

Exercise 4.3.26. *Let X be a metric space and let $x_0 \in X$. Suppose that $r > 0$. Prove or disprove: $\overline{B_r(x_0)} = \{x \in X \mid d(x, x_0) \leq r\}$.*

Exercise 4.3.27. *For definitions and notations for this exercise see Project 2.6.1.*

(*i*) *Consider the set of 2×2 matrices over $\mathbb{R}$, that is $M_2(\mathbb{R})$. Make this into a metric space by identifying it with $\mathbb{R}^4$ with the usual metric. Show that $GL_2(\mathbb{R})$ is an open subset of $M_2(\mathbb{R})$ and that $\overline{GL_2(\mathbb{R})} = M_2(\mathbb{R})$.*

(*ii*) *Show that $SL_2(\mathbb{R})$ is a closed subset of $GL_2(\mathbb{R})$.*

Exercise 4.3.28. *Let A be a subset of a metric space X and let x_0 be an isolated point of A. Show that x_0 is in the boundary of A if and only if x_0 is an accumulation point of ${}^cA$.*

Exercise 4.3.29. *As usual, let $\mathbb{R}$ be an ordered field with the least upper bound property. Give $\mathbb{R}$ the discrete metric. Show that $\mathbb{R}$ is still an ordered field with the least upper bound property, but that neither the rational nor the irrational numbers are dense in $\mathbb{R}$. Determine what other relevant properties of $\mathbb{R}$ with the usual metric do not hold with the discrete metric.*

Corresponding to the notion of closure is the idea of the *interior* of a set.

Definition 4.3.30. *Let A be a subset of a metric space X. The* interior *of A is the union of all open sets that are contained in A.*

The interior of A is the largest open set contained in A. We denote the interior of A by A°. Obviously $A^\circ \subseteq A$ and $A^\circ = A$ iff A is open.

Examples 4.3.31.

(i) *Let $X = \mathbb{R}^3$ with the usual metric and $A = \{(x, y, z) \mid z \geq 0\}$. Then $A^\circ = \{(x, y, z) \mid z > 0\}$.*

(ii) *Let X be a discrete metric space and let A be any subset of X. Then $A^\circ = A$ and $\overline{A} = A$, so that $A = A^\circ = \overline{A}$.*

Exercise 4.3.32. *Show that, in the usual metric on $\mathbb{R}$, the interior of $\mathbb{Q}$ is empty, that is $\mathbb{Q}^\circ = \varnothing$, but the interior of $\bar{\mathbb{Q}}$ is $\mathbb{R}$, that is, $(\bar{\mathbb{Q}})^\circ = \mathbb{R}$.*

Exercise 4.3.33. *Look at combinations of interior, closure, and boundary and determine how many different possibilities result. For this exercise only, let "I" stand for interior, "B" stand for boundary, and "C" stand for closure. Let X be a metric space and let $A \subseteq X$. How many possible sets can be made from A with these operations? For example, $I(I(A)) = I(A)$ but $C(I(A))$ is not necessarily A. Is it $C(A)$? Explore all possibilities of applying combinations of I, C, and B.* Hint: *There are only a finite number.*

Another important concept in the theory of metric spaces is that of diameter.

Definition 4.3.34. *Let A be a nonempty subset of a metric space X. The* diameter of A *is*

$$\operatorname{diam}(A) = \sup_{x,y \in A} d(x, y).$$

Note that we may have $\operatorname{diam}(A) = \infty$.

Exercise 4.3.35.

(*i*) *Show that the diameter of a set is* 0 *iff the set consists of a single point.*

(*ii*) *Suppose A is a nonempty subset of a metric space X. Show that* $\operatorname{diam}(A) = \operatorname{diam}(\overline{A})$.

Definition 4.3.36. *Let A be a nonempty subset of $\mathbb{R}^n$. We say that A is* convex *if, given any two points $\mathbf{p}, \mathbf{q} \in A$, the set of points $\{(1-t)\mathbf{p} + t\mathbf{q} \mid t \in \mathbb{R}, 0 \leq t \leq 1\}$ is a subset of A.*

Example 4.3.37. *The unit ball B^n contained in $\mathbb{R}^n$, in the usual metric, is a convex set.*

Exercise 4.3.38. *Show that the unit ball in $\ell_n^p(\mathbb{R})$, for $1 \leq p \leq \infty$, is a convex set in $\mathbb{R}^n$.*

Definition 4.3.39. *Let A be a subset of $\mathbb{R}^n$ with the usual metric. The* convex hull *of A is the intersection of all convex sets containing A. The* closed convex hull *of A is the intersection of all closed convex sets containing A.*

Exercise 4.3.40. *Let A be a nonempty subset of $\mathbb{R}^n$ and let C be the convex hull of A.*

(*i*) *Prove or disprove the following statement. The closed convex hull of A is $\overline{C}$.*

(*ii*) *Show that the diameter of A is the diameter of C.*

Remark 4.3.41. *The concept of convex set in $\mathbb{R}^n$ does not involve a metric in $\mathbb{R}^n$. However, a particular metric is often used to define subsets of $\mathbb{R}^n$ that may or may not be convex.*

Exercise 4.3.42.

(*i*) *Describe the closed convex hull of the unit ball in $\ell_n^p(\mathbb{R})$ for $1 \leq p \leq \infty$.*

(*ii*) *Suppose $0 < p < 1$. For $\mathbf{x} \in \mathbb{R}^n$, define,*

$$\|\mathbf{x}\|_p = \left(\sum_{k=1}^{n} |x_k|^p \right)^{\frac{1}{p}}.$$

Define $S_p = \{\mathbf{x} \in \mathbb{R}^n \mid \|\mathbf{x}\|_p \leq 1\}$. Determine whether S_p is convex. If not, find the closed convex hull of S_p.

Example 4.3.43. *We now branch out in a slightly different direction. Suppose that X is a set and $F = \mathbb{R}$ or $\mathbb{C}$. Denote by $\mathcal{B}(X, F)$ the set of all bounded functions from X to F. Thus, $f \in \mathcal{B}(X, F)$ iff there is a real* *number M such that $|f(x)| \leq M$ for all $x \in X$. For $f \in \mathcal{B}(X, F)$, define $\|f\| = \sup\{|f(x)| \mid x \in X\}$ (the* sup norm*). For f, $g \in \mathcal{B}(X, F)$, define $d(f, g) = \|f - g\|$ (the* sup metric*). It follows easily from the definition of* sup *that d is a metric on $\mathcal{B}(X, F)$. In this example, a closed ball of radius r around a function f is the collection of all functions whose graphs lie within an "r-strip" around the graph of f.*

Exercise 4.3.44.

(i) *Let $F = \mathbb{R}$ or $\mathbb{C}$. Show that $\mathcal{B}(X, F)$, with d as defined above, is a metric space.*

(ii) *For $f, g \in \mathcal{B}(X, F)$, define $(f + g)(x) = f(x) + g(x)$ and $(fg)(x) = f(x)g(x)$. Also, for $\alpha \in F$ define $(\alpha f)(x) = \alpha f(x)$. Show that, with these operations, $\mathcal{B}(X, F)$ is a commutative algebra with 1 over F (see Definition 2.3.4). Of course, scalar multiplication can be thought of as simply multiplication by a constant function.*

This is a step up in our examples of metric spaces. While previous examples are important, spaces of functions are the most significant examples of metric spaces in analysis.

4. Limits and Continuous Functions

The consideration of function spaces leads us to the notion of continuous function. Before we define continuous functions, we introduce the idea of limit.

Definition 4.4.1. *Suppose $(a_n)_{n \in \mathbb{N}}$ is a sequence of points in a metric space X. We say that a point $L \in X$ is the* limit *of the sequence $(a_n)_{n \in \mathbb{N}}$ as n goes to infinity if, for any $\varepsilon > 0$, there exists $N_\varepsilon \in \mathbb{N}$ such that $d(a_n, L) < \varepsilon$ whenever $n \geq N_\varepsilon$. When the limit exists, we say that $(a_n)_{n \in \mathbb{N}}$* converges *to L, and write*

$$\lim_{n \to \infty} a_n = L.$$

Sometimes, we simply say that $(a_n)_{n \in \mathbb{N}}$ converges in X *without mentioning L explicitly.*

As in Chapter 3, we have a concept of Cauchy sequences in a metric space.

Definition 4.4.2 (See Definitions 3.5.2, 3.6.12)**.** *Let X be a metric space and let $(a_n)_{n \in \mathbb{N}}$ be a sequence in X. We say that $(a_n)_{n \in \mathbb{N}}$ is a* Cauchy sequence *if, for any $\varepsilon > 0$, there exists $N_\varepsilon \in \mathbb{N}$ such that $d(a_n, a_m) < \varepsilon$ whenever $n, m \geq N_\varepsilon$.*

It may be that a sequence in a metric space is a Cauchy sequence even though it does not converge. For example, as we observed in Chapter 3, Cauchy sequences in $\mathbb{Q}$ with the usual metric do not necessarily converge in $\mathbb{Q}$. This leads us to the following exercise.

Exercise 4.4.3. *Suppose that X is a metric space and that the sequence $(a_n)_{n\in\mathbb{N}}$ converges in X. Show that, for any $\varepsilon > 0$ there exists $N_\varepsilon \in \mathbb{N}$ such that $d(a_n, a_m) < \varepsilon$ whenever $n, m \geq N_\varepsilon$. Thus, a convergent sequence is a Cauchy sequence.*

Exercise 4.4.4. *Let $(a_n)_{n\in\mathbb{N}}$ be a Cauchy sequence in a discrete metric space X. Show that there exists $N \in \mathbb{N}$ such that $d(a_n, a_m) = 0$, that is, $a_n = a_m$, for all $n, m \geq N$. Hence, the sequence is convergent. Such a sequence is called* eventually constant. *Note that an eventually constant sequence in any metric space is convergent, and in fact, it converges to the eventual constant.*

There is a standard litany associated to the notions of convergent sequence and Cauchy sequence. For example, from Exercise 4.4.3, we see that in any metric space, a convergent sequence is a Cauchy sequence. In $\mathbb{R}$ or $\mathbb{C}$ with the usual metric, every Cauchy sequence converges. In $\mathbb{Q}$ with the usual metric, many Cauchy sequences do not converge. The best kinds of metric spaces (at least our favorite kinds) are the ones in which "convergent sequence" and "Cauchy sequence" are synonymous.

Definition 4.4.5. *Suppose that X is a metric space. We say that X is a* complete metric space *if every Cauchy sequence in X converges.*

Examples 4.4.6. *The following metric spaces are complete. (If this seems repetitive, don't worry about it.) The proofs of i and ii are in Chapter 3:*

(*i*) *$\mathbb{R}$ with the usual metric;*

(*ii*) *$\mathbb{C}$ with the usual metric;*

(*iii*) *any discrete metric space.*

The rational numbers $\mathbb{Q} \subset \mathbb{R}$ are not complete in the usual metric, but they are complete in the discrete metric.

Exercise 4.4.7. *Prove that a closed subset of a complete metric space is a complete metric space with the inherited metric.*

Exercise 4.4.8. *Show that, for $1 \leq p \leq \infty$, the spaces $\ell_n^p(\mathbb{R})$ and $\ell_n^p(\mathbb{C})$ are complete metric spaces.*

We now turn to an investigation of convergence and completeness in the spaces $\mathbb{R}^n$ and $\mathbb{C}^n$ with the usual metrics. Our approach here is very similar to the one that we took in $\mathbb{R}$ (see Section 3.6). One big difference is that, since there is no notion of order in $\mathbb{R}^n$, the idea of monotonicity has no meaning. However, we will use it one variable at a time. The following lemmas and theorems for $\mathbb{R}^n$ and $\mathbb{C}^n$ will be proved for $\mathbb{R}^n$ and left as exercises for $\mathbb{C}^n$.

Lemma 4.4.9. *Every bounded sequence in $\mathbb{R}^n$ (or $\mathbb{C}^n$) with the usual metric has a convergent subsequence.*

Proof. Let $(a_m)_{m\in\mathbb{N}}$ be a bounded sequence in $\mathbb{R}^n$. Write $a_m = (a_{m,1}, a_{m,2}, \ldots, a_{m,n})$. We prove the lemma by induction on n. For $n = 1$, this is the content of Lemma 3.6.10. Assume the lemma is true for $n-1$. Let a'_m be the $(n-1)$-tuple $(a_{m,1}, a_{m,2}, \ldots, a_{m,n-1})$. Then $(a'_m)_{m\in\mathbb{N}}$ is a bounded sequence in $\mathbb{R}^{n-1}$. By the induction hypothesis $(a'_m)_{m\in\mathbb{N}}$ has a convergent subsequence in $\mathbb{R}^{n-1}$. Label this convergent subsequence $(a'_{m_j})_{j\in\mathbb{N}}$. Now the sequence $(a_{m_j,n})_{j\in\mathbb{N}}$ is a bounded sequence in $\mathbb{R}$ and hence has a convergent subsequence which we shall not name. Again, taking the corresponding subsequence of $(a_{m_j})_{j\in\mathbb{N}}$, we get a convergent subsequence of the original subsequence $(a_m)_{m\in\mathbb{N}}$. ☠

Exercise 4.4.10.

(*i*) *For practice, carry out the above proof in $\mathbb{C}^n$.*

(*ii*) *Prove the above lemma by proceeding coordinate by coordinate. You will notice that the indexing gets quite messy.*

Theorem 4.4.11 (Bolzano-Weierstrass). *If A is a bounded infinite subset of $\mathbb{R}^n$ or $\mathbb{C}^n$, then A has an accumulation point.*

Proof. (We'll do $\mathbb{R}^n$. You do $\mathbb{C}^n$.) Since A is infinite there exists a sequence $(x_k)_{k\in\mathbb{N}}$ in A, where $x_k \neq x_j$ if $k \neq j$. Then $(x_k)_{k\in\mathbb{N}}$ is a bounded sequence in $\mathbb{R}^n$ and by Lemma 4.4.9 has a convergent subsequence. If this subsequence converges to x_0, then x_0 is an accumulation point of A. ☠

Remark 4.4.12. *As in Example* 4.3.43, *we let $\mathcal{B}(X, F)$ denote either $\mathcal{B}(X,\mathbb{R})$ or $\mathcal{B}(X,\mathbb{C})$. There are two types of convergence to be discussed in this space. The first is called* uniform convergence, *that is, convergence with respect to the metric defined in the example. In this case, a sequence $(f_n)_{n\in\mathbb{N}}$ in $\mathcal{B}(X,F)$ is a Cauchy sequence if, given $\varepsilon > 0$, there exists $N_\varepsilon \in \mathbb{N}$ such that $\sup_{x\in X} |f_n(x) - f_m(x)| < \varepsilon$ for $n, m \geq N_\varepsilon$. Thus, if a sequence $(f_n)_{n\in\mathbb{N}}$ is a Cauchy sequence in $\mathcal{B}(X,F)$, then, for a fixed $x_0 \in X$, the sequence $(f_n(x_0))_{n\in\mathbb{N}}$ is a Cauchy sequence in $\mathbb{R}$ or $\mathbb{C}$. Since $\mathbb{R}$ and $\mathbb{C}$ are complete, this sequence has a limit. Set $f(x_0) = \lim_{n\to\infty} f_n(x_0)$. As x_0 varies, this defines a function $f : X \to \mathbb{R}$ or $\mathbb{C}$. This function $f : X \to \mathbb{R}$ or $\mathbb{C}$ is called the* pointwise limit *of the sequence $(f_n)_{n\in\mathbb{N}}$. From the discussion above, uniform convergence of a sequence $(f_n)_{n\in\mathbb{N}}$ of functions in $\mathcal{B}(X,F)$*

implies the existence of a pointwise limit f, or phrased slightly differently, uniform convergence implies pointwise convergence.

Observe that even if a sequence does not converge uniformly, it may still have a pointwise limit in $\mathcal{B}(X,F)$. For example, define the following sequence of functions in $\mathcal{B}([0,1],\mathbb{R})$:

$$f_n(x) = \begin{cases} 2n^2x & \text{if } 0 \le x \le \frac{1}{2n}, \\ -2n^2(x-\frac{1}{n}) & \text{if } \frac{1}{2n} \le x \le \frac{1}{n}, \\ 0 & \text{if } \frac{1}{n} \le x \le 1. \end{cases}$$

Then, for each $x \in [0,1]$, we have $\lim_{n\to\infty} f_n(x) = 0$. So, the sequence $(f_n)_{n\in\mathbb{N}}$ converges pointwise to the function $f(x) = 0$. However, it is clear that this convergence is not uniform. Note that all the functions f_n, as well as the limit function f, are continuous by elementary calculus.

We now ask whether a Cauchy sequence $(f_n)_{n\in\mathbb{N}}$ in $\mathcal{B}(X,F)$ converges uniformly to its pointwise limit f.

Theorem 4.4.13. *The spaces $\mathcal{B}(X,\mathbb{R})$ and $\mathcal{B}(X,\mathbb{C})$ are complete metric spaces.*

Proof. As above, we let $\mathcal{B}(X,F) = \mathcal{B}(X,\mathbb{R})$ or $\mathcal{B}(X,\mathbb{C})$. Suppose that $(f_n)_{n\in\mathbb{N}}$ is a Cauchy sequence in $\mathcal{B}(X,F)$ and denote by f the pointwise limit of $(f_n)_{n\in\mathbb{N}}$ (which exists by Remark 4.4.12). We want to show that the sequence $(f_n)_{n\in\mathbb{N}}$ converges uniformly to f. To this end, choose $\varepsilon > 0$ and $N \in \mathbb{N}$ such that $\sup_{x\in X} |f_n(x) - f_m(x)| < \varepsilon/2$ when $n, m \ge N$. Fix $x_0 \in X$ and choose an integer $N(x_0) \ge N$ such that $|f_{N(x_0)}(x_0) - f(x_0)| < \varepsilon/2$. Then $|f_n(x_0) - f(x_0)| \le |f_n(x_0) - f_{N(x_0)}(x_0)| + |f_{N(x_0)}(x_0) - f(x_0)| < \varepsilon$ if $n \ge N$.

To complete the proof, we must show that the function f is bounded, that is, $f \in \mathcal{B}(X,F)$. But, from the above inequality, it follows that $|f(x)| < |f_n(x)| + \varepsilon$ for all $x \in X$. ☠

We now turn to one of the most important ideas about functions on metric spaces.

Definition 4.4.14. *Let (X,d) and (X',d') be metric spaces. A function $f : X \to X'$ is* continuous *at the point $x_0 \in X$ if, for any $\varepsilon > 0$, there is a $\delta > 0$ such that $d'(f(x), f(x_0)) < \varepsilon$ whenever $x \in X$ and $d(x,x_0) < \delta$.*

This is the old familiar ε-δ definition. It is simply the statement that

$$\lim_{x\to x_0} f(x) = f(x_0).$$

More generally, the limit of a function $f(x)$ at x_0 is $L \in X'$, and we write

$$\lim_{x\to x_0} f(x) = L$$

if, for every $\varepsilon > 0$, there exists a $\delta > 0$ such that $d'(f(x), L) < \varepsilon$ whenever $0 < d(x, x_0) < \delta$.

Exercise 4.4.15. *Suppose that X and X' are metric spaces as above and that $x_0 \in X$. Show that f is continuous at x_0 iff for every sequence $(x_n)_{n\in\mathbb{N}}$ in X that converges to x_0 in X, we have*

$$\lim_{n\to\infty} f(x_n) = f(x_0)$$

in X'.

Note that another way of saying that f is continuous at x_0 is the following: given $\varepsilon > 0$, there exists $\delta > 0$ such that $f(B_\delta(x_0)) \subseteq B_\varepsilon(f(x_0))$.

In discussing continuity, one must be careful about the domain of the function. For example, define $f : \mathbb{R} \to \mathbb{R}$ by the equation

$$f(x) = \begin{cases} 0 & \text{if } x \notin \mathbb{Q}, \\ 1 & \text{if } x \in \mathbb{Q}. \end{cases}$$

Then f is not continuous at any point of $\mathbb{R}$. However, suppose we restrict f to be a function from $\mathbb{Q}$ to $\mathbb{Q}$. This means that $f(x) = 1$ on $\mathbb{Q}$ and is continuous at every point of $\mathbb{Q}$.

Exercise 4.4.16. *Define $f : \mathbb{R} \to \mathbb{R}$ by*

$$f(x) = \begin{cases} 1/q & \text{if } x = p/q \text{ (reduced to lowest terms, } x \neq 0\text{)}, \\ 0 & \text{if } x = 0 \text{ or } x \notin \mathbb{Q}. \end{cases}$$

Show that f is continuous at 0 and every irrational point. Show that f is not continuous at any nonzero rational point.

Continuity is called a *pointwise property* or *local property* of a function f, that is, as in Exercise 4.4.16, a function may be continuous at some points, but not at others. We often deal with functions $f : X \to X'$ that are continuous at every point of X. In this case, we simply say that f is *continuous* without reference to any particular point.

Theorem 4.4.17. *Suppose that (X, d) and (X', d') are metric spaces. Then a function $f : X \to X'$ is continuous iff for any open set $V \subset X'$, the set $f^{-1}(V)$ is an open set in X.*

Proof. First suppose that f is continuous. Let V be an open set in X'. Suppose $x_0 \in f^{-1}(V)$. Take $\varepsilon > 0$ such that $B_\varepsilon(f(x_0)) \subset V$. Then there exists $\delta > 0$ such that $f(B_\delta(x_0)) \subseteq B_\varepsilon(f(x_0))$, and so $B_\delta(x_0) \subseteq f^{-1}(B_\varepsilon(f(x_0))) \subseteq f^{-1}(V)$. So $f^{-1}(V)$ is open.

The second half of the proof is easy. You do it. 

Exercise 4.4.18.

(*i*) *Let X and X' be metric spaces and assume that X has the discrete metric. Show that any function $f : X \to X'$ is continuous.*

(*ii*) *Let $X = \mathbb{R}$ with the usual metric and let $f : X \to X$ be a polynomial function. Show that f is continuous.*

(*iii*) *Let $X = \mathbb{R}$ with the usual metric and $X' = \mathbb{R}$ with the discrete metric. Describe all continuous functions from $X \to X'$.*

Remark 4.4.19. *In a general topological space (see Project 4.1), the definition of continuity is ordinarily stated by saying that the inverse image of an open set is open (see Theorem 4.4.17 above, and Definition* 4.6.1.13 *below). However, in metric spaces, the definition of continuity using limits is often more useful.*

Definition 4.4.20. *A subset A of a metric space X is* bounded *if $X = \varnothing$ or there exist a point $x \in X$ and $r > 0$ such that $A \subseteq B_r(x)$.*

Exercise 4.4.21. *Suppose that (X, d) and (X', d') are metric spaces and that $f : X \to X'$ is continuous. For each of the following statements, determine whether or not it is true. If the assertion is true, prove it. If it is not true, give a counterexample.*

(*i*) *If A is an open subset of X, then $f(A)$ is an open subset of X'.*

(*ii*) *If B is a closed subset of X', then $f^{-1}(B)$ is a closed subset of X.*

(*iii*) *If A is a closed subset of X, then $f(A)$ is a closed subset of X'.*

(*iv*) *If A is a bounded subset of X, then $f(A)$ is a bounded subset of X'.*

(*v*) *If B is a bounded subset of X', then $f^{-1}(B)$ is a bounded subset of X.*

(*vi*) *If $A \subseteq X$ and x_0 is an isolated point of A, then $f(x_0)$ is an isolated point of $f(A)$.*

(*vii*) *If $A \subseteq X$, $x_0 \in A$, and $f(x_0)$ is an isolated point of $f(A)$, then x_0 is an isolated point of A.*

(*viii*) *If $A \subseteq X$ and x_0 is an accumulation point of A, then $f(x_0)$ is an accumulation point of $f(A)$.*

(*ix*) *If $A \subseteq X$, $x_0 \in X$, and $f(x_0)$ is an accumulation point of $f(A)$, then x_0 is an accumulation point of A.*

(*x*) *Do any of your answers to the above questions change if we assume X and X' are complete?*

Definition 4.4.22. *Let (X, d) and (X', d') be metric spaces. A continuous function $f : X \to X'$ is a* homeomorphism *if*

(a) *f is a bijection, and*

(b) *the function f^{-1} is also continuous.*

Theorem 4.4.23. *Suppose $1 \leq p < q \leq \infty$. Then the identity map $I(x) = x$ from $\ell_n^p(\mathbb{R})$ to $\ell_n^q(\mathbb{R})$ is a homeomorphism.*

Proof. From Exercise 4.3.5, it is clear that, if $p < q$, then the unit ball in $\ell_n^p(\mathbb{R})$ is contained in the unit ball in $\ell_n^q(\mathbb{R})$. Take $(x_1, x_2, \ldots, x_n) \in \mathbb{R}^n$ and suppose $\max_{1 \leq i \leq n}\{|x_i|\} \leq 1/n$. Then $|x_1| + \cdots + |x_n| \leq 1$. This shows that the ball of radius $1/n$ in the ℓ_n^∞ metric is contained in the ball of radius 1 in the ℓ_n^1 metric. In particular, this last fact shows that if we take the unit ball in $\ell_n^q(\mathbb{R})$ and multiply each coordinate by a factor of $1/n$, then the resulting set of points is contained in the unit ball in $\ell_n^p(\mathbb{R})$. This is enough to show that I is a homeomorphism.

Exercise 4.4.24. *Show that $\ell_n^p(\mathbb{C})$ and $\ell_n^q(\mathbb{C})$ are homeomorphic.*

Definition 4.4.25. *A homeomorphism $f : X \to X'$ is an* isometry *if*

$$d'(f(x_1), f(x_2)) = d(x_1, x_2)$$

for all $x_1, x_2 \in X$.

Exercise 4.4.26. *Suppose that we had defined an isometry to be a bijection $f : X \to X'$ such that $d'(f(x_1), f(x_2)) = d(x_1, x_2)$ for all $x_1, x_2 \in X$. Show that with this definition, any isometry is a homeomorphism.*

Exercise 4.4.27. *Let $X = \mathbb{R}$ with the discrete metric and $X' = \mathbb{R}$ with the usual metric. Define $f : X \to X'$ by $f(x) = x$. Show that f is a continuous bijection that is not a homeomorphism.*

Exercise 4.4.28. *Let (X, d) be a metric space. Let G be the collection of all homeomorphisms from X to X. Prove that, under composition of functions, G is a group and the collection of all isometries of X is a subgroup of G.*

Definition 4.4.29. *Suppose that (X, d) is a metric space. Define $\mathcal{BC}(X, F)$ to be the subset of $\mathcal{B}(X, F)$ consisting of continuous functions from X to F. We take the metric on $\mathcal{BC}(X, F)$ to be the same as that on $\mathcal{B}(X, F)$. If X is compact, then all continuous functions from X to F are bounded (see Exercise 4.5.8(ii) below); so, when X is compact, we will sometimes write $\mathcal{C}(X, F)$ in place of $\mathcal{BC}(X, F)$.*

Theorem 4.4.30. *The space $\mathcal{BC}(X, F)$ is a complete metric space.*

Proof. Suppose that $(f_n)_{n \in \mathbb{N}}$ is a Cauchy sequence in $\mathcal{BC}(X, F)$. Then by Theorem 4.4.13, $(f_n)_{n \in \mathbb{N}}$ converges to a function $f \in \mathcal{B}(X, F)$. All we need to show is that f is a continuous function. Now, given $\varepsilon > 0$, there exists N such that $\sup_{x \in X} |f_n(x) - f(x)| < \varepsilon/3$ whenever $n \geq N$. Fix $x_0 \in X$. Then, for any $x \in X$ and $n \geq N$,

$$\begin{aligned} |f(x) - f(x_0)| &\leq |f(x) - f_n(x)| + |f_n(x) - f_n(x_0)| + |f_n(x_0) - f(x_0)| \\ &< \varepsilon/3 + |f_n(x) - f_n(x_0)| + \varepsilon/3. \end{aligned}$$

Since f_n is continuous, we can choose $\delta > 0$ such that $|f_n(x) - f_n(x_0)| < \varepsilon/3$ whenever $d(x, x_0) < \delta$. But then $|f(x) - f(x_0)| < \varepsilon$ when $d(x, x_0) < \delta$, so f is continuous.

Remark 4.4.31. *So we have proved (see Theorems 4.4.13 and 4.4.30) that the uniform limit of bounded functions is a bounded function and the uniform limit of bounded continuous functions is a bounded continuous function. We will find these facts very useful.*

Exercise 4.4.32. *Show that $\mathcal{BC}(X, F)$ is a subalgebra of $\mathcal{B}(X, F)$. That is, $\mathcal{BC}(X, F)$ is a vector subspace of $\mathcal{B}(X, F)$ that is closed under pointwise multiplication.*

Exercise 4.4.33. *In Remark* 4.4.12, *we saw an example in which the pointwise limit of a sequence of functions was continuous even though the convergence was not uniform. Now consider the sequence of functions $f_n : [0, 1] \to [0, 1]$ where $f_n(x) = x^n$. Find the pointwise limit of the sequence $(f_n)_{n \in \mathbb{N}}$ and show that it is not continuous.*

Exercise 4.4.34. *Define a sequence of functions $f_n : (0, 1) \to \mathbb{R}$ by*

$$f_n(x) = \begin{cases} \frac{1}{q^n} & \text{if } x = \frac{p}{q} \neq 0 \\ 0 & \text{otherwise} \end{cases}$$

for $n \in \mathbb{N}$. Find the pointwise limit f of the sequence $(f_n)_{n \in \mathbb{N}}$ and show that $(f_n)_{n \in \mathbb{N}}$ converges to f uniformly.

There is an additional property of continuous functions that is important for future applications.

Definition 4.4.35. *Let (X, d) and (X', d') be metric spaces, and let f be a continuous function from X to X'. We say that f is* uniformly continuous *if, given $\varepsilon > 0$, there exists $\delta > 0$ such that, for any pair $x, y \in X$, we have $d'(f(x), f(y)) < \varepsilon$ whenever $d(x, y) < \delta$.*

So, f is uniformly continuous if it is continuous at every point and, for a given $\varepsilon > 0$, we can find a corresponding δ that is independent of the point.

Exercise 4.4.36. *Let $X = X' = \mathbb{R}$ with the usual metric.*

(i) *Show that a polynomial function $p(x)$ on $\mathbb{R}$ is uniformly continuous if and only if* $\deg(p(x)) < 2$.

(ii) *Show that $f(x) = \sin(x)$ is uniformly continuous on $\mathbb{R}$.*

Exercise 4.4.37. *Let $X = (0, \infty)$ and determine whether the following functions are uniformly continuous on X:*

(i) $f(x) = 1/x$;

(ii) $f(x) = \sqrt{x}$;

(iii) $f(x) = \ln(x)$;

(iv) $f(x) = x\ln(x)$.

5. Compactness, Completeness and Connectedness

Now, we consider a distinguished class of subsets of metric spaces.

Definition 4.5.1 (see Definition 3.6.28). *Let A be a nonempty subset of a metric space X. A family $\{U_j\}_{j\in J}$ of open subsets of X is called an* open covering *(or* open cover*) of A if*

$$A \subseteq \bigcup_{j\in J} U_j.$$

If $\{U_j\}_{j\in J}$ is an open cover of A, we say that this cover has a finite subcovering *if there is a finite subcollection $U_{j_1}, U_{j_2}, \ldots, U_{j_n}$ satisfying*

$$A \subseteq \bigcup_{k=1}^{n} U_{j_k}.$$

Examples 4.5.2.

(i) *Let $A = (0,1) \subseteq \mathbb{R}$ with the usual metric. For $j \in \mathbb{N}$, with $j \geq 2$, define $U_j = (\frac{1}{j}, 1)$. Then $(0,1) \subseteq \bigcup_{j\in\mathbb{N}} U_j$, but there is no finite subcover.*

(ii) *Let X be a discrete metric space. For any point $j \in X$, set $U_j = \{j\}$. Then $\{U_j\}_{j\in X}$ is an open cover of X, which has a finite subcover iff X is a finite set.*

(iii) *We saw in Theorem 3.6.27, that if A is a closed and bounded set in $\mathbb{R}$ with the usual metric, then every open cover of A has a finite subcover.*

Here is one of the big ideas in the theory of metric spaces.

Definition 4.5.3 (see Definitions 3.6.29 and 3.9.17). *Let A be a subset of a metric space X. We say that A is* compact *if every open covering of A has a finite subcovering.*

Recall that the Heine–Borel Theorem in $\mathbb{R}$ (and $\mathbb{C}$) with usual metric states that a subset is compact if and only if it is closed and bounded. The statement of the Heine–Borel theorem is certainly not true in a general metric space. For example, take $\mathbb{R}$ with the discrete metric. Then, $\mathbb{R}$ is closed and bounded in this metric. Take an open covering consisting of the individual points in $\mathbb{R}$. This covering does not have a finite subcovering.

For emphasis, we note that the definition insists that for every open covering, there must be a finite subcovering. For example, given any subset A of a metric space X, we have that $\{X\}$ is an open covering which is already a finite subcovering. So while this particular open covering has a finite subcover, this does not necessarily imply that other open coverings have finite subcoverings.

Hence, in a general metric space, the closed bounded sets are not necessarily compact. However, we do have one half of the statement of the Heine–Borel theorem in general metric spaces.

Theorem 4.5.4. *If a subset A of a metric space X is compact, then A is closed and bounded.*

Proof. Recall that a set in a metric space is bounded if and only if it is contained in a ball of finite radius with center at some point. If A is non–empty, take a point $a \in A$ and consider the open covering $\{B_n(a) \mid n \in \mathbb{N}\}$. Since A is compact, this cover has a finite subcovering, and in fact, there is an integer N so that $A \subseteq B_N(a)$. Hence, A is bounded.

To prove that A is closed, we assume that x_0 is an accumulation point of A and prove that $x_0 \in A$. Suppose not. Then, for each $a \in A$, let $r_a = d(a, x_0)/2$. The collection $\{B_{r_a}(a) \mid a \in A\}$ is an open cover of A and hence has a finite subcover $\{B_{r_1}(a_1), B_{r_2}(a_2), \ldots, B_{r_n}(a_n)\}$. Let $r = \min\{r_1, r_2, \ldots, r_n\}$. Then $B_r(x_0) \cap B_{r_j}(a_j) = \varnothing$ for all j. Hence, $B_r(x_0) \cap A = \varnothing$, which contradicts the definition of an accumulation point. So $x_0 \in A$.

Corollary 4.5.5. *If A is a compact subset of a metric space X, then every infinite subset of A has an accumulation point in A.*

Proof. Suppose A is a compact set and that C is an infinite subset of A with no accumulation point in A. Then, for each $a \in A$, there is an open ball $B(a)$ centered at a such that $(B(a) \setminus \{a\}) \cap C = \varnothing$. The collection $\{B(a) \mid a \in A\}$ covers A. So, by compactness, we can extract a finite subcover, $\{B(a_1), \ldots, B(a_n)\}$. Thus, $C \subset A \subset B(a_1) \cup \ldots \cup B(a_n)$, and each $B(a_j)$ contains at most one element of C (at its center). This implies that C has at most n elements.

Corollary 4.5.6. *Let A be a compact set in a metric space. Then, every infinite sequence in A has a subsequence that converges to a point in A.*

Exercise 4.5.7. *Prove that the Heine–Borel theorem holds in $\mathbb{R}^n$ and $\mathbb{C}^n$ with the usual metrics. (Hint: see the proof of Theorem* 3.9.18.*)*

Exercise 4.5.8.

(*i*) *Let $f : X \to X'$ be a continuous map of metric spaces. Show that if $A \subseteq X$ is compact, then $f(A) \subseteq X'$ is compact.*

(*ii*) *Suppose that X is a compact metric space. Show that a continuous function $f : X \to \mathbb{R}$ ($\mathbb{R}$ with the usual metric) is bounded.*

(*iii*) *Suppose that X is a compact metric space. Show that a continuous function $f : X \to \mathbb{R}$ ($\mathbb{R}$ with the usual metric) attains a maximum and minimum value on X.*

Exercise 4.5.9. *Suppose X and X' are metric spaces with X compact.*

(*i*) *If $f : X \to X'$ is continuous on X, show that f is uniformly continuous on X.*

(*ii*) *If $f : X \to X'$ is a continuous bijection, show that f is a homeomorphism.*

Exercise 4.5.10 (Dini's Theorem)**.** *Let X be a compact metric space. Suppose f and $(f_n)_{n\in\mathbb{N}}$ are real-valued continuous functions on X. Suppose that, for each $x \in X$, the sequence $(f_n(x))_{n\in\mathbb{N}}$ is a monotonic sequence converging to $f(x)$. Show that $(f_n)_{n\in\mathbb{N}}$ converges to f uniformly.*

Exercise 4.5.11. *Suppose that A and B are nonempty subsets of a metric space X. The* distance *between A and B is defined by*

$$d(A, B) = \inf\{d(a, b) \mid a \in A, b \in B\}.$$

We say that the distance between A and B is assumed *if there exist $a_0 \in A$ and $b_0 \in B$ such that $d(A, B) = d(a_0, b_0)$. Determine whether or not the distance between A and B is necessarily assumed in (i)–(iii):*

(*i*) *A is closed and B is closed;*

(*ii*) *A is compact and B is closed;*

(*iii*) *A is compact and B is compact.*

(*iv*) *What happens in the above cases if we assume that X is complete?*

At this point, we introduce an alternate notion of compactness.

Definition 4.5.12 (see Definition 3.6.30 and Exercise 3.9.21)**.** *A subset A of a metric space X is* sequentially compact *if every sequence in A has a subsequence that converges to an element of A.*

Exercise 4.5.13. *If X is a metric space, and $A \subset X$, we say that A is* totally bounded *if, for any $\varepsilon > 0$, A can be covered by a finite number of balls of radius ε. Show that a sequentially compact metric space is totally bounded.*

One of the most important facts about metric spaces is that compactness and sequential compactness are equivalent. We have already proved that compactness implies sequential compactness. To prove the converse, we need the following lemma.

Lemma 4.5.14. *Let X be a metric space. If $A \subset X$ has the property that every infinite subset of A has an accumulation point in X, then there exists a countable collection of open sets $\{U_i \mid i \in \mathbb{N}\}$ such that, if V is any open set in X and $x \in A \cap V$, then there is some U_i such that $x \in U_i \subset V$.*

Proof. We claim that, for each $n \in \mathbb{N}$, there is a finite set of points $x_1, \ldots, x_{N(n)}$ in A such that the set of open balls $B_{\frac{1}{n}}(x_1), B_{\frac{1}{n}}(x_2), \ldots,$ $B_{\frac{1}{n}}(x_{N(n)})$ covers A. Otherwise, there exists $n \in \mathbb{N}$ such that no finite collection of balls of radius $\frac{1}{n}$ centered at points of A can cover A. For each $k \in \mathbb{N}$, assume A is infinite and define an infinite sequence of points of A inductively as follows. Take $y_1 \in A$. Then $B_{\frac{1}{n}}(y_1)$ does not cover A. So choose $y_2 \in A \setminus B_{\frac{1}{n}}(y_1)$. Then $B_{\frac{1}{n}}(y_1) \cup B_{\frac{1}{n}}(y_2)$ does not cover A and $d(y_1, y_2) \geq \frac{1}{n}$. Assume $y_1, \ldots, y_k$ have been chosen so that $B_k = B_{\frac{1}{n}}(y_1) \cup \ldots \cup B_{\frac{1}{n}}(y_k)$ does not cover A, and $d(y_i, y_j) \geq \frac{1}{n}$ for all $i \neq j$. Choose $y_{k+1} \in A \setminus B_k$. The infinite sequence $(y_k)_{k \in \mathbb{N}}$ does not have an accumulation point anywhere, which is a contradiction.

Taking all these balls $\{B_{\frac{1}{n}}(x_j) \mid n \in \mathbb{N} \text{ and } 1 \leq j \leq N(n)\}$ gives the required collection. ∎

Exercise 4.5.15. *Verify that the above collection satisfies the conclusion of the lemma.*

Exercise 4.5.16. *Let X be a metric space. If $A \subset X$ has the property that every infinite subset of A has an accumulation point in A, show that for any open covering of A, there exists a countable subcovering.*

Now comes a major Theorem.

Theorem 4.5.17. *In any metric space, a subset A is compact if and only if it is sequentially compact.*

Proof. We have already proved in Corollary 4.5.6 that compactness implies sequential compactness.

For the converse, suppose that $A \subset X$ is sequentially compact. Then any infinite subset of A contains a countable subset, which defines a sequence in A. By sequential compactness, this sequence has a subsequence that converges to a point $a \in A$. Since this point is clearly an accumulation point of A, we can apply Lemma 4.5.14 and Exercise 4.5.16 to conclude that, for any open cover $\mathcal{U}$ of A, we can find a countable subcover $\mathcal{U}'$.

From this open cover, $\mathcal{U}'$, we wish to extract a finite subcover. Let $\mathcal{U}' = \{U_j \mid j \in \mathbb{N}\}$. Suppose that, for each n, the union $U_1 \cup \ldots \cup U_n$ does not cover A. Then, for each n, there exists $x_n \in A \setminus (U_1 \cup \ldots \cup U_n)$. This defines a sequence $(x_n)_{n \in \mathbb{N}}$ in A, which by sequential compactness has a convergent subsequence, say with limit $x \in A$. Since $\mathcal{U}'$ covers A, x must be contained in U_N for some N. But then, U_N contains infinitely many elements of the sequence, and hence contains some x_m with $m > N$. This is a contradiction. ☠

Exercise 4.5.18.

(i) *Show that a compact metric space is complete.*

(ii) *Show that a totally bounded complete metric space is compact.*

Note that Theorem 4.5.17 gives another proof of the Heine–Borel Theorem in $\mathbb{R}^n$ and $\mathbb{C}^n$.

Exercise 4.5.19. *Prove this.*

Compact sets in $\mathbb{R}^n$ with the usual metric have many interesting properties, some of which are illustrated in the following exercises.

Exercise 4.5.20. *Let B be a compact convex subset of $\mathbb{R}^n$ with the usual metric. Define the* nearest point function *$p : {}^cB \to B$ as follows. For $x \in {}^cB$, we set $p(x)$ to be the closest point to x that lies in B. Show that:*

(i) *the function $p(x)$ is well defined;*

(ii) *the point $p(x)$ lies in the boundary of B;*

(iii) *the function $p(x)$ is surjective onto the boundary of B.*

In the next exercise, we continue with the terminology of the preceding exercise. Define the supporting hyperplane at $p(x)$ to be the hyperplane through $p(x)$ orthogonal to the vector $p(x) - x$. Define the supporting half space at $p(x)$ to be the set $H_{p(x)} = \{y \in \mathbb{R}^n \mid (y - p(x)) \cdot (p(x) - x) \geq 0\}$. (Note that the supporting hyperplane and supporting half space really depend on x, not just on $p(x)$.)

Exercise 4.5.21.

(*i*) *Show that, for each* $x \in {}^cB$, *the set* B *is a subset of* $H_{p(x)}$.

(*ii*) *Show that* $B = \bigcap_{z \in \partial B} H_z$. *(Note that* $H_z = H_{p(x)}$ *for some* $x \in {}^cB$.*)*

(*iii*) *Does the above process work when* B *is a closed convex unbounded subset of* $\mathbb{R}^n$ *with the usual metric?*

Here are a few more interesting facts and ideas about metric spaces. The first involves the notion of separability.

Definition 4.5.22. *Let* (X, d) *be a metric space. A subset* $A \subseteq X$ *is said to be* dense *in* X *if* $\overline{A} = X$.

Exercise 4.5.23. *It is clear that* X *is dense in* X. *Is it possible that the only subset of* X *that is dense in* X *is* X *itself?*

Definition 4.5.24. *Let* (X, d) *be a metric space. We say that* X *is* separable *if there exists a countable subset of* X *that is dense in* X.

Example 4.5.25. *The spaces* $\mathbb{R}^n$ *and* $\mathbb{C}^n$ *with the usual metrics are separable. As a countable dense subset, we can take the collection of all points in* $\mathbb{R}^n$ *whose coordinates are rational numbers, or the set of all points in* $\mathbb{C}^n$ *whose coordinates have the property that the real and imaginary parts are rational numbers.*

Theorem 4.5.26. *If* (X, d) *is a compact metric space, then* X *is separable.*

Proof. For each $n \in \mathbb{N}$, consider the collection of open balls $\{B_{\frac{1}{n}}(x) \mid x \in X\}$. This is an open covering of X, and hence, there is a finite subcovering $\mathcal{U}_n$. Take the union over $n \in \mathbb{N}$ of the centers of the balls in $\mathcal{U}_n$. This is a countable collection of points in X which is obviously dense. ☠

Exercise 4.5.27. *Suppose* X *and* X' *are metric spaces with* X *separable. Let* $f : X \to X'$ *be a continuous surjection. Show that* X' *is separable.*

As shown in Example 4.5.25, separable metric spaces do not have to be compact. Many of the important metric spaces in mathematics are separable, but there are some very important examples of non-separable metric spaces.

Exercise 4.5.28. *Determine the conditions, if they exisit, for which the following metric spaces are separable:*

(*i*) $\mathbb{R}$,

(*ii*) $B(X, F)$,

(*iii*) $BC(X, F)$.

Another important idea in metric spaces is connectedness. It has a funny definition because we begin by defining a non-connected set.

Definition 4.5.29. *Let X be a metric space and let $A \subset X$. We say that A is* not connected *(or* disconnected*) if there exist open sets $U, V \subset X$ such that*

(a) $U \cap A \neq \varnothing$ *and* $V \cap A \neq \varnothing$,

(b) $(U \cap A) \cap (V \cap A) = \varnothing$,

(c) $A = (U \cap A) \cup (V \cap A)$.

We say that A is disconnected *by the open sets U and V.*

Definition 4.5.30. *Let X be a metric space and $A \subset X$. We say that A is* connected *if A is not disconnected.*

Exercise 4.5.31.

(*i*) *Show that a subset A of $\mathbb{R}$ in the usual metric is connected iff A is an interval.*

(*ii*) *Show that a convex subset of $\mathbb{R}^n$ with the usual metric is a connected set.*

The basic theorem about connected sets is the following.

Theorem 4.5.32. *Let X, X' be metric spaces and $f : X \to X'$ a continuous function. If A is a connected subset of X, then $f(A)$ is connected subset of X'. That is, the continuous image of a connected set is connected.*

Proof. Let U and V be open sets in X', and assume that U and V disconnect $f(A)$. Then, $f^{-1}(U)$ and $f^{-1}(V)$ are open sets in X that disconnect A.

Corollary 4.5.33 (Intermediate Value Theorem)**.** *Let X be a metric space, and take $\mathbb{R}$ with the usual metric. Let $f : X \to \mathbb{R}$ be a continuous function. Let A be a connected subset of X and let $I = f(A)$. Then I is an interval in $\mathbb{R}$, and if $x_0 \in I$ there exists $a_0 \in A$ such that $f(a_0) = x_0$.*

Exercise 4.5.34. *Use the Corollary to show the following. Take $\mathbb{R}$ with the usual metric, and let $f : \mathbb{R} \to \mathbb{R}$ be given by $f(x) = x^n$ for $n \in \mathbb{N}$. If b is a positive real number, show that there exists a unique positive real number a such that $a^n = b$.*

Exercise 4.5.35.

(i) *Show that an open ball in* $\mathbb{R}^n$ *or* $\mathbb{C}^n$ *with the usual metric is a connected set.*

(ii) *Show that a closed ball in* $\mathbb{R}^n$ *or* $\mathbb{C}^n$ *with the usual metric is a connected set.*

(iii) *Show that* $GL(2, \mathbb{R})$ *with the metric inherited from* $M_2(\mathbb{R})$ *as in Exercise* 4.3.27 *is not a connected set. (Hint: use the fact that the determinant is a continuous function.)*

(iv) *Show that* $GL(2, \mathbb{C})$ *with the metric inherited from* $M_2(\mathbb{C})$ *is a connected set.*

If a metric space X is not connected, then it can be decomposed into subsets called connected components.

Definition 4.5.36. *If* X *is a metric space and* x_0 *is in* X*, then the* connected component of x_0 in X *is the union of the connected sets that contain* x_0.

Exercise 4.5.37.

(i) *Let* X *be a metric space and take* $x_0 \in X$. *Show that the connected component of* x_0 *is a connected set in* X.

(ii) *Show that if* A *is a connected subset of* X *that contains* x_0, *then* A *is contained in the connected component of* x_0.

(iii) *Show that if* A *is a connected subset of a metric space, then* $\overline{A}$ *is connected. Deduce that connected components are closed.*

Examples 4.5.38.

(i) *Let* $X = \mathbb{R}^\times$ *the set of nonzero real numbers with the usual metric. This metric space has two connected components, namely, the positive real numbers and the negative real numbers.*

(ii) *The connected components of* $GL(2, \mathbb{R})$ *with the usual metric are* $GL^+(2, \mathbb{R}) = \{x \in GL(2, \mathbb{R}) \mid \det\ x > 0\}$ *and* $GL^-(2, \mathbb{R}) = \{x \in GL(2, \mathbb{R}) \mid \det x < 0\}$.

Exercise 4.5.39. *Let* $O(n, \mathbb{R})$ *and* $SO(n, \mathbb{R})$ *(see pp. 81 and 85) be metric spaces with the metric inherited from* $GL(n, \mathbb{R})$. *Show that* $O(n, \mathbb{R})$ *is not connected and that* $SO(n, \mathbb{R})$ *is connected.*

Definition 4.5.40. *A metric space* X *is* totally disconnected *if the connected component of each point is the point itself.*

Example 4.5.41. *A discrete metric space* X *is totally disconnected.*

Exercise 4.5.42.

(i) *Find an example of a metric space that is totally disconnected but not discrete.*

(ii) *Find an example of a complete metric space that is totally disconnected but not discrete.*

Obviously, complete metric spaces play a special role among all metric spaces. We now present a procedure through which any metric space can be embedded as a dense subset of a complete metric space.

Theorem 4.5.43. *Let (X, d) be a metric space. Then there exists a complete metric space $(\tilde{X}, \tilde{d})$, and an injection $\phi : X \to \tilde{X}$, such that*

(1) *$\phi : X \to \phi(X)$ is an isometry,*

(2) *$\phi(X)$ is dense in $\tilde{X}$.*

Proof. Consider the set X' of all Cauchy sequences in X. We define an equivalence relation on X' by saying that $(x_n)_{n\in\mathbb{N}}$ is equivalent to $(y_n)_{n\in\mathbb{N}}$ if $\lim_{n\to\infty} d(x_n, y_n) = 0$.

Exercise 4.5.44. *Prove that this is an equivalence relation.*

Let $\tilde{X}$ be the set of equivalence classes. We first define a metric on $\tilde{X}$. Let $\{(x_n)_{n\in\mathbb{N}}\}$ and $\{(x'_n)_{n\in\mathbb{N}}\}$ be elements of $\tilde{X}$. We note that $(d(x_n, x'_n))_{n\in\mathbb{N}}$ is a Cauchy sequence in $\mathbb{R}$. This follows from the fact that $|d(x_n, x'_n) - d(x_m, x'_m)| \leq d(x_n, x_m) + d(x'_n, x'_m)$. We set

$$\tilde{d}(\{(x_n)_{n\in\mathbb{N}}\}, \{(x'_n)_{n\in\mathbb{N}}\}) = \lim_{n\to\infty} d(x_n, x'_n).$$

This limit exists because the real numbers are known to be complete (see Theorem 3.6.14).

Exercise 4.5.45. *Show that $\tilde{d}$ is well defined.*

Now define $\phi : X \to \tilde{X}$ by $\phi(x) = \{(x_k)_{k\in\mathbb{N}}\}$ where $x_k = x$ for all $k \in \mathbb{N}$. It is clear that ϕ is an isometry from X to $\phi(X)$.

There are two things left to do. First, show $\phi(X)$ is dense in $\tilde{X}$, and second, show that $(\tilde{X}, \tilde{d})$ is complete.

Let $\tilde{x} = \{(x_n)_{n\in\mathbb{N}}\} \in \tilde{X}$. Pick $\varepsilon > 0$. Since the sequence $(x_n)_{n\in\mathbb{N}}$ is Cauchy in X, there exists an integer N such that $d(x_N, x_m) < \varepsilon$ if $m \geq N$. Now consider the class of the constant sequence $(x_N) = \phi(x_N)$. Then $\tilde{d}(\tilde{x}, \phi(x_N)) = \lim_{n\to\infty} d(x_n, x_N) \leq \varepsilon$ and hence $\phi(X)$ is dense in $\tilde{X}$.

To show that $\tilde{X}$ is complete, take a Cauchy sequence $(\tilde{y}_n)$ in $\tilde{X}$. Remember, each $\tilde{y}_n$ is an equivalence class of Cauchy sequences in X. For each $n \in \mathbb{N}$, by density, choose $\tilde{z}_n \in \phi(X)$ such that $\tilde{d}(\tilde{y}_n, \tilde{z}_n) < \frac{1}{n}$. Then

$\tilde{d}(\tilde{z}_n, \tilde{z}_m) \leq \tilde{d}(\tilde{z}_n, \tilde{y}_n) + \tilde{d}(\tilde{y}_n, \tilde{y}_m) + \tilde{d}(\tilde{y}_m, \tilde{z}_m) < \frac{1}{n} + \tilde{d}(\tilde{y}_n, \tilde{y}_m) + \frac{1}{m}$. This implies that $(\tilde{z}_n)_{n\in\mathbb{N}}$ is Cauchy in $\tilde{X}$. Let $x_n = \phi^{-1}(\tilde{z}_n)$. Then, since ϕ is an isometry, $(x_n)_{n\in\mathbb{N}}$ is Cauchy in X. Let $\tilde{y}$ be the element of $\tilde{X}$ defined by the equivalence class of this Cauchy sequence, that is $\tilde{y} = \{(x_n)_{n\in\mathbb{N}}\}$. Then, $\tilde{d}(\tilde{y}_n, \tilde{y}) \leq \tilde{d}(\tilde{y}_n, \tilde{z}_n) + \tilde{d}(\tilde{z}_n, \tilde{y}) < \frac{1}{n} + \tilde{d}(\tilde{z}_n, \tilde{y})$. Observe that $\tilde{d}(\tilde{z}_n, \tilde{y}) = \lim_{k\to\infty} d(x_n, x_k)$. Since $(x_n)_{n\in\mathbb{N}}$ is Cauchy in X, for n and k large, $d(x_n, x_k)$ can be made arbitrarily small. This completes the proof.

Definition 4.5.46. *The metric space $\tilde{X}$ in the above theorem is called the* completion *of X.*

Exercise 4.5.47. *If (X, d) is already a complete metric space, show that (X, d) and $(\tilde{X}, \tilde{d})$ are isometric.*

Exercise 4.5.48. *Prove that $(\tilde{X}, \tilde{d})$ is unique up to isometry. That is, if (X', d') is a complete metric space such that X is isometric to a dense subset of X', then $(\tilde{X}, \tilde{d})$ and (X', d') are isometric.*

Remark 4.5.49. *One might ask at this point, "Why did we write Chapter 3 at all?" Why not just take the rational numbers with the usual metric and complete them by the above process to get the real numbers? Sorry folks, but in the proof of the above theorem, we used the fact that the real numbers are complete. In Chapter 5, we will have a simple, yet significant example of the completion of a metric space, namely, the p-adic completion of $\mathbb{Q}$ relative to a prime p. This emphasizes the fact that while $\mathbb{R}$ is the most familiar example of a completion of $\mathbb{Q}$ with respect to a metric, there are in fact infinitely many other completions of $\mathbb{Q}$.*

Exercise 4.5.50. *Let (X, d) be a metric space, and for any $x, y \in X$, let $d'(x, y) = \frac{d(x,y)}{1+d(x,y)}$.*

(i) *Show that d' defines a metric on X.*

(ii) *Show that U is open in (X, d) if and only if U is open in (X, d').*

(iii) *If a set A is compact in (X, d), is A necessarily compact in (X, d')?*

(iv) *If (X, d') is complete, is (X, d) necessarily complete?*

This exercise is intended to illustrate that, without additional structure, metric spaces can be twisted, expanded, or shrunken without disturbing the open sets too badly. This possibility can be eliminated by introducing an underlying algebraic structure. This can be seen in several places throughout the chapter when a metric is defined on a vector space or an algebra.

6. Independent Projects

6.1. General Point Set Topology.

6.1.1. *Basic Notions.*

Definition 4.6.1.1. *Given a set X and $\tau \subset \wp(X)$, we say that τ is a* topology *on X provided that:*

(a) *the sets $X, \varnothing \in \tau$;*

(b) *if $\{U_i\}_{i \in I} \subset \tau$, then* $\displaystyle\bigcup_{i \in I} U_i \in \tau$;

(c) *if $\{U_i\}_{i=1}^{n} \subset \tau$, then* $\displaystyle\bigcap_{i=1}^{n} U_i \in \tau$.

The pair (X, τ) is commonly referred to as a *topological space*. When the topology is clear or already given, the symbol τ is often suppressed in the notation.

Exercise 4.6.1.2.

(*i*) *If X is a set and $\alpha = \{\varnothing, X\}$, show that α is a topology on X. This is called the* indiscrete topology *on X.*

(*ii*) *If X is a set and $\omega = \wp(X)$, show that ω is a topology on X. This is called the* discrete topology *on X.*

(*iii*) *If X is a set and τ is a topology on X, show that $\alpha \subset \tau \subset \omega$ with α and ω as above.*

Exercise 4.6.1.3. *Let X be a metric space, and let τ be the collection of all open sets. Show that τ is a topology on X. The topology on $\mathbb{R}^n$ given by the usual metric is often called the* usual topology.

Exercise 4.6.1.4. *Let $X = \mathbb{R}$. Let $\tau = \{\varnothing\} \cup \{\text{all sets with finite complement}\}$. Show that τ is a topology on X. This is called the* finite complement topology *on $\mathbb{R}$.*

Exercise 4.6.1.5. *Let $X = \mathbb{R}$. Let $\tau = \{\varnothing, X\} \cup \bigcup_{a \in \mathbb{R}} \{(a, \infty)\}$. Show that τ is a topology on X.*

Definition 4.6.1.6. *Let (X, τ) be a topological space. A subset U of X is* open *relative to τ if $U \in \tau$. A subset V of X is* closed *relative to τ if $X \setminus V \in \tau$. We say that N is a* neighborhood *of $x \in X$ if there exists $U \in \tau$ such that $x \in U \subset N$.*

Exercise 4.6.1.7. *Show that a subset U of X is open iff, for all $x \in U$, there is a neighborhood of x contained in U.*

Proposition 4.6.1.8. *The closed sets of a topological space X satisfy the following properties:*

(*i*) *the sets $\varnothing, X$ are closed;*

(*ii*) *if $\{V_i\}_{i\in I}$ is a collection of closed sets, then $\bigcap_{i\in I} V_i$ is closed;*

(*iii*) *if $\{V_i\}_{i=1}^n$ is a finite collection of closed sets, then $\bigcup_{i=1}^{n} V_i$ is closed.*

Proof. This is immediate from DeMorgan's Laws. 

Definition 4.6.1.9 (see Definition 4.3.16). *Given a topology τ on X and a set $E \subset X$, a point $x \in X$ is called an* accumulation point *of E if, for all neighborhoods N of x, we have $(N \cap E) \setminus \{x\} \neq \varnothing$.*

Exercise 4.6.1.10.

(*i*) *Show that set E is closed iff it contains all of its accumulation points.*

(*ii*) *Show that the union of a set with its accumulation points is closed.*

(*iii*) *Show that the intersection of all closed sets containing E is equal to the union of E with its accumulation points.*

Remark 4.6.1.11. *The theory of closure, boundary, and interior operators can now be repeated for topological spaces as it was for metric spaces (see Section 4.3).*

Exercise 4.6.1.12. *Formulate a definition of density in a general topological space (see Definition 4.5.22).*

We now turn to the notion of continuous functions on general topological spaces.

Definition 4.6.1.13. *If (X, τ) and (Y, σ) are topological spaces, we say that a map $f : X \to Y$ is* continuous *if, for all $V \in \sigma$, the set $f^{-1}(V) \in \tau$. In other words, the inverse image of every open set in Y is an open set in X. In addition, if $f : X \to Y$ is a continuous bijection such that f^{-1} is also continuous, then we say that f is a* homeomorphism.

Remark 4.6.1.14. *Recall that in metric spaces the definition of continuity given above is equivalent to the ε-δ definition (see Theorem 4.4.17).*

Proposition 4.6.1.15. *If X, Y and Z are topological spaces and $f : X \to Y$ and $g : Y \to Z$ are continuous functions, then $g \circ f : X \to Z$ is a continuous function.*

Proof. Take U an open set in Z. Because g is continuous, the set $g^{-1}(U)$ is open in Y, and because f is continuous, the set $f^{-1}(g^{-1}(U)) = (g \circ f)^{-1}(U)$ is open in X.

Definition 4.6.1.16. *If X and Y are topological spaces, a map $f : X \to Y$ is an* open map *if, for every open set U contained in X, the set $f(U)$ is open in Y.*

Exercise 4.6.1.17.

(*i*) *Show that a homeomorphism is an open map.*

(*ii*) *Find topological spaces X, Y, and an open map $f : X \to Y$ such that there exists a closed set V in X with $f(V)$ not closed in Y.*

(*iii*) *Let X and Y be metric spaces. Suppose $f : X \to Y$ has the property that, for each ball $B \subset X$ centered at $x \in X$, the image $f(B)$ contains a ball centered at $f(x)$. Show that f is an open map.*

Definition 4.6.1.18. *Given a topological space (X, τ), a* base *(or* basis*) for the topology τ on X is a collection $\mathcal{B} \subset \tau$ such that every element of τ is a union of elements of $\mathcal{B}$.*

Definition 4.6.1.19. *Let X be a set, and let $\mathcal{C}$ be a collection of subsets of X that includes $\varnothing$ and X. The* topology generated by *$\mathcal{C}$ is the intersection of all the topologies on X that contain $\mathcal{C}$.*

Exercise 4.6.1.20. *Let (X, τ) be a topological space, and let $\mathcal{B}$ be a base for the topology. Show that τ is the topology generated by $\mathcal{B}$.*

Exercise 4.6.1.21. *Given a collection $\mathcal{C}$ of subsets of a set X, show that arbitrary unions and finite intersections of elements of $\mathcal{C}$ are in the topology generated by $\mathcal{C}$. Is it possible that the topology generated by $\mathcal{C}$ contains more elements than these?*

Theorem 4.6.1.22. *Let (X, τ) be a topological space with a countable base $\mathcal{B}$. Let $E \subset X$ be an uncountable set. Then there exists $x \in E$ such that x is an accumulation point of E.*

Proof. Suppose that no point in E is an accumulation point of E. Then, given any $x \in E$, there exists an open set U_x so that $U_x \cap E = \{x\}$. As $\mathcal{B}$ is a basis, there exists $B_x \in \mathcal{B}$ such that $x \in B_x \subset U_x$. This implies $B_x \cap E = \{x\}$. Note that if $x, y \in E$ and $x \neq y$, then $B_x \neq B_y$. It follows that there is a one-to-one map from E into $\mathcal{B}$ given by $x \mapsto B_x$. This contradicts the uncountability of E.

Definition 4.6.1.23. *A topological space (X, τ) is* separable *if there is a countable dense subset in X, that is, there is a countable subset $A \subset X$ such that $\overline{A} = X$.*

Exercise 4.6.1.24.

(*i*) *Show that a topological space* (X, τ) *that has a countable base is separable.*

(*ii*) *Prove or disprove: A topological space* (X, τ) *that is separable has a countable base.*

(*iii*) *Let* X *and* Y *be topological spaces, and suppose that there exists a continuous surjection* $f : X \to Y$. *Prove or disprove: if* X *is separable, then* Y *is separable.*

6.1.2. *Separation Properties.* Although metric spaces are the most common spaces in analysis, there are strong mathematical reasons for considering different topologies that occur in other parts of mathematics. Some idea of the unusual behavior that can arise in non-metric topologies is given by separation properties. Note that separability is *not* a separation property! Here are some of the most common.

Definition 4.6.1.25. *(Separation properties) Let* (X, τ) *be a topological space.*

(a) *The space* (X, τ) *is* T_0 *if for every pair of distinct points* $x, y \in X$, *there is a neighborhood* N *of one of the points that does not contain the other point.*

(b) *The space* (X, τ) *is* T_1 *if points are closed.*

(c) *The space* (X, τ) *is* T_2 *(commonly called* Hausdorff*) if, for every* $x, y \in X$, *there are open sets* U, V *so that* $x \in U$, $y \in V$ *and* $U \cap V = \varnothing$.

(d) *The space* (X, τ) *is* T_3 *(commonly called* regular*) if it is* T_2 *and, given any* $x \in X$ *and a neighborhood* N *of* x, *there is a closed neighborhood* V *of* x *such that* $V \subset N$.

(e) *The space* (X, τ) *is* T_4 *(commonly called* normal*) if it is* T_1 *and, given two closed sets* A *and* B *with* $A \cap B = \varnothing$, *there exist open sets* U *and* V *such that* $A \subset U$ *and* $B \subset V$ *and* $U \cap V = \varnothing$.

Exercise 4.6.1.26. *Show that metric spaces satisfy all of the above separation properties.*

Exercise 4.6.1.27.

(*i*) *Show that, if* (X, τ) *is* T_i, *then it is* T_{i-1} *for* $i = 1, 2, 3, 4$.

(*ii*) *Let* $X = \mathbb{R} \cup \{\infty\}$, *and let* $\tau = \{E \subset X \mid {}^cE$ *is finite, and* $\infty \in E\} \cup \{\varnothing\}$. *Show that* (X, τ) *is* T_0 *but not* T_1.

(*iii*) *Let* $X = \mathbb{R}$ *with the finite complement topology. Show that* X *is* T_1 *but not* T_2.

(*iv*) *Find an example of a topological space that is T_2 but not T_3.*

(*v*) *Find an example of a topological space that is T_3 but not T_4.*

The following lemma demonstrates the type of theorem that follows from assuming certain separation properties in a topological space.

Lemma 4.6.1.28. *(Urysohn) If A and B are disjoint closed subsets of a normal topological space X, then there is a continuous function $f : X \to [0,1]$ such that $f(A) = 0$ and $f(B) = 1$.*

Proof. Let $D = \{p2^{-q} \mid p, q \in \mathbb{N}\}$. We define $F : D \to \wp(X)$ and then use it to get the desired function. For $t \in D$ with $t > 1$ let $F(t) = X$, and let $F(1) = X \setminus B$. Using the assumption that X is normal, we pick $F(0)$ to be some open set containing A such that $\overline{F(0)} \cap B = \varnothing$. For $t \in D$ with $0 < t < 1$, we write $t = (2m+1)2^{-n}$ and choose, inductively on n and m, $F(t)$ to be an open set containing $\overline{F(2m \cdot 2^{-n})}$ and such that $\overline{F(t)} \subset F((2m+2) \cdot 2^{-n})$. This is possible because X is normal. Now we define $f : X \to [0,1]$. Let $f(x) = \inf\{t \mid x \in F(t)\}$. The function is 0 on A because $A \subset F(t)$ for all $t \in D$. The function f is 1 on B because $F(t) \subset X \setminus B$ for all $t \leq 1$ and $F(t) = X$ for $t > 1$.

Now we show that f is continuous. Observe that all sets of the form $\{t \mid t < s\}$ and $\{t \mid t > s\}$ generate the topology on $[0,1]$, and it suffices to check that the inverse images of these sets are open. Notice that $\{x \mid f(x) < s\} = \bigcup_{\{j \in D \mid j < s\}} F(j)$. For each $j \in D$, the set $F(j)$ is open and the arbitrary unions of open sets are open. Likewise, $\{x \mid f(x) \leq s\} = \bigcap_{\{j \in D \mid j > s\}} \overline{F(j)}$. This is an intersection of closed sets, hence is closed. Thus, $f^{-1}(\{t \mid t > s\})$ is open. ☹

6.1.3. *New Topologies from Old.*

Definition 4.6.1.29. *(Relative topology) Let (X, τ) be a topological space, and let $Y \subset X$. The* relative topology *on Y is the collection $\{E \cap Y \mid E \in \tau\}$.*

The relative topology on Y is sometimes called the *subspace topology*.

Exercise 4.6.1.30.

(*i*) *Let (X, τ) be a topological space, and let $Y \subset X$ have the relative topology. Show that the inclusion map $i : Y \to X$ is continuous.*

(*ii*) *Let X, Y be as above. Determine which of the separation properties, $T_0, \ldots, T_4$, are preserved by the relative topology on Y.*

Definition 4.6.1.31. *Let (X_1, τ_1) and (X_2, τ_2) be two topological spaces. Let $X = X_1 \times X_2$ be the Cartesian product. Then the* product topology *on X is the topology generated by the collection $\mathcal{C} = \{E_1 \times E_2 \mid E_1 \in \tau_1 \text{ and } E_2 \in \tau_2\}$.*

It is clear that the above definition can be extended to the product of a finite number of topological spaces.

Example 4.6.1.32.

(i) *The usual topologies on $\mathbb{R}^n$ and $\mathbb{C}^n$ are standard examples of product topologies.*

(ii) *The space $\mathbb{C}$ may be regarded topologically as $\mathbb{R} \times \mathbb{R}$ with the product topology.*

Definition 4.6.1.33. *Let $\{(X_i, \tau_i)\}_{i \in I}$ be a collection of topological spaces, and let $X = \prod_{i \in I} X_i$ be the Cartesian product. Then the* product topology *on X is the topology generated by the collection $\mathcal{C} = \{\prod_{i \in I} E_i \mid E_i \in \tau_i \text{ for all } i \in I, \text{ and } E_i = X_i \text{ for all but finitely many } i \in I\}$.*

Exercise 4.6.1.34.

(i) *For each $i \in \mathbb{N}$, let X_i be the closed interval $[0, 1]$ with the usual topology. Find the open sets in $X = \prod_{i \in \mathbb{N}} X_i$.*

(ii) *Let $A = \{x \in X \mid x_1 \in [0, 1] \text{ and } x_i = 0 \text{ for } i \geq 2\}$. Is the relative topology on A the usual topology on $[0, 1]$?*

Exercise 4.6.1.35. *If the index set is infinite, is there a reason that we do not define the product topology to be generated by all sets of the form $\prod_{i \in I} E_i$, where each $E_i \in \tau_i$?*

Exercise 4.6.1.36. *Let $\{(X_i, \tau_i)\}_{i \in I}$ be a collection of topological spaces and let $X = \prod_{i \in I} X_i$ with the product topology.*

(i) *For each $i \in I$, let $p_i : X \to X_i$ be the projection, defined by $p_i(x) = x_i$. Show that p_i is continuous.*

(ii) *Let Y be a topological space and let $f : Y \to X$. Show that f is continuous if and only if $p_i \circ f$ is continuous for all $i \in I$.*

Definition 4.6.1.37. *Let (X, τ) be a topological space, and let Y be a set. If $f : X \to Y$ is a function, we define the* quotient topology *σ associated to f on Y as follows. Given $E \subset Y$ we say that $E \in \sigma$ if $f^{-1}(E) \in \tau$.*

Exercise 4.6.1.38. *Show that with this definition, (Y, σ) is a topological space.*

One of the most natural examples of the quotient topology occurs when $X = G$, a group that is also a topological space, and H is a subgroup of G. We then take Y to be the coset space G/H (see Project 4.6.3 below) and give it the quotient topology associated with the function $g \mapsto gH$.

Exercise 4.6.1.39. *Let $G = \mathbb{R}$ with the usual topology, and let $H = \mathbb{Z}$. Show that G/H with the quotient topology is homeomorphic to S^1 (see Example 4.3.19(ii)).*

Exercise 4.6.1.40. *Let X be a topological space and let Y be a space with the quotient topology given by the function $f : X \to Y$. If Z is a topological space, show that $g : Y \to Z$ is continuous iff $g \circ f$ is continuous.*

6.1.4. *Compactness.*

Definition 4.6.1.41 (see Definition 4.5.3). *A subset K of a topological space X is* compact *if every cover of K by open sets admits a finite subcover. We say that a space X is* locally compact *if every $x \in X$ has a compact neighborhood in X.*

Exercise 4.6.1.42.

(*i*) *Show that every closed subset of a compact space is compact.*

(*ii*) *Show that every closed subset of a locally compact space is locally compact.*

Exercise 4.6.1.43. *If X is Hausdorff, then any compact set $K \subset X$ is closed.*

Exercise 4.6.1.44. *If $f : X \to Y$ is a continuous map, then for any compact set $K \subset X$, the set $f(K)$ is compact in Y.*

Exercise 4.6.1.45. *Show that, if X is compact and Y is Hausdorff, then every bijective continuous function $f : X \to Y$ is a homeomorphism.*

Exercise 4.6.1.46. *If X and Y are compact topological spaces, show that $X \times Y$ with the product topology is a compact topological space.*

Adventure 4.6.1.47. *Prove Tychynoff's Theorem, which states: If $\{(X_i, \tau_i)\}_{i\in I}$ is a collection of compact topological spaces, then $X = \prod_{i\in I} X_i$ with the product topology is a compact topological space.*

6.2. Fundamental Theorem of Algebra.

Here is a proof of the Fundamental Theorem of Algebra promised in Chapter 3.

Exercise 4.6.2.1. *Let P be a polynomial of positive degree with coefficients in $\mathbb{C}$. Show that there exists $z_0 \in \mathbb{C}$ such that $|P(z_0)| \leq |P(z)|$ for all $z \in \mathbb{C}$. Then show that, by considering the polynomial $P(z + z_0)$, we may assume $z_0 = 0$.*

Theorem 4.6.2.2 (The Fundamental Theorem of Algebra). *The field $\mathbb{C}$ is algebraically closed, that is, any nonconstant polynomial with coefficients in $\mathbb{C}$ has a root in $\mathbb{C}$.*

Proof. Let $P \in \mathbb{C}[z]$ be a polynomial of positive degree. By Exercise 4.6.2.1, we may assume $|P(z)|$ has a minimum at 0. There exists $n \geq 1$ and $a, b \in \mathbb{C}$ with $b \neq 0$ so that

$$P(z) = a + bz^n + z^{n+1}Q(z),$$

where $Q \in \mathbb{C}[z]$. Suppose that $P(0) = a \neq 0$, and choose an n-th root w of $-a/b$ in $\mathbb{C}$.

By continuity, there exists t with $0 < t < 1$ so that $t|w^{n+1}Q(tw)| < |a|$. Now, we have

$$\begin{aligned} P(tw) &= a + b(tw)^n + (tw)^{n+1}Q(tw) \\ &= (1 - t^n)a + (tw)^{n+1}Q(tw) \end{aligned}$$

because $bw^n = -a$. Hence,

$$\begin{aligned} |P(tw)| &\leq (1 - t^n)|a| + t^{n+1}|w^{n+1}Q(tw)| \\ &< (1 - t^n)|a| + t^n|a| = |a| = |P(0)|. \end{aligned}$$

This is a contradiction, and hence we must have $P(0) = a = 0$.

Exercise 4.6.2.3. *Find ten other proofs of the Fundamental Theorem of Algebra.*

Starting with any field F, we wish to define an algebraic closure of F. We first define an algebraic extension of F.

Definition 4.6.2.4. *Let F be a field and E be a field containing F as a subfield of E. We say that E is an* algebraic extension *of F if, given $\alpha \in E$, there exists a non-0 polynomial $p(x)$ with coefficients in F such that $p(\alpha) = 0$.*

Definition 4.6.2.5. *Let F a field. A field E containing F is an* algebraic closure *of F if E is an algebraic extension of F and E is algebraically closed.*

The following sequence of statements leads to the existence and uniqueness, up to isomorphism, of an algebraic closure of F.

Fact 4.6.2.6.

(1) *The field F is contained in an algebraically closed field E.*

(2) *There is an extension E of F that is both algebraically closed and algebraic over F.*

(3) *Suppose F is a field and E is an algebraic extension of F. Let σ be a monomorphism (injective homomorphism) of F into an algebraically closed field L. Then σ can be extended to a monomorphism of E into L.*

(4) *If L and L′ are algebraically closed fields that are algebraic over F, then there exists an isomorphism $\tau : L \to L'$ such that τ is the identity on F.*

Exercise 4.6.2.7. *Prove the above statements. Use Lang's* Algebra, *Chapter 5, if you must.*

Exercise 4.6.2.8. *Show that if F is algebraically closed, then the algebraic closure of F is F.*

Remark 4.6.2.9. *The Fundamental Theorem of Algebra shows that $\mathbb{C}$ is algebraically closed. In fact, $\mathbb{C}$ is the algebraic closure of $\mathbb{R}$. (You should prove, by writing down polynomials, that $\mathbb{C}$ is an algebraic extension of $\mathbb{R}$.)*

Exercise 4.6.2.10.

(i) *Show that $\mathbb{A}_{\mathbb{R}}$, the field of real algebraic numbers, is not algebraically closed.*

(ii) *Show that $\mathbb{A}$, the field of algebraic numbers, is the algebraic closure of $\mathbb{Q}$.*

6.3. Topological Groups.

Definition 4.6.3.1. *A set G is a* topological group *provided that*

(a) *G is a group,*

(b) *G is a Hausdorff topological space, and*

(c) *the map $(g, h) \mapsto gh$ from $G \times G \to G$ and the map $g \mapsto g^{-1}$ from $G \to G$ are continuous.*

Examples 4.6.3.2. *We have already encountered numerous examples of topological groups in this book:*

(i) $(\mathbb{R}, +)$ *and* $(\mathbb{C}, +)$;

(ii) $(\mathbb{R}^\times, \cdot)$ *and* $(\mathbb{C}^\times, \cdot)$;

(iii) $(\mathbb{R}^n, +)$ *and* $(\mathbb{C}^n, +)$;

(iv) $(M_n(\mathbb{R}), +)$, $(M_n(\mathbb{C}), +)$;

(v) $GL_n(\mathbb{R})$ *and* $GL_n(\mathbb{C})$;

(vi) $SL_n(\mathbb{R})$ *and* $SL_n(\mathbb{C})$;

(vii) *the groups B, A, and N as defined in Project 2.6.1 (see p. 81);*

(viii) $O(n, \mathbb{R})$ *and* $SO(n, \mathbb{R})$.

In the first three examples, we have the usual topology. For $M_n(\mathbb{R})$ and $M_n(\mathbb{C})$, we take the topology from $\mathbb{R}^{n^2}$ and $\mathbb{C}^{n^2}$, respectively. In the last four examples, we have the group operation of matrix multiplication and the *topology inherited from $M_n(\mathbb{R})$ or $M_n(\mathbb{C})$. It is clear in the first four examples that the group operations are continuous. For the last four examples, we note that matrix multiplication is a polynomial function in the coordinates.*

Exercise 4.6.3.3. *Prove that the inverse maps $g \mapsto g^{-1}$ in the last four examples are continuous.*

Remark 4.6.3.4. *Any group with the discrete topology is a topological group. This can be interesting when the group is infinite but it is notably uninteresting when the group is finite.*

Definition 4.6.3.5. *The map $g \mapsto g_0 g$ from $G \to G$ is called* left multiplication by g_0. *It should be clear what* right multiplication by g_0 *means.*

Exercise 4.6.3.6.

(*i*) *Show that left multiplication is a homeomorphism.*

(*ii*) *Show that $g \mapsto g^{-1}$ is a homeomorphism.*

From the definition of a topological group, one can immediately prove several properties about neighborhoods of points in such a group.

Exercise 4.6.3.7.

(*i*) *If $g, h \in G$, show that for every neighborhood W of gh, there exist neighborhoods U of g and V of h such that $UV \subset W$.*

(*ii*) *If $g \in G$, show that for every neighborhood V of g^{-1}, there exists a neighborhood U of g such that $U^{-1} \subset V$.*

(*iii*) *If $g, h \in G$, show that for every neighborhood W of gh^{-1}, there exist neighborhoods U of g and V of h such that $UV^{-1} \subset W$.*

Exercise 4.6.3.8.

(*i*) *If $F \subset G$ is closed and $g \in G$, show that gF, Fg, and F^{-1} are closed.*

(*ii*) *If $S \subset G$ is any subset and $U \subset G$ is open, show that US, SU, and U^{-1} are open.*

For every pair of elements $g, h \in G$, left multiplication by hg^{-1} is a homeomorphism that maps g to h. Hence, to verify local properties of G, it suffices to verify them at one point, usually the identity.

As an example, we will show that all topological groups are regular. Recall that a Hausdorff topological space X is regular if and only if, for all $x \in X$ and for all neighborhoods U of x, there exists a neighborhood V of x such that $\overline{V} \subset U$.

Proposition 4.6.3.9. *A topological group G is regular.*

Proof. It suffices to consider neighborhoods of the identity e. Let U be a neighborhood of e. Since $ee^{-1} = e$, there exists a neighborhood V of e such that $VV^{-1} \subset U$. We will show that $\overline{V} \subset U$.

Let $p \in \overline{V}$. Then every neighborhood of p intersects V. Since pV is open and $p \in pV$ (since $e \in V$), there exists a point $a \in pV \cap V$. We write $a = pb$ with $b \in V$, and hence $p = ab^{-1}$. Thus $p = ab^{-1} \in VV^{-1} \subset U$. ☹

Exercise 4.6.3.10. *If $P, Q \subset G$ are compact, show that PQ is compact.*

Exercise 4.6.3.11. *Given any open set U containing e, show that there exists an open set $V \subset U$ such that $e \in V$ and $V = V^{-1}$.*

Exercise 4.6.3.12. *If G is connected, any neighborhood U of e generates G.*

Chapter 5

Complete Metric Spaces and the p-adic Completion of $\mathbb{Q}$

...I have tried to draw the conclusions from the developments of the last thirty years, whereby locally compact groups, measure and integration have been seen to play an increasingly important role in classical number theory. ...In retrospect, we see now that the real numbers appear there as one of the infinitely many completions of the prime field, one which is neither more nor less interesting to the arithmetician than its p-adic companions, and that there is at least one language and one technique, that of the adeles, for bringing them all together under one roof and making them cooperate for a common purpose.

– *André Weil,*
Basic Number Theory

In this chapter, we study some interesting ideas related to the concept of completeness in metric spaces. These ideas are all basic tools in mathematics.

These include:

(1) the Contraction Mapping Theorem and applications to differential equations;

(2) the Baire Category Theorem and its consequences;

(3) the Stone-Weierstrass theorem;

(4) the p-adic completion $\mathbb{Q}_p$ of $\mathbb{Q}$ for a given prime p.

1. The Contraction Mapping Theorem and Its Applications

Definition 5.1.1. *Let X be a metric space and f a map from X to X. We say that f is a* contraction mapping *of X if there exists a real number α, with $0 < \alpha < 1$, such that $d(f(x), f(y)) \leq \alpha d(x, y)$ for every pair $x, y \in X$.*

Exercise 5.1.2. *Show that a contraction mapping is continuous.*

Exercise 5.1.3. *Let f be a polynomial function from $\mathbb{R}$ to $\mathbb{R}$. Give conditions on f so that f is a contraction mapping.*

Definition 5.1.4. *Let X be a metric space and f a map from X to X. A point $x_0 \in X$ is a* fixed point *of f if $f(x_0) = x_0$.*

Exercise 5.1.5.

(*i*) *Let $f : [0, 1] \to [0, 1]$ be a continuous function. Show that f has a fixed point.*

(*ii*) *Find a continuous function $f : \mathbb{R} \to \mathbb{R}$ that does not have a fixed point.*

Theorem 5.1.6 (Contraction Mapping Theorem). *Let X be a complete metric space and let $f : X \to X$ be a contraction mapping with constant α. Then f has a unique fixed point $x_0 \in X$.*

Proof. Let x_1 be any element of X. Define $x_2 = f(x_1)$, $x_3 = f(x_2) = f(f(x_1)) = f^2(x_1)$, and in general $x_n = f^{n-1}(x_1)$. Then, if $n > m$, we have

$$\begin{aligned}
d(x_m, x_n) &= d(f^{m-1}(x_1), f^{n-1}(x_1)) \\
&\leq \alpha^{m-1} d(x_1, f^{n-m}(x_1)) \\
&\leq \alpha^{m-1}(d(x_1, x_2) + d(x_2, x_3) + \cdots + d(x_{n-m}, x_{n-m+1})) \\
&\leq \alpha^{m-1}(d(x_1, x_2) + \alpha d(x_1, x_2) + \cdots + \alpha^{n-m-1} d(x_1, x_2)) \\
&\leq \frac{\alpha^{m-1}}{1-\alpha} d(x_1, x_2).
\end{aligned}$$

It follows that $(x_n)_{n\in\mathbb{N}}$ is a Cauchy sequence in X that converges since X is complete. Let $x_0 = \lim_{n\to\infty} x_n$. From the continuity of f, it follows that $f(x_0) = x_0$.

Exercise 5.1.7. *Show that x_0 is the unique fixed point of f.* 

Exercise 5.1.8. (i) *Let $B = B_1(0)$ be the unit ball in the usual metric on $\mathbb{R}^n$, and let f be a map from B to B. We say that f satisfies a* Lipschitz condition *if there exists a constant C such that $|f(x) - f(y)| \leq C|x - y|$ for all $x, y \in B$. Show that, if $0 < C < 1$, then f is a contraction mapping. Show that, if $C \geq 1$, then f need not be a contraction mapping.*

(ii) *Let $T : \ell_n^p(\mathbb{R}) \to \ell_n^q(\mathbb{R})$, $1 \leq p, q \leq \infty$, be a linear transformation. When is T a contraction mapping?*

The following theorem, sometimes called *Picard's Theorem*, gives a direct application of the Contraction Mapping Theorem to a problem in analysis.

Theorem 5.1.9 (Picard's Theorem). *Let B be a ball of radius r in $\mathbb{R}^2$ with center at (x_0, y_0). Suppose that $f : B \to \mathbb{R}$ is a continuous function that satisfies a Lipschitz condition in the second variable, that is, there is a constant C such that $|f(x, y) - f(x, y')| \leq C|y - y'|$ for all $(x, y), (x, y') \in B$. Then there exists a $\delta > 0$ such that the differential equation $dy/dx = f(x, y)$ has a unique solution $y = \phi(x)$, satisfying $\phi(x_0) = y_0$, in the interval $|x - x_0| < \delta$.*

Proof. Without loss of generality, we can assume that f is bounded on B, that is, there exists a constant M so that $|f(x, y)| \leq M$ for all $(x, y) \in B$. Take a $\delta > 0$ such that $C\delta < 1$ and $\{(x, y) \mid |x - x_0| \leq \delta, |y - y_0| \leq M\delta\} \subset B$. We now work inside the space $X = \{\phi \in \mathcal{C}([x_0 - \delta, x_0 + \delta]) \mid |\phi(x) - y_0| \leq M\delta\}$. If we define a metric on X with the sup norm, then, by Theorem 4.4.30 and Exercise 4.5.8(ii), X is a complete metric space. Now, take the mapping $T : X \to X$ defined by $T\phi(x) = y_0 + \int_{x_0}^{x} f(t, \phi(t))\, dt$. It is obvious that $T\phi \in X$ and that $\|T\phi - T\phi'\| \leq C\delta\|\phi - \phi'\|$, where $\|\cdot\|$ represents the sup norm. Thus, T is a contraction mapping on X, and there is a unique function $\phi \in X$ so that $T\phi = \phi$. It is easy to check that the solutions to the differential equation are precisely the fixed points of T, so the proof is complete. ☠

The Contraction Mapping Theorem can also be applied to systems of differential equations, see for example Kolmogorov and Fomin's book "Introduction to Real Analysis".

The following exercise assumes the reader is familiar with some basic concepts in calculus, especially integration theory.

Exercise 5.1.10. *Take $\mathcal{C}([0, 1], \mathbb{R})$ with the* sup *metric and let $k(x, y) : [0, 1] \times [0, 1] \to \mathbb{R}$ be a continuous function satisfying* $\sup_{0 \leq x \leq 1} \int_0^1 |k(x, y)|\, dy < 1$. *Given a function $g(x) \in \mathcal{C}([0, 1], \mathbb{R})$ show there is a unique solution*

$f(x) \in \mathcal{C}([0,1],\mathbb{R})$ *to the equation*

$$f(x) - \int_0^1 k(x,y)f(y)\,dy = g(x).$$

2. The Baire Category Theorem and Its Applications

The topic of Baire category is fundamental in several parts of mathematics, in particular, in measure theory and the study of bounded linear operators on Banach spaces. The word category should not be confused with the notions of "categories and functors." These ideas occur in many parts of mathematics, but they will not be found in this book.

We begin with some simple ideas in metric spaces.

Definition 5.2.1. *Let X be a metric space. A subset $A \subseteq X$ is said to be* nowhere dense *if $\complement(\bar{A})$ is dense in X. A set $A \subset X$ is said to be of the* first category *if A is a countable union of nowhere dense sets. A set $A \subset X$ is said to be of the* second category *if A is not of the first category.*

Examples 5.2.2.

(i) *Let $A = \mathbb{Z}^n$, the set of integer lattice points in $\mathbb{R}^n$ with the usual metric. Then A is nowhere dense and hence of the first category.*

(ii) *Let $[0,1] \subset \mathbb{R}$ with the usual metric, and let A be the Cantor set. Then A is nowhere dense in $[0,1]$.*

(iii) *In a discrete metric space, the only nowhere dense set is the empty set.*

(iv) *A set containing a single point in a complete metric space is nowhere dense if and only if the point is not isolated.*

Exercise 5.2.3.

(i) *Show that a subset A of a metric space X is nowhere dense iff the interior of $\bar{A}$ is empty.*

(ii) *Suppose U is an open set in a metric space X. Show that $\bar{U} \setminus U$ is nowhere dense in X.*

(iii) *Suppose F is a closed subset of a metric space X. Show that $F \setminus F^{\circ}$ is nowhere dense in X.*

(iv) *Show that a countable union of sets of the first category is of the the first category.*

This is a good time to create a family of sets that is interesting for a number of purposes. The sets are called *generalized Cantor sets* and are a generalization of the Cantor set in Exercise 3.6.26 (but note that the Cantor set is not actually a generalized Cantor set). They are constructed as follows. Choose a real number α, with $0 < \alpha < 1$. Then delete successively from $[0,1]$ the following sequence of open intervals. First, remove the open interval $(1/2 - \alpha/4, 1/2 + \alpha/4)$. From the two remaining closed intervals, remove the middle open intervals each of length $\alpha/8$. Continuing inductively, we remove a sequence of open intervals whose total length is $\sum_{n=1}^{\infty} \alpha/2^n = \alpha$.

The remaining set of points is denoted by C_α. It is a consequence of elementary measure theory that the "length" of C_α is $1 - \alpha$.

Definition 5.2.4. *A subset A of a metric space is* perfect *if every point of A is an accumulation point of A.*

Remark 5.2.5. *Note that we saw in Exercise* 3.6.26 *that the ordinary Cantor set in the closed interval $[0,1]$ is a perfect set.*

Exercise 5.2.6. *For any α, with $0 < \alpha < 1$, show that C_α is a nowhere dense perfect set in $[0,1]$ with the usual metric.*

In the discussion of category, the crucial issue is not whether a given set is dense. For example, the rational numbers in $\mathbb{R}$ with the usual metric form a dense subset and are of the first category, while the unit interval in $\mathbb{R}$ is not dense in $\mathbb{R}$ and is of the second category.

Exercise 5.2.7.

(i) *Show that the irrational numbers are of the second category in $\mathbb{R}$ with the usual metric.*

(ii) *Determine if each of the following sets is of the first or second category in $\mathbb{R}^n$ with the usual metric:*
   (a) $A = \{(x_1, x_2, \ldots, x_n) \mid x_j \in \mathbb{Q}$ *for* $j = 1, 2, \ldots, n\}$;
   (b) $A = \{(x_1, x_2, \ldots, x_n) \mid$ *at least k of the coordinates are rational*$\}$ *for a fixed number k;*
   (c) $A = \{(x_1, x_2, \ldots, x_n) \mid$ *at least 1 coordinate is irrational*$\}$.

The following theorems of Baire are extremely important.

Theorem 5.2.8 (Baire). *Suppose that X is a complete metric space, and let $(U_n)_{n \in \mathbb{N}}$ be a collection of dense open subsets of X. Then $\bigcap_{n \in \mathbb{N}} U_n$ is dense in X.*

Proof. Let $U \subseteq X$ be a nonempty open set. We claim that $U \cap (\bigcap_{n \in \mathbb{N}} U_n) \neq \varnothing$. To show this, choose $x_1 \in U \cap U_1$ and $r_1 > 0$ so that $\bar{B}_{r_1}(x_1) \subseteq U_1 \cap U$. Next, since U_2 is open and dense, we can choose $x_2 \in B_{r_1}(x_1) \cap U_2$ and r_2, with $0 < r_2 < r_1/2$ such that $\bar{B}_{r_2}(x_2) \subset B_{r_1}(x_1) \cap U_2$. Proceeding inductively, we choose $x_n \in B_{r_{n-1}}(x_{n-1})$ and r_n, with $0 < r_n < r_{n-1}/2$, such that $\bar{B}_{r_n}(x_n) \subseteq B_{r_{n-1}}(x_{n-1}) \cap U_n$. It is clear that $(x_n)_{n \in \mathbb{N}}$ is a Cauchy sequence and, since X is complete, this sequence converges to a point x_0 in X. It follows immediately that x_0 is in U, and this proves the theorem.

Corollary 5.2.9 (Baire Category Theorem). *Let X be a complete metric space. Then X is of the second category in itself.*

Proof. This is clear from the theorem above. 

Exercise 5.2.10. *Let X be a complete metric space and $(F_n)_{n \in \mathbb{N}}$ a countable collection of closed sets in X such that $X = \bigcup_{n \in \mathbb{N}} F_n$. Show that $U = \bigcup_{n \in \mathbb{N}} F_n^\circ$ is dense.*

Exercise 5.2.11. *Show that a complete metric space with no isolated points is uncountable.*

A basic theorem that shows the usefulness of Baire Category is the Uniform Boundedness Principle. This is often thought of as a theorem about linear operators on Banach spaces, which we do not discuss in this book. But it is really a theorem about continuous functions on complete metric spaces.

Theorem 5.2.12 (Uniform Boundedness). *Let X be a complete metric space and let $S \subset \mathcal{C}(X, \mathbb{R})$. Suppose that, for each $x \in X$, there is a constant M_x such that $|f(x)| \leq M_x$ for all $f \in S$. Then there are a non-empty open subset $U \subset X$ and a constant M so that $|f(x)| < M$ for all $f \in S$ and all $x \in U$.*

Proof. For $n \in \mathbb{N}$ and $f \in S$, let $S_{n,f} = \{x \in X \mid |f(x)| \leq n\}$. Let $S_n = \bigcap_{f \in S} S_{n,f}$. Since f is continuous, $S_{n,f}$ is closed, and hence, S_n is closed. For each $x \in X$, there is an n such that $|f(x)| < n$ for all $f \in S$. Hence $X = \bigcup_{n \in \mathbb{N}} S_n$. The Baire Category theorem of X implies there exists an $N \in \mathbb{N}$ so that S_N is not nowhere dense. Since S_N is closed, it contains an open ball U and, for each $x \in U$, we have $|f(x)| \leq N$ for all $f \in S$.

Exercise 5.2.13.

(i) *With the notation of Theorem 5.2.12, give an example of a set S of continuous functions such that $\sup_{x \in X} M_x = \infty$.*

(ii) *Does your answer to (i) change if X is a compact metric space?*

3. The Stone–Weierstrass Theorem

Throughout this section F represents $\mathbb{R}$ or $\mathbb{C}$.

Definition 5.3.1. *Let A be a collection of functions from a set X to F. We say that the collection A* separates points *if, for every pair of distinct points $x_1, x_2 \in X$, there is a function $f \in A$ such that $f(x_1) \neq f(x_2)$.*

Example 5.3.2. *If $X = [0,1]$, then $\mathcal{C}(X, \mathbb{R})$ separates points. This is easy to see just by drawing a picture.*

Exercise 5.3.3.

(i) *Show that polynomial functions in $\mathcal{C}([0,1], \mathbb{R})$ separate points.*

(ii) *Does the class of functions $\{\sin(2\pi n x) \mid n \in \mathbb{N}\}$ in $\mathcal{C}([0,1], \mathbb{R})$ separate points?*

Definition 5.3.4. *A real polynomial function $f : \mathbb{R}^n \to \mathbb{R}$ is a finite linear combination of expressions of the form $x_1^{m_1} x_2^{m_2} \cdots x_n^{m_n}$ where $m_1, m_2, \ldots, m_n$ are non-negative integers. The coefficients of a polynomial may be taken from $\mathbb{Z}$, $\mathbb{Q}$, or $\mathbb{R}$. The resulting sets of polynomials are denoted by $\mathbb{Z}[x_1, \ldots, x_n]$, $\mathbb{Q}[x_1, \ldots, x_n]$, and $\mathbb{R}[x_1, \ldots, x_n]$, respectively.*

Example 5.3.5. *A typical polynomial in $\mathbb{R}[x_1, x_2, x_3, x_4]$ looks like $\sqrt{2}x_1^3 x_2 x_3^2 x_4 + \pi x_1 x_2^5 x_4^{15} - 11 x_1 x_4$.*

Exercise 5.3.6.

(i) *Show that $R[x_1, x_2, \ldots, x_n]$ is a commutative ring with 1 for $R = \mathbb{Z}, \mathbb{Q}$, or $\mathbb{R}$. Find the units (invertible elements) in each of these rings.*

(ii) *Find the possible images of a polynomial in $\mathbb{R}[x_1, \ldots, x_n]$.*

Theorem 5.3.7 (Weierstrass). *Let A be a compact set in $\mathbb{R}^n$. Then every continuous function $f : A \to \mathbb{R}$ is the uniform limit of a sequence of real polynomials in $\mathbb{R}[x_1, \ldots, x_n]$.*

Theorem 5.3.8 (Stone). *Let X be a compact metric space. Let A be an algebra of continuous, real valued functions on X, and suppose that A separates points. Then $\bar{A}$, the uniform closure of A, either coincides with $\mathcal{C}(X, \mathbb{R})$ or with $\mathcal{C}_{x_0}(X, \mathbb{R}) = \{f \in \mathcal{C}(X, \mathbb{R}) \mid f(x_0) = 0\}$, for some point $x_0 \in X$.*

Note that Stone's theorem implies Weierstrass's theorem simply by letting $A = \mathbb{R}[x_1, x_2, \ldots, x_n]$. Before we attempt the proof, it will be helpful to gather some preliminary lemmas.

Lemma 5.3.9. *Let A be an algebra of real valued, continuous functions on a compact metric space X. Then, for $f \in A$, $|f|$ is in the uniform closure of A. That is, there is a sequence $(f_n)_{n \in \mathbb{N}}$ in A so that $(f_n)_{n \in \mathbb{N}}$ converges uniformly to $|f|$.*

Proof. Since X is compact, we know that f is bounded (see Exercise 4.5.8(ii)). Choose $C \in \mathbb{R}$, $C > 0$, so that $|f(x)| \leq C$ for all $x \in X$. Let $u = \frac{1}{C} f$. Then $u \in A$ and $\|u\| \leq 1$. Now we construct a sequence $(w_n)_{n \in \mathbb{N}}$ in A converging uniformly to $|u|$.

Let $w_0 = 0$, and define w_n inductively by the relation

$$w_{n+1} = w_n + \frac{u^2 - w_n^2}{2}.$$

Before proceeding further, notice if we formally took limits in n, we would have a relation of the form $w = w + (u^2 - w^2)/2$, which would imply that $w^2 = u^2$. With a little luck, we may also show that $w \geq 0$ and hence $w = |u|$.

First notice that $0 \leq w_1 - w_0 = w_1 = u^2/2 \leq u^2 \leq |u|$. Now suppose $w_k - w_{k-1} \geq 0$, and $w_k \leq |u|$ for $1 \leq k \leq n$. Then, $w_n \geq 0$ and $w_{n+1} - w_n = \frac{u^2-w_n^2}{2} = \frac{|u|+w_n}{2}(|u| - w_n) \geq 0$. Also, keeping in mind that $|u| \leq 1$, we have

$$\begin{aligned} 0 \leq w_{n+1} = w_n + \frac{u^2 - w_n^2}{2} &= w_n + (\frac{|u| + w_n}{2})(|u| - w_n) \\ &\leq w_n + |u| - w_n = |u|. \end{aligned}$$

Hence, by induction, $(w_n)_{n\in\mathbb{N}}$ is an increasing sequence of functions and $0 \leq w_n \leq |u|$ for all n. Now, as suggested in the beginning of the proof, we let w be the pointwise limit of $(w_n)_{n\in\mathbb{N}}$, which exists by Lemma 3.6.9. Then, $w = |u|$, and by Dini's Theorem, 4.5.10 we know that the sequence $(w_n)_{n\in\mathbb{N}}$ converges uniformly to $|u|$.

Definition 5.3.10. *Let V be a vector space of real valued continuous functions on a metric space X. We say that V is a* lattice *if $|f| \in V$ whenever $f \in V$.*

Exercise 5.3.11. *Let V be a lattice on a metric space X. If f, g are in V, set $f \wedge g = \min(f, g)$ and $f \vee g = \max(f, g)$. Show that $f \wedge g$ and $f \vee g \in V$.*

Lemma 5.3.12. *Let X be a compact metric space and L a lattice of continuous functions on X. Suppose that, for any $x, y \in X$ with $x \neq y$ and $a, b \in \mathbb{R}$, there is a function $f_{xy} \in L$ satisfying $f_{xy}(x) = a$ and $f_{xy}(y) = b$. Then, for each $f \in C(X, \mathbb{R})$, there is a sequence $(f_n)_{n\in\mathbb{N}} \in L$ so that $(f_n)_{n\in\mathbb{N}}$ converges uniformly to f.*

Proof. Take $f \in C(X, \mathbb{R})$ and $\varepsilon > 0$. For any $x, y \in X$, we identify the function f_{xy} and the sets U_{xy} and V_{xy} as follows. Let $a = f(x)$ and $b = f(y)$. Take $f_{xy} \in L$ so that $f_{xy}(x) = a$ and $f_{xy}(y) = b$. We take $U_{xy} = \{z \in X \mid f_{xy}(z) < f(z) + \varepsilon\}$ and $V_{xy} = \{z \in X \mid f(z) - \varepsilon < f_{xy}(z)\}$. Notice that for any $x, y \in X$, the sets U_{xy} and V_{xy} are open and, in addition, both contain x and y.

Fix y. Then by compactness, there exists a finite number of points $x_1, x_2, \ldots, x_n$ so that $\{U_{x_1y}, U_{x_2y}, \ldots, U_{x_ny}\}$ covers X. Set $h_y = \min(f_{x_1y}, f_{x_2y}, \ldots, f_{x_ny})$. By Exercise 5.3.11, we have $h_y \in L$ and $h_y(z) < f(z) + \varepsilon$ for all $z \in X$. Notice that $f(z) - \varepsilon < h_y(z)$ for $z \in V_y = \bigcap_{i=1}^n V_{x_iy}$.

Now let $y \in X$ vary, and for each y, construct h_y and V_y as above. By compactness, we can select an open cover $\{V_{y_1}, V_{y_2}, \ldots, V_{y_m}\}$ of X. Put $l = \max(h_{y_1}, h_{y_2}, \ldots, h_{y_m})$. Then $l \in L$ and $f(z) - \varepsilon < l(z) < f(z) + \varepsilon$.

Finally, to construct $(f_n)_{n\in\mathbb{N}}$, we let $\varepsilon = 2^{-n}$ and choose f_n to be the function l constructed above. ☠

We are ready to return to the proof of Stone's theorem.

Proof. (of Theorem 5.3.8) There are two cases to consider. First, suppose that, for each $x_0 \in X$, there is an $f \in A$ so that $f(x_0) \neq 0$. Take $x_1, x_2 \in X$ so that $x_1 \neq x_2$. Then there is a function $f \in A$ so that $f(x_1) \neq 0$ and $f(x_1) \neq f(x_2)$. To see this, take functions $h, g \in A$ so that $g(x_1) \neq g(x_2)$ and $h(x_1) \neq 0$. Then take

$$f = \begin{cases} g & \text{if } g(x_1) \neq 0 \\ h & \text{if } g(x_1) = 0 \text{ and } h(x_1) \neq h(x_2) \\ g + h & \text{if } g(x_1) = 0 \text{ and } h(x_1) = h(x_2). \end{cases}$$

If $f(x_2) \neq 0$, let $u(x) = (f(x)/f(x_2)) - (f(x)/f(x_2))^2$. Then $u \in A$, $u(x_1) \neq 0$ and $u(x_2) = 0$.

Hence, we can find f_1 and f_2 in A so that $f_1(x_1) = 1$, $f_1(x_2) = 0$, $f_2(x_1) = 0$, and $f_2(x_2) = 1$. Now for any $a, b \in \mathbb{R}$, take $f = af_1(x) + bf_2(x)$. Then $f(x_1) = a$ and $f(x_2) = b$. From Lemma 5.3.9, we have that $\bar{A}$, the uniform closure of A, is a lattice. From Lemma 5.3.12, $\bar{A} = \mathcal{C}(X, \mathbb{R})$. This concludes the proof in the first case.

Now we turn to the case when there is an element $x_0 \in X$ so that $f(x_0) = 0$ for all $f \in A$. Let $A' = \{g \in \mathcal{C}(X, \mathbb{R}) \mid g(x) = c + f(x) \text{ for some } c \in \mathbb{R} \text{ and } f \in A\}$. We have that A' is an algebra satisfying the conditions for the first part of the theorem. In particular, if $h(x) \in \mathcal{C}_{x_0}(X, \mathbb{R})$ and $\varepsilon > 0$, there is a function $f \in A$ and $c \in \mathbb{R}$ so that $\sup_{x\in X} |h(x) - c - f(x)| < \varepsilon$. Looking at x_0, we see that $|c| < \varepsilon$. Hence $\sup_{x\in X} |h(x) - f(x)| < 2\varepsilon$. ☠

Exercise 5.3.13. *Let X, Y be compact metric spaces. Show that the set $\{(x, y) \mapsto f(x)g(y) \mid f \in \mathcal{C}(X, \mathbb{R}) \text{ and } g \in \mathcal{C}(Y, \mathbb{R})\}$ is uniformly dense in $\mathcal{C}(X \times Y, \mathbb{R})$.*

Exercise 5.3.14.

(i) *Prove the complex version of the Stone–Weierstrass theorem. Let X be a compact metric space. Let A be an algebra of continuous complex valued functions on X with the property that, if $f \in A$ then $\bar{f} \in A$. Assume that A separates points and there is no point $x \in X$ such that $f(x) = 0$ for all $f \in A$. Show that the uniform closure of A is $\mathcal{C}(X, \mathbb{C})$.*

(ii) *A* trigonometric polynomial *from* $\mathbb{T} = \{z \in \mathbb{C} \mid |z| = 1\}$ *to* $\mathbb{C}$ *is a function of the form* $f(e^{i\theta}) = \sum_{j=-n}^{n} a_n e^{ij\theta}$, *where the coefficients are in* $\mathbb{C}$. *Show that the set of trigonometric polynomials is uniformly dense in* $C(\mathbb{T}, \mathbb{C})$.

4. The p-adic Completion of $\mathbb{Q}$

The simplest example of the completion of an incomplete metric space is called the p-adic completion of $\mathbb{Q}$. The p in this case refers to a prime integer p, and the metric is that defined below. This metric plays a significant role in analysis, number theory, theoretical physics, and other areas.

The process of completing a metric space was carried out in Chapter 4. As mentioned there, that process for completing a metric space cannot be used to obtain the real numbers from the rational numbers because the method uses the fact that the real numbers are complete with respect to the usual metric. Note that in Chapter 3, we presented two methods for completing the rational numbers to the real numbers, namely, Cauchy sequences (see Section 3.5) and Dedekind cuts (see Section 3.10.1).

In this section we will use some algebraic ideas from group theory and ring theory that have not been discussed previously. They will be defined and named in the context we are developing. For more information, the reader can consult Dummit and Foote's "Algebra" or Lang's "Algebra."

4.1. Definitions and Basic Properties.

Definition 5.4.1. *Let p be a prime in $\mathbb{Z}$. For $r \in \mathbb{Q}^\times$, we write $r = p^k(\frac{a}{b})$ where a and b are relatively prime integers not divisible by p. Define the* p-adic absolute value $|\cdot|_p$ *on* $\mathbb{Q}$ *by*

$$|r|_p = p^{-k} \text{ if } r \neq 0 \quad \text{and} \quad |0|_p = 0.$$

Exercise 5.4.2. *Show that $|\cdot|_p$ has the following properties for all $r, s \in \mathbb{Q}$:*

(i) $|r|_p \geqslant 0$, *and* $|r|_p = 0$ *if and only if* $r = 0$;

(ii) $|rs|_p = |r|_p \cdot |s|_p$;

(iii) $|r + s|_p \leq \max(|r|_p, |s|_p)$;

(iv) $|r + s|_p = \max(|r|_p, |s|_p)$ *if* $|r|_p \neq |s|_p$.

Note that i and ii are familiar properties of the usual absolute value on $\mathbb{Q}$, while iii, known as the non-Archimedean Triangle Inequality, *is stronger than the usual triangle inequality on $\mathbb{Q}$, which asserts that*

$$|r + s| \leq |r| + |s|, \qquad r, s \in \mathbb{Q}.$$

The absolute value $|\cdot|_p$ gives a metric on $\mathbb{Q}$ defined by

$$d_p(r,s) = |r-s|_p, \qquad r,s \in \mathbb{Q}.$$

Exercise 5.4.3.

(*i*) *Show that d_p is a metric.*

(*ii*) *Find a Cauchy sequence in $\mathbb{Q}$ relative to $|\cdot|_p$ that does not converge in $\mathbb{Q}$. This shows that $\mathbb{Q}$ is not complete with respect to $|\cdot|_p$.*

We denote by $\mathbb{Q}_p$ the completion of $\mathbb{Q}$ with respect to the metric d. We can define addition and multiplication on $\mathbb{Q}_p$ so that $\mathbb{Q}_p$ becomes a field. Recall that elements of $\mathbb{Q}_p$ are equivalence classes of Cauchy sequences from $\mathbb{Q}$ relative to $|\cdot|_p$. The process of turning $\mathbb{Q}_p$ into a field proceeds exactly as in the case of the real numbers (see section 3.5).

Definition 5.4.4. *Addition and multiplication on $\mathbb{Q}_p$ are defined as follows:*

$$[a_n] + [b_n] = [a_n + b_n]; \text{ and}$$
$$[a_n]\cdot[b_n] = [a_n b_n].$$

Next, we must extend $|\cdot|_p$ to $\mathbb{Q}_p$. Observe that, if $(a_n)_{n\in\mathbb{N}}$ is a Cauchy sequence in $\mathbb{Q}$ with respect to $|\cdot|_p$, then $(|a_n|_p)_{n\in\mathbb{N}}$ is a Cauchy sequence in $\mathbb{R}$. So if $[a_n] \in \mathbb{Q}_p$, then the absolute value on $\mathbb{Q}_p$ can be defined by

$$|[a_n]|_p = \lim_{n\to\infty} |a_n|_p$$

Note that if $\lim_{n\to\infty} |a_n|_p \neq 0$, then the sequence $(|a_n|_p)_{n\in\mathbb{N}}$ is eventually constant and hence converges to the eventual constant.

Exercise 5.4.5.

(*i*) *Show that addition, multiplication, and $|\cdot|_p$ are well-defined on $\mathbb{Q}_p$.*

(*ii*) *Show that $\mathbb{Q}_p$ is a field with the operations given above.*

(*iii*) *Show that $|\cdot|_p$ on $\mathbb{Q}_p$ satisfies the same properties as it does in $\mathbb{Q}$ (see (5.4.2)).*

(*iv*) *Show that the image of $\mathbb{Q}_p$ under $|\cdot|_p$ is the same as that of $\mathbb{Q}$ under $|\cdot|_p$, that is, $\{p^k \mid k \in \mathbb{Z}\} \cup \{0\}$.*

(*v*) *Show that $\mathbb{Q}_p$ cannot be made into an ordered field.*

Definition 5.4.6. *The field $\mathbb{Q}_p$ is called a* p-adic field. *It is also called the* p-adic completion of $\mathbb{Q}$.

4.2. The Additive Structure of $\mathbb{Q}_p$.

We begin by defining several sets in $\mathbb{Q}_p$ that play an important role in our study of p-adic fields.

Definition 5.4.7. *Define the following subsets of* $\mathbb{Q}_p$*:*

(a) $R_p = \{x \in \mathbb{Q}_p \mid |x|_p \leq 1\}$;

(b) $\wp = \{x \in R_p \mid |x|_p < 1\} = \{x \in R_p \mid |x|_p \leq \frac{1}{p}\}$; *and*

(c) $U_p = \{x \in R_p \mid |x|_p = 1\}$.

The set R_p *is called the* ring of integers in $\mathbb{Q}_p$. *The set* $\wp$ *is called the* maximal ideal *in* R_p. *The set* U_p *is called the* group of units *in* R_p.

There are several simple facts about the additive structure of $\mathbb{Q}_p$ related to the above subsets. We present some of them with proof, and others we leave as exercises.

Exercise 5.4.8. *Show that* R_p *is a commutative ring with* 1.

Proposition 5.4.9. *The set* $\wp$ *is a subgroup of* R_p*, and*

$$R_p = \bigcup_{0 \leq k \leq p-1} k + \wp.$$

Proof. It follows from the non-Archimedean triangle inequality that $\wp$ is an additive subgroup of R_p. Let $x \in R_p$. If $|x|_p < 1$, then $x \in \wp$. Suppose $|x|_p = 1$. Since $\mathbb{Q}$ is dense in $\mathbb{Q}_p$, there is some $r \in \mathbb{Q}$ such that $r = a/b$ with $(a, b) = (a, p) = (b, p) = 1$ and $|r - x|_p < 1$. Hence, $x + \wp = r + \wp$. Since p and b are relatively prime, there exists an integer k with $0 < k \leq p - 1$ such that p divides $a - kb$. Hence, $|a - kb|_p < 1$, and also $|\frac{a-kb}{b}|_p < 1$ by Exercise 5.4.5(iii) since $p \nmid b$. Thus, $|k - \frac{a}{b}|_p < 1$. It follows that $k + \wp = r + \wp = x + \wp$, so that $x \in k + \wp$. ☠

Exercise 5.4.10.

(*i*) *Show that* U_p *is in fact the set of* units *in* R_p*, that is, the set of elements in* R_p *that have multiplicative inverses in* R_p.

(*ii*) *Show that* U_p *is a group under multiplication.*

(*iii*) *Show that* $\wp$ *is an* ideal *in* R_p*, that is, if* a *is in* $\wp$ *and* $x \in R_p$*, then* $ax \in \wp$.

(*iv*) *Show that* $\wp$ *is a* maximal ideal *in* R_p. *That is, if* $x \in U_p$*, then the smallest ideal containing* x *and* $\wp$ *is all of* R_p.

(*v*) *For* $n \in \mathbb{Z}$*, define* $\wp^n = p^n R_p = \{p^n x \mid x \in R_p\} = \{x \in \mathbb{Q}_p \mid |x|_p \leq p^{-n}\}$. *Show that* $\wp^n$ *is a subgroup of* $(\mathbb{Q}_p, +)$.

(*vi*) *Show that* $\wp^n \setminus \wp^{n+1} = p^n U_p$.

(*vii*) *Show that, if* $n > 0$*,* $\wp^n$ *is an ideal in* R_p*, that is, if* $a \in \wp^n$ *and* $x \in R_p$*, then* $ax \in \wp^n$.

(*viii*) *Show that* $\mathbb{Q}_p = \bigcup_{n\in\mathbb{Z}} \wp^n$.

(*ix*) *Show that* $\mathbb{Q}_p^\times = \bigcup_{n\in\mathbb{Z}} p^n U_p$.

Definition 5.4.11. *If n is an integer, the set $p^n U_p$ is called a* shell *in $\mathbb{Q}_p$.*

4.3. The Topological Structure of $\mathbb{Q}_p$. We now consider the topology on $\mathbb{Q}_p$ determined by the metric associated to $|\cdot|_p$.

Exercise 5.4.12. *If x_0 is an element of $\mathbb{Q}_p$ and $r > 0$, show that there is an integer n such that $B_r(x_0) = B_{p^{-n}}(x_0) = x_0 + \wp^{n+1} = \{x \in \mathbb{Q}_p \mid |x - x_0|_p < p^{-n}\} = \{x \in \mathbb{Q}_p \mid |x - x_0|_p \leq p^{-n-1}\}$.*

This shows that the open balls in $\mathbb{Q}_p$ are simply cosets of some power of $\wp$.

Proposition 5.4.13. *For each $n \in \mathbb{Z}$, the subsets $\wp^n$ and $p^n U_p$ are both open and closed in $\mathbb{Q}_p$.*

Proof. First, consider $p^n U_p$ for some $n \in \mathbb{Z}$. If $x \in p^n U_p$, then $|x|_p = p^{-n}$. If $k > n$, then the ball $x + \wp^k$ is contained in $p^n U_p$ by Exercise 5.4.5(iii). This proves that $p^n U_p$ is open. Now, consider $\wp^n$. If $x \in \wp^n$ and $k > n$, then the ball $x + \wp^k$ is contained in $\wp^n$. Hence $\wp^n$ is open. To show that $\wp^n$ is closed, notice that $\mathbb{Q}_p \setminus \wp^n = \bigcup_{k<n} p^k U_p$, which is open. Finally, $p^n U_p$ is the complement of $\wp^{n+1}$ in $\wp^n$ so that $p^n U_p$ is closed. ☠

Corollary 5.4.14. *If $n \in \mathbb{Z}$ and $x \in \mathbb{Q}_p$, then $x + \wp^n$ is both open and closed.*

Corollary 5.4.15. *Any open set A in $\mathbb{Q}_p$ can be written as a disjoint union of cosets of the subgroups $\wp^n$, for $n \in \mathbb{Z}$.*

Proof. If A is empty, then we are done, so suppose that it is not. Suppose further that A is bounded. Then the set S of integers n such that A contains some coset of $\wp^n$ is bounded below. By the Well Ordering Principle, applied to a suitable shift of S, we see that S has a least element, say n_0. Let $A_0 = a_0 + \wp^{n_0}$ be a coset of $\wp^{n_0}$ contained in A. By Corollary 5.4.14, A_0 is closed, so $A \backslash A_0$ is open. If $A \backslash A_0$ is empty, then we are done. Otherwise, repeat to get A_1, and so on.

Exercise. *Prove that this algorithm terminates, so that we have writtten A as a disjoint union of cosets $A_0, A_1, \ldots$ of the desired form.*

Exercise. *Explain how to reduce the case of general A to the case of bounded A. (Hint: Consider the intersection of an arbitrary open set A with cosets of R_p.)* ☠

It is now easy to prove some of the basic topological properties of $\mathbb{Q}_p$. We present them in the form of exercises.

Exercise 5.4.16. *Show that the ring of integers R_p is a maximal compact subring of $\mathbb{Q}_p$.*

Exercise 5.4.17. *Show that the field $\mathbb{Q}_p$ has the Bolzano-Weierstrass property, that is, if A is a bounded infinite subset of $\mathbb{Q}_p$, then A has an accumulation point in $\mathbb{Q}_p$.*

Exercise 5.4.18. *Show that $\mathbb{Q}_p$ has the Heine-Borel property, that is, if A is a closed, bounded subset of $\mathbb{Q}_p$, then A is compact.*

Exercise 5.4.19. *Show that the field $\mathbb{Q}_p$ is a locally compact field, that is, every point in $\mathbb{Q}_p$ has a neighborhood whose closure is compact. In fact, show that every point in $\mathbb{Q}_p$ has a neighborhood that is both open and compact.*

The ring of p-adic integers modulo its maximal ideal, $R_p/\wp$, is isomorphic to the finite field $\mathbb{F}_p$ with p elements. This is a consequence of Proposition 5.4.9, which implies that

$$U_p = \bigcup_{1\leqslant k\leqslant p-1} (k+\wp).$$

The field $\mathbb{F}_p$ is the same, of course, as $\mathbb{Z}_p$, the field of integers modulo p (see Exercise 1.6.28(v)).

Exercise 5.4.20. *Show that the set of cosets $k+\wp$ such that $0 \leq k \leq p-1$ can be made into a field that is isomorphic to $\mathbb{Z}_p$ by defining addition as usual and multiplication by $(k+\wp)(j+\wp) = kj+\wp$.*

Exercise 5.4.21. *Show that $\mathbb{Z}_p^{\times}$, the multiplicative group of the field $\mathbb{Z}_p$, is a cyclic group.*

Continuing this idea, we see that a shell in $\mathbb{Q}_p$ (see Definition 5.4.11) consists of elements of $\mathbb{Q}_p$ of a fixed absolute value, and may be written

$$p^n U_p = \bigcup_{1\leqslant k\leqslant p-1} (p^n k + \wp^{n+1}).$$

The next statement follows from the discussion just completed.

Exercise 5.4.22. *The ring of ordinary integers $\mathbb{Z}$ is dense in R_p relative to $|\cdot|_p$.*

Definition 5.4.23. *The* valuation map $\nu : \mathbb{Q}_p \to \mathbb{Z} \cup \{+\infty\}$ *is defined by the following rule:*

$$p^{-\nu(x)} = |x|_p \quad \text{if } x \neq 0,$$
$$\nu(0) = +\infty.$$

(See Exercise 5.4.5(iv).)

With this definition, we can write:

(a) $R_p = \{x \in \mathbb{Q}_p \mid \nu(x) \geq 0\}$;

(b) $\wp = \{x \in R_p \mid \nu(x) > 0\}$;

(c) $U_p = \{x \in R_p \mid \nu(x) = 0\}$.

We now consider the convergence of infinite series in $\mathbb{Q}_p$. The situation here is simpler than that in Project 3.10.2. In real and complex analysis, determining whether or not an infinite series converges can be a delicate matter. The p-adic case is different.

Theorem 5.4.24. *Let $a_n \in \mathbb{Q}_p$ for all $n \in \mathbb{N}$. Then $\sum_{n=1}^{\infty} a_n$ converges in $\mathbb{Q}_p$ if and only if $\lim_{n\to\infty} a_n = 0$.*

Proof. The "only if" part is clear, just as in the real and complex cases (see Exercise 3.10.2.5).

Now suppose that $\lim_{n\to\infty} a_n = 0$. This means that, given $k \geq 0$, we can pick $N \in \mathbb{N}$ such that $|a_n|_p < p^{-k}$ for all $n > N$. Thus, for all $m > n > N$

$$|s_m - s_n|_p = |a_{n+1} + \cdots + a_m|_p \leq \max_{n+1 \leq i \leq m} |a_i|_p < p^{-k},$$

the first inequality following from the non-Archimedean Triangle Inequality. Therefore, the sequence $(s_n)_{n\in\mathbb{N}}$ of partial sums is Cauchy, and so must converge by the completeness of $\mathbb{Q}_p$. ☠

From the decomposition $\mathbb{Q}_p^{\times} = \bigcup_{n\in\mathbb{Z}} p^n U_p$ into shells, one can express any non-zero x as an infinite series $x = \sum a_k p^k$, where the $a_k \in \{0, 1, \ldots, p-1\}$ are uniquely determined, and there are only finitely many $k < 0$ (possibly none) for which $a_k \neq 0$. In fact, the first non-zero term in the series is the one corresponding to the valuation of x, and one can write x in a *p-adic expansion*:

$$x = \sum_{k=\nu(x)}^{\infty} a_k p^k$$

where $a_{\nu(x)} \neq 0$.

It follows immediately that the p-adic expansion of x converges to x.

Definition 5.4.25. *The* tail *of the p-adic expansion of x is defined as follows:*

$$\lambda(x) = \begin{cases} \displaystyle\sum_{k=\nu(x)}^{-1} a_k p^k & \textit{if } \nu(x) < 0, \\ 0 & \textit{if } \nu(x) \geq 0. \end{cases}$$

So $x \in R_p$ if and only if $\lambda(x) = 0$.

4.4. The Multiplicative Structure of $\mathbb{Q}_p$.

Given $x \in \mathbb{Q}_p^\times$, we can write $x = p^{\nu(x)}u$ for a unique $u \in U_p$, namely, $u = xp^{-\nu(x)}$. Hence $\mathbb{Q}_p^\times$ has a direct product decomposition as

$$\mathbb{Q}_p^\times \cong \{p^n \mid n \in \mathbb{Z}\} \times U_p \cong \mathbb{Z} \times U_p.$$

Definition 5.4.26. *If $n \in \mathbb{N}$, we define $U_{p,n} = 1+\wp^n = \{x \in U_p \mid |1-x|_p \leq p^{-n}\}$. For convenience, we write $U_{p,0} = U_p$.*

Observe that $U_{p,1} = 1 + \wp$. This set is a group and is called the group of *principal units* in R_p. The sets $U_{p,m}$ are all subgroups of U_p under multiplication, and $U_p = U_{p,0} \supset U_{p,1} \supset U_{p,2} \supset \cdots \supset \{1\}$. This is a neighborhood basis for the topology at 1, that is, every open set that contains 1 contains one of these open sets.

It follows from the previous section (see Exercise 5.4.20) that $U_p/U_{p,1} \cong \mathbb{F}_p^\times$, so the index of $U_{p,1}$ in U_p is $p-1$. More generally, the indices of these multiplicative subgroups are $[U_{p,n} : U_{p,m}] = p^{m-n}$ for $m \geqslant n \geqslant 1$ and $[U_p : U_{p,m}] = (p-1)p^{m-1}$.

Recall that $\mathbb{F}_p^\times$ is a cyclic group. It turns out that we can lift a generator of $\mathbb{F}_p^\times$ to U_p. We now have a more refined direct product decomposition

$$\mathbb{Q}_p^\times \cong \mathbb{Z} \times U_p \cong \mathbb{Z} \times \mathbb{Z}_{p-1} \times U_{p,1}.$$

Proposition 5.4.27. *There exists $\varepsilon \in U_p$ such that $\varepsilon^{p-1} = 1$ and $\varepsilon^n \neq 1$ for $0 < n < p-1$. Moreover, $U_p = U_{p,1} \cup \varepsilon U_{p,1} \cup \varepsilon^2 U_{p,1} \cup \ldots \cup \varepsilon^{p-2} U_{p,1}$.*

There are two ways to prove this. Both begin by considering the roots of the polynomial $f(X) = X^{p-1} - 1$. From the theory of finite fields, there exists an element α of $R_p/\wp \cong \mathbb{F}_p$ such that $\alpha^{p-1} = 1$, and $\alpha^n \neq 1$ for all $0 < n < p-1$. Our task then is to "lift" α to a suitable element in U_p.

Now, we have a choice. We could apply Hensel's Lemma (see Gouvea's "p-adic Numbers: An Introduction"), which addresses this kind of lifting problem. However, we will instead apply a p-adic analogue of Newton's method. This involves finding an approximate solution, showing that any approximate solution can be improved, and showing that the successive improvements converge to a solution.

First, we need an easy lemma.

Lemma 5.4.28. *If $|1-x|_p = r < 1$, then $|1-x^{-1}|_p = r$.*

Proof. Exercise. ☠

Proof. (of Proposition 5.4.27) Let $f(X)$ and α be as above. Choose any $a_0 \in U_{p,0} \setminus U_{p,1}$ such that $\eta(a_0) = \alpha$, where $\eta : R_p \to R_p/\wp$ is the natural map. Then $|f(a_0)|_p < 1$, so a_0 is an approximate zero for f.

Suppose $|f(b)|_p = r < 1$. Let $c = b - f(b)/f'(b)$, where f' is the derivative of f. We have

$$c = b - \frac{b^{p-1}-1}{(p-1)b^{p-2}} = b\big(1 - \tfrac{1}{p-1}(1-b^{1-p})\big),$$

so

$$\begin{aligned}
|f(c)|_p &= \left|b^{p-1}(1 - \tfrac{1}{p-1}(1-b^{1-p}))^{p-1} - 1\right|_p \\
&= \left|b^{p-1}\left(1 - (1-b^{1-p}) + \binom{p-1}{2}\left(\frac{1-b^{1-p}}{p-1}\right)^2 + \cdots\right) - 1\right|_p \\
&= \left|1 + b^{p-1}\binom{p-1}{2}\left(\frac{1-b^{1-p}}{p-1}\right)^2 + \cdots - 1\right|_p \\
&= \left|\binom{p-1}{2}(1-b^{1-p})^2 + \cdots\right|_p \\
&\leq r^2.
\end{aligned}$$

This last step follows from the non-Archimedean triangle inequality and the fact that every omitted term is a product of a p-adic integer and a power (of order at least two) of $(1-b^{1-p})$, which by the lemma has absolute value r. Thus, c is a better approximate solution than b, and

$$|c-b|_p = \left|\frac{b^{p-1}-1}{(p-1)b^{p-2}}\right|_p = |b^{p-1}-1|_p = r.$$

Now, use the procedure of the preceding paragraph to refine our approximate solution a_0 to a better solution a_1. Repeating this process, we get a Cauchy sequence $(a_n)_{n\in\mathbb{N}}$ in U_p. Let ε be the limit of this sequence in U_p. By the continuity of f, we see that ε is a zero of f.

Since $\eta(\varepsilon) = \alpha$, it is clear that $\varepsilon^n \neq 1$ for all $0 < n < p-1$.

So ε is a primitive $(p-1)$st root of unity in U_p. As stated in the proposition, the existence of such an ε allows us to write U_p as a disjoint union of multiplicative cosets

$$U_p = \bigcup_{k=0}^{p-2} \varepsilon^k U_{p,1}.$$

Note that $\varepsilon \notin U_{p,1}$. Otherwise, there would be some $x \in \wp \setminus \{0\}$ such that $(1+x)^{p-1} = 1$, and this is not possible.

Exercise 5.4.29. *Prove this last statement.*

Returning to the additive structure for a moment, we can also write R_p as a disjoint union of additive cosets of the prime ideal,

$$R_p = \wp \cup \bigcup_{k=0}^{p-2} (\varepsilon^k + \wp).$$

Next, we consider the structure of the group $(\mathbb{Q}_p^\times)^2$ of squares of elements of $\mathbb{Q}_p^\times$, and, in light of our direct product decomposition for $\mathbb{Q}_p^\times$, we must consider $U_{p,1}^2$.

Proposition 5.4.30. *If p is odd, then $U_{p,1}^2 = U_{p,1}$.*

Proof. Let $\alpha \in U_{p,1}$. Then, as in the proof of Proposition 5.4.27, we are looking for a zero of a polynomial, in this case $f(X) = X^2 - \alpha$. As before, we start with an approximate solution, and then use Newton's method to refine it to an exact one.

Define a sequence $(a_n)_{n\in\mathbb{N}}$ inductively by setting $a_0 = 1$, and

$$a_{i+1} = a_i - \frac{f(a_i)}{f'(a_i)}.$$

As in the proof of Proposition 5.4.27, this is a Cauchy sequence, and its limit is a square root of α.

Exercise 5.4.31. *In the last proof, where did we use the fact that p was odd?*

Remark 5.4.32. *If $p = 2$, then $U_{2,1}^2 = U_{2,3}$ (see Serre's "A Course in Arithmetic").*

If p is odd, then $(\mathbb{Q}_p^\times)^2 \cong 2\mathbb{Z}\times 2\mathbb{Z}_{p-1}\times U_{p,1}$. In particular, $[\mathbb{Q}_p^\times : (\mathbb{Q}_p^\times)^2] = 4$ in this case. Any quadratic extension of $\mathbb{Q}_p$ has the form $\mathbb{Q}_p(\sqrt{\alpha})$, and is determined by the class of α in $\mathbb{Q}_p^\times/(\mathbb{Q}_p^\times)^2$, which must be nontrivial. Therefore, $\mathbb{Q}_p$ has three quadratic extensions, and they arise from adjoining $\sqrt{p}$, $\sqrt{\varepsilon}$, or $\sqrt{p\varepsilon}$ to $\mathbb{Q}_p$.

When $p = 2$, we have $U_{2,0} = U_{2,1}$, and thus the decomposition $\mathbb{Q}_2^\times \cong \mathbb{Z} \times U_{2,1}$. Hence, $(\mathbb{Q}_2^\times)^2 \cong 2\mathbb{Z} \times U_{2,3}$. Thus $[\mathbb{Q}_2^\times : (\mathbb{Q}_2^\times)^2] = 8$, and $\mathbb{Q}_2$ has seven distinct quadratic extensions.

5. Challenge Problems

The following collection of problems is intended to provide students with challenging experiences, some of which are based on the material in this book and others of which are designed to test the ingenuity and creativity of the solver. These problems range in difficulty from rather easy to somewhat impossible. We leave it to the reader to decide which of these holds.

Problem 5.1. *If r and s are rational numbers such that $r+s$ and rs are integers, must r and s be integers?*

Problem 5.2. *Show that, for $n \geq 2$,*

$$1+\frac{1}{2}+\frac{1}{3}+\cdots+\frac{1}{n}$$

is never an integer.

Problem 5.3. *Show that, if $n \geq 2$, the integer $n! = n(n-1)(n-2)\cdots 2 \cdot 1$ is never a perfect square. (Do not use Bertrand's postulate.)*

Problem 5.4. *Suppose f is a function from the real numbers to the real numbers satisfying $|f(x)-f(y)| = |x-y|$ for all real numbers x, y. What can you say about f?*

Problem 5.5. *A* lattice point *in the Euclidean plane is a point for which both coordinates are integers. Show that there does not exist an equilateral triangle in the plane whose vertices are lattice points. Find those regular polygons in the plane whose vertices are lattice points.*

Problem 5.6. *If $f : \mathbb{R} \to \mathbb{R}$ is a polynomial function such that $f(\mathbb{Q}) \subseteq \mathbb{Q}$ and $f(\mathbb{R} \setminus \mathbb{Q}) \subseteq \mathbb{R} \setminus \mathbb{Q}$, show that $f(x) = ax + b$ with $a, b \in \mathbb{Q}$.*

Problem 5.7. *There are five regular polyhedra: the tetrahedron, the cube, the octahedron, the dodecahedron, and the icosahedron. Which of these can be embedded in $\mathbb{R}^3$ as lattice polyhedra (that is, with vertices in $\mathbb{Z}^3$)?*

Problem 5.8. *Let $T : \mathbb{R}^4 \to \mathbb{R}^4$ be the function defined by $T(a,b,c,d) = (|a-b|, |b-c|, |c-d|, |a-d|)$.*

- (*i*) *If $a, b, c, d \in \mathbb{Z}$, show that there exists $n \in \mathbb{N}$ such that $T^n(a,b,c,d) = (0,0,0,0)$ where $T^n = T \circ T \circ \cdots \circ T$ (n times).*
- (*ii*) *Given a positive integer M, show that there exist $a, b, c, d \in \mathbb{Z}$ such that $T^M(a,b,c,d) \neq (0,0,0,0)$ but $T^{M+1}(a,b,c,d) = (0,0,0,0)$.*
- (*iii*) *Find an element $(a,b,c,d) \in \mathbb{R}^4$ such that $T^n(a,b,c,d) \neq (0,0,0,0)$ for all $n \in \mathbb{N}$.*

Problem 5.9. *Find* $\mathrm{Aut}(\mathbb{A})$, *the automorphism group of the field of algebraic numbers (see Definition 3.9.30).*

Problem 5.10. *Find* $\mathrm{Aut}(\mathbb{A}_{\mathbb{R}})$, *the automorphism group of the field of real algebraic numbers (see Definition 3.9.30).*

Problem 5.11. *Find* $\mathrm{Aut}(\mathbb{C})$, *the automorphism group of the field of complex numbers.*

Problem 5.12. *Suppose that α is an irrational real number. Show that there exists an infinite number of rational numbers of the form p/q such that*

$$|\alpha - p/q| < 1/(\sqrt{5}q^2).$$

Show that this result is the best possible.

Problem 5.13. *Let k be a positive integer. There is a longest finite sequence $x_1, x_2, \ldots, x_n$ from $\{1, 2, \ldots, k\}$ such that for no $i < j \le n/2$ is $x_i, x_{i+1}, \ldots, x_{2i}$ a subsequence of $x_j, x_{j+1}, \ldots, x_{2j}$. Let $n(k)$ be the length of a longest such finite sequence. Show that $n(1) = 3$, $n(2) = 11$, and find $n(3)$.*

Problem 5.14. *Suppose that a real number x has the following decimal expansion, $x = 0.101001000100001\ldots$. Show that x is irrational. Determine whether x is algebraic or transcendental.*

Problem 5.15. *How many congruent regular tetrahedra, with edge length 1, can be packed inside a sphere of radius 1, if each tetrahedron has a vertex at the center of the sphere?*

Problem 5.16. *Find all possible areas of lattice squares in $\mathbb{R}^2$. (Hint: the first answer you get is probably not the final answer we're looking for.)*

Problem 5.17. *Find all possible volumes of lattice cubes in $\mathbb{R}^3$.*

Problem 5.18. *Find all possible volumes of lattice hypercubes in $\mathbb{R}^n$, for $n > 3$.*

Problem 5.19. *Suppose X_1 and X_2 are compact metric spaces. Consider the metric spaces $C(X_1)$ and $C(X_2)$ with the* sup *metric. Show that $C(X_1)$ is isometric to $C(X_2)$ if and only if X_1 is homeomorphic to X_2.*

Problem 5.20. *Suppose A is a subset of $\mathbb{R}^2$. Show that A can contain at most one point p such that A is isometric to $A \setminus \{p\}$ with the usual metric.*

Problem 5.21. *Show that any continuous function $f : S^n \to \mathbb{R}^n$ maps some two antipodal points to the same point in $\mathbb{R}^n$, that is there exists $x \in S^n$ so that $f(x) = f(-x)$.*

Problem 5.22. *Let S be any bounded subset of $\mathbb{R}^n$ with diameter $d > 0$. Find those n for which S can be partitioned into $n+1$ subsets, each of which has diameter less than d. (This is Borsuk's problem. It is known that it can be done for $n = 2, 3$ and that it can't for large values of n that are getting smaller annually.)*

Problem 5.23. *Find* $\mathrm{Aut}(\mathbb{Q}_p)$*, the automorphism group of the field $\mathbb{Q}_p$.*

Problem 5.24. *Describe the algebraic closure of $\mathbb{Q}_p$ and show that it is not a locally compact field in the natural topology.*

Problem 5.25. *Show that every rational number has a periodic p-adic expansion and determine the length of the period.*

Problem 5.26. *Show that there cannot exist a function $f : \mathbb{R} \to \mathbb{R}$ that is continuous at the rational numbers and discontinuous at the irrational numbers.*

Index